ROCKET PROPULSION ELEMENTS

ROCKET PROPULSION

An Introduction to the Engineering

NEW YORK · JOHN WILEY & SONS, INC.

London · Chapman & Hall, Ltd.

ELEMENTS

of Rockets

SECOND EDITION

GEORGE P. SUTTON

Engineering Section Chief,
Rocketdyne, A Division of
North American Aviation, Inc.

Instructor,
University Extension,
University of California

Library of Congress Catalog Card Number: 56-8967

Printed in the United States of America

Preface to the Second Edition

This book has been revised to include a broader treatment of the basic elements and the technical problems and a more comprehensive and complete description of the physical mechanisms, applications, and designs of rocket propulsion systems.

The progress in this new field has indeed been rapid, particularly in the past few years. This new edition attempts to keep up to date with the changes in the state of the art. Some of the technical features and the underlying principles have been clarified further. The new material, new data, new illustrations, the changes and additions to every chapter, and the writing of several new chapters have made this book approximately 60 per cent larger than the first edition.

The contents of the book are now organized into three broad categories. Several revised chapters are concerned exclusively with liquid propellant rockets, their working fluids, and their design. The second category consists of three new chapters on solid propellant rocket fundamentals, working substances, and solid propellant rocket design. The major part of this text (namely Chapters 1 through 5 and Chapters 12 and 13) concerns general principles of thermodynamics, chemistry, heat transfer, flight theory, historical background, and testing methods; this last broad category is general and applies to both liquid and solid propellant rockets. The new chapter on heat transfer is intended to explain the thermal limitations of rocket combustion devices.

These changes are intended to make the book more valuable for the industry indoctrination of new engineers and for use in college courses. For the benefit of the student, more examples and problems (some with answers) have been added. For the practicing engineer, extra data, tables, and curves have been included. For example, the data on physical properties and performance of rocket propellants have been expanded. For the researcher a new bibliography has been compiled; it lists approximately 650 references to other pertinent publications in the technical literature.

Symbols and terminology have been made to agree with existing industrial practice and official standards, such as the *American Standard Letter Symbols for Rocket Propulsion* proposed by the American Standard Association's Y10-17 subcommittee.

GEORGE P. SUTTON

Los Angeles, California
July, 1956

Acknowledgments

It is again a pleasure to acknowledge my appreciation to the many friends and associates who have helped me in writing this book. Again, I can mention only a few here. In particular I want to thank C. S. Coe, P. Albanese, W. T. Rinehart, J. Scheer, G. F. Emerich, A. T. Sutor, J. A. Hyer, M. I. Willinski, R. B. Dillaway, M. H. Rosenblum, V. R. Degner, and T. F. Dixon for their help and suggestions, their interest and time in reading certain sections, and their courtesy in calling improvements to my attention.

The first edition was used as a text in a number of technical colleges and in several military and industrial indoctrination courses. I am indebted to many professors, students, and instructors for calling errors and shortcomings to my attention. All of these have been considered in the revised edition. I look forward to receiving more of these suggestions.

My company, Rocketdyne, a Division of North American Aviation, Inc., has again helped substantially in making this revision possible. My wife has labored long and patiently over the manuscript and the proof. I appreciate the cooperation of the Armed Forces, various government agencies, and various leading industrial organizations in furnishing illustrations, data, and information. The specific items and their sources are listed in the text.

GEORGE P. SUTTON

Preface to the First Edition

The object of this book is to present the basic elements and the technical problems of rocket propulsion and to describe the physical mechanisms and designs of rocket propulsion systems.

The progress made in this new field has indeed been very rapid in the last decade. Nevertheless, a number of principles and technical features are not yet fully crystallized or understood, and it is therefore difficult to describe them clearly. I hope that this publication will help to clarify the thinking and to stimulate interest in further investigations.

The book will, I hope, prove useful not only as a reference to those engaged in the rocket propulsion field but also as a college textbook. Emphasis has been placed on a practical treatment of the subject matter by including examples, problems, tabulated data, and illustrations. Compared with the vast literature which exists in other branches of knowledge, there are very few works which deal specifically with the many phases of rocket propulsion. This book, as the chapter titles show, is an attempt to present in one volume the fundamental elements and the practical aspects of the various phases of rocket propulsion. Certain topics, such as interplanetary navigation and underwater rockets, have been omitted because their engineering problems are not very well defined at this time. For a detailed explanation or proof of various principles of the basic engineering sciences, the reader is referred to references on such subjects as thermodynamics or gas turbines. Emphasis has been placed more on liquid propellant rocket units, since their fields of application are of greater general interest than those of solid propellant units. The thermodynamic, thermochemical, and ballistic principles as presented in Chapters 3, 4, and 8 apply to both types. The last chapter in the book is devoted entirely to the general problems of solid propellant rocket propulsion. References for further study are given at the end of each chapter and with several significant tables and illustrations.

The book has been the outgrowth of an upper division rocket propulsion course at the Extension Division of the University of California at Los Angeles. This course has been given successfully several times to graduate and undergraduate students of various branches of engineering with widely different training and experience. The reader's familiarity with elementary physics, chemistry, mechanics, and thermodynamics is presupposed.

The text and the figures have been submitted and checked by military authorities. This requirement limited in part the amount of experimental and calculated data which could be presented, since a large part of the technical information on this subject cannot be published for security reasons.

GEORGE P. SUTTON

Los Angeles, California
December, 1948

Acknowledgments

It is a pleasure to acknowledge my indebtedness to the many friends and associates who have helped me to write this book. I can mention here only a few.

Dr. W. Bollay and Dr. E. M. Redding gave freely of their time. They read the entire manuscript and offered much good constructive criticism. Chapter 4 was revised by J. Friedman, Chapter 6 was edited by P. R. Vogt and H. S. Fowler, Chapter 7 was improved by T. B. Carvey and J. L. Dooley, Chapter 8 was checked by R. Mahin and B. Augenstein, and Chapter 10 was read by T. F. Dixon. M. Sanz and D. Fisher collected the physical properties of metals. S. Greenfield helped with several sections. My wife labored long and patiently over correspondence and proof.

Credit belongs to J. C. Dillon of the University of California for his helpfulness in the upper division courses mentioned in the Preface, and to M. C. Beebe and all the students of the course who aided in clarifying specific passages.

In the text I have listed the sources and references from which data, illustrations, and information have been obtained. I appreciate the cooperation of the Armed Forces, various agencies, and leading companies in allowing me to reproduce their photographs and data.

North American Aviation, Inc., aided me in submitting the manuscript to military authorities for security clearance.

George P. Sutton

Contents

Chapter 1

Classification and Definitions

The idea of jet propulsion is old, and only in the last few years has it been found to be useful and practical. Recent intensive research and engineering effort has resulted in the development of this new prime mover. Many different types of jet propulsion systems have been successfully designed for a large variety of applications. This chapter gives their general classification and a number of basic definitions.

Jet propulsion is a means of locomotion whereby a reaction is imparted to a device by the momentum of ejected matter. There are essentially two types of jet propulsion: *rocket propulsion,* wherein the matter to be ejected is stored within the device, and *duct propulsion,* wherein the surrounding fluid is ducted through the device and accelerated to a greater momentum by mechanical or thermal means prior to ejection.

1 Ducted Propulsion Units

Ducted propulsion units include the following main types.

Mechanical Compression Units

The working fluid is compressed by mechanical means, burned, and expanded in a nozzle. This compression is usually accomplished by a mechanical compressor, which is driven by a turbine (*turbojets*) or by other means. The momentum of the ducted fluid is increased and thus produces a propulsive force. A typical turbojet unit is shown in Figure 1–1.

Pure Ducts

These units are similar in principle to the mechanical compression units, except that no compressors or turbines are used.

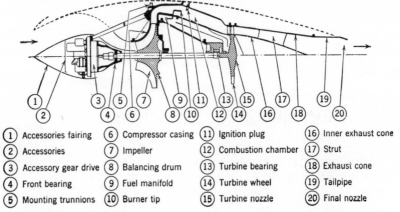

① Accessories fairing	⑥ Compressor casing	⑪ Ignition plug	⑯ Inner exhaust cone
② Accessories	⑦ Impeller	⑫ Combustion chamber	⑰ Strut
③ Accessory gear drive	⑧ Balancing drum	⑬ Turbine bearing	⑱ Exhaust cone
④ Front bearing	⑨ Fuel manifold	⑭ Turbine wheel	⑲ Tailpipe
⑤ Mounting trunnions	⑩ Burner tip	⑮ Turbine nozzle	⑳ Final nozzle

FIGURE 1–1. Turbojet engine employing a centrifugal air compressor. (Reproduced from D. F. Warner and E. L. Auyer, *Mechanical Engineering*, November 1945.)

Compression of flowing fluids is achieved by proper shaping of the duct. *Ramjets* are ducts wherein the medium is air, while the *Hydroduct* is an underwater propulsion unit which uses water. A schematic diagram of a ramjet is shown in Figure 1–2.

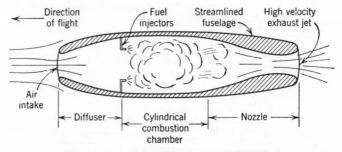

FIGURE 1–2. Schematic diagram of ramjet.

Pulse Jets

While the previous two types rely on a continuous flow of the medium, a pulse jet works on an intermittent principle similar to a conventional piston engine. The *Aeropulse* (example: German V-1) and the *Hydropulse* (similar to Aeropulse, but uses water as the medium of propulsion) are typical of the pulse jet type. The medium is repetitively admitted, compressed, heated, and expanded. A schematic diagram of a V-1 type pulse jet is shown in Figure 1–3.

These ducted units are mentioned here in order to give a complete picture of propulsion devices.* While a ducted propulsion system carries only its own fuel, a *rocket* carries all its own propellant. By *propellant* is meant both a fuel and an oxidizer, or

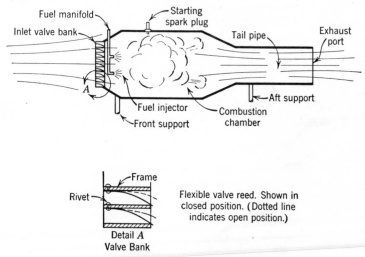

FIGURE 1–3. Schematic diagram of pulse jet.

a mixture of both. When the rocket unit operates, a chemical reaction occurs which generates high temperature, high pressure gases; these, in turn, are ejected through a nozzle. While ducted units depend on the surrounding medium for proper operation, a rocket is independent of its environment.† A rocket is, therefore, capable of operating in air at any altitude, in water, in any other gaseous or fluid medium, or in a vacuum. A rocket system is the best known power plant which is theoretically able to drive interplanetary vehicles.

---

* A general introduction to the several types of propulsion units will be found in the references listed under Section 1.1 of the Reference Bibliography at the end of this book.

† The pressure of the surrounding medium influences the rocket performance slightly, as explained on pages 15, 65, and 71.

2   Classification of Rockets

Rocket propulsion units can generally be classified according to any of the following headings:

(*a*) Type of application
> Airplane power plant or airplane auxiliary power plant
> Assisted take-off unit
> Rocket projectile
> Guided missile power plant
> Satellite and space vehicles
> Other applications

(*b*) Type of propellant used
> Liquid propellant
> Solid propellant
> Gaseous propellant
> Combination of liquid, solid, and/or gaseous propellant

(*c*) Size of unit

(*d*) Type of construction, feed systems, etc.

Type of Application of Rocket Units

Since the rocket can reach a performance which is not equaled by other prime movers, it has its own fields of application and does

FIGURE 1–4. The X-1A supersonic research airplane undergoing a hold-down rocket firing test. Its predecessor, the X-1 airplane, completed its first supersonic flight in October of 1947. (Courtesy Bell Aircraft Corporation.)

not compete with other propulsion devices. Further discussion of different applications are to be found in Chapters 2 and 12 and in the references listed in Section 7 of the Reference Bibliography.

FIGURE 1–5. Enlarged motion picture frame of first American rocket plane with spouting rocket flame (1943). (Courtesy Northrup Aircraft, Inc.)

Airplane Power Plant. A rocket propulsion system may be used as a primary or as an auxiliary power plant of an airplane. Typical examples of planes fully powered by rockets are the German

FIGURE 1–6. Liquid propellant assisted take-off unit on test stand. (North American Aviation Photograph.)

Me 163 fighter and the American Bell XS-1. Auxiliary rocket power plants have been installed on the German Me 262 World War II fighter and on American research aircraft and fighter airplanes. These auxiliary rocket systems permit "super-performance," that is improved performance (speed, rate of climb, ceiling altitude), and some increased maneuverability of airplanes, particularly at high altitudes. Pictures of rocket-propelled airplanes are shown in Figures 1–4 and 1–5.

Assisted take-off units are used to provide conventional airplanes with additional power during take-off. They permit planes to take off with a heavier payload and to clear obstacles on shorter airport strips. Many of the units can be dropped or parachuted from the airplane after they have served their purpose in the take-off operation. In Figure 1–6 a liquid rocket assisted take-off unit is shown during a static test firing, and in Figure 2–10 another unit is shown permanently installed in an airplane.

Rocket projectiles have their main application as weapons. They are essentially unguided missiles. An explosive charge, a smoke charge, or some other military payload is propelled during the first part of its flight by a suitable simple rocket system; during the remainder of the flight, the projectile is a freely flying body. The accuracy of projectiles is not so high as the accuracy of artillery and small arms, but because of the simplicity of rocket projectiles and the light weight of their launching mechanisms they can more readily be fired in greater numbers. Rocket projectiles have also been used as mail carriers to reach snowed-in villages in mountainous country. Rocket projectiles are shown in cross section in Figure 1–7 and on Navy launching racks in Figure 1–8.

Guided missiles are similar to rocket projectiles, but they are usually larger, and their flight path is controlled by an automatic mechanism or pilot. Although the main application of guided missiles is a military one (German V-2), they are also used as vehicles for scientific instruments. The art of warfare is now being revolutionized by the manifold applications of this weapon. The weapons may be subdivided into several classes, depending on their launching method and type of target, including ground-to-ground, ground-to-air (antiaircraft), air-to-air, air-to-ground, ship-to-air, and ship-to-ship missiles. Their military payload consists usually of an explosive, smoke, or shrapnel charge. More recently atomic bombs have been considered. Figure 1–9 is a picture of a V-2 guided missile (ground-to-ground type).

Advanced *space missiles* are intended for interplanetary travel

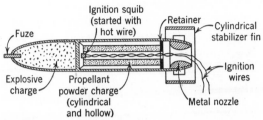

FIGURE 1-7. Diagram of unguided projectile powered by solid propellant rocket.

FIGURE 1-8. Loading rocket projectiles on launchers aboard ship. (Official U. S. Navy Photograph.)

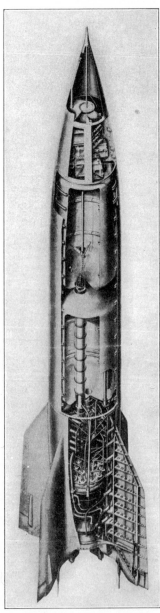

FIGURE 1-9. V-2 missile, internal arrangement.

and research. Even *satellite vehicles*, the simpler form of space travel, require two or more stages in the vehicle design for accomplishing their mission. In multiple stage vehicles each stage has its own propellant supply, rocket engines, and structure. When the propellants of one stage have been consumed by its rocket system, then this stage of the vehicle is separated and dropped from the rest of the vehicle and at approximately the same time the rocket engine of the next stage is started. In this manner dead weight is dropped off and the propulsive energy is used efficiently in imparting very high velocities only to that portion of the multiple stage missile which contains the useful load.

Sounding rockets are essentially rocket-propelled missiles which carry instruments to measure meteorological data at high altitudes. The *Wac Corporal* built by the California Institute of Technology is a good example. (See Figure 1-10.) These missiles may be guided or unguided.

Many *other applications* of rockets can be mentioned, such as rocket-powered race cars, rocket-driven small boats, rockets to assist heavy trucks out of a muddy road, even a rocket-powered railroad car, "Fourth of July" rockets, and underwater rockets for torpedoes and submarines.

FIGURE 1–10. The Wac Corporal sounding rocket being set into launching tower. (Courtesy Jet Propulsion Laboratory, California Institute of Technology.)

Type of Propellants

Liquid propellant rockets employ liquid propellants which are fed under pressure from tanks into a thrust chamber.* A typical

---

* The term *"thrust chamber,"* used for the assembly of the injector, nozzle, and chamber, is preferred by several official agencies and has therefore been

liquid propellant system is schematically shown in Figure 1–11. The liquid propellants usually consist of a liquid *oxidizer* (for example, liquid oxygen) and a liquid *fuel* (for example, gasoline).

In the thrust chamber the propellants react to form hot gases, which in turn are accelerated and ejected at a high velocity through a nozzle, thereby imparting momentum to the system.

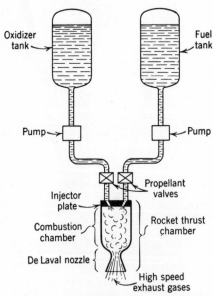

FIGURE 1–11. Simplified schematic diagram of liquid propellant rocket system.

A liquid rocket unit usually permits repetitive operation and can be started and shut off at will. If the thrust chamber is provided with adequate cooling capacity, it is possible to run liquid rockets for periods exceeding an hour, dependent only on the propellant supply. A liquid rocket propulsion system is, however, relatively complicated in design, for it requires several precision valves, a complex feed mechanism with propellant pumps, turbines or a propellant pressurizing device, and a relatively intricate combustion or thrust chamber.

used in this book. However, other terms, such as *rocket motor, thrust cylinder,* or *combustor,* are still used in the literature.

In *solid propellant rockets* all the propellant to be burned is contained within the combustion chamber. This type of propulsion unit is particularly adaptable to short duration firing (one-tenth to 25 seconds). Long duration solid rocket units require an excessively heavy and large combustion chamber. These propulsion systems are and have been used widely for jet-assisted take-off units on Navy flying boats, fighter planes, and rocket projectiles. A solid propellant assisted take-off unit is shown in Figure 1–12. An airplane using solid propellant rocket assisted take-off units is shown in Figure 1–13. The propellant charge contains all the chemical elements for complete burning. Once ignited, it burns at a nearly constant rate on the exposed surface of the charge. Since there are no feed systems, valves, or pumps such as there are in liquid units, solid propellant rockets are relatively simple in construction.

Gaseous propellant rockets employ gaseous propellants. Although various gaseous propellants have been used ex-

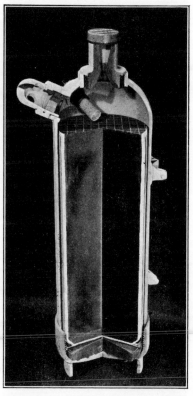

FIGURE 1–12. Restricted burning solid propellant assisted take-off unit of 1000-lb thrust and 12 to 14 sec duration. Note liner surrounding dark propellant charge, safety burst diaphragm, igniter, and nozzle with protective cap. Exterior of unit can be seen in Figure 9–6. (Courtesy Aerojet-General Corporation.)

perimentally, little application of this type of propellant is anticipated. The main difficulty is that compressed gases require excessively large and heavy propellant tanks.

Occasionally *combinations of liquid and solid propellants* have been proposed and used experimentally. An example is a combustion chamber filled with solid carbonaceous material into which a liquid oxidizing agent is injected.

Figure 1–13. Solid propellant rocket assisted take-off unit helps plane to take off from runway. (Official U. S. Navy Photograph.)

Size

The size of rocket propulsion systems can usually be compared with respect to several basic physical quantities.

Actual Weight. Units ranging in weight from a few pounds to approximately 30,000 pounds have been flown successfully.

Thrust. Rockets with less than one pound of thrust up to over 60,000 pounds of thrust have been operated successfully.

Duration. Solid rocket units operating only a fraction of a second and liquid rocket units operating several hours have been built and fired.

Thrust-to-Weight Ratio. This quantity is often used for comparing performance of rocket units.

Total Impulse. This is the product of thrust and duration. It is defined in a subsequent section and is used for comparing rocket units.

3   Combination of Ducted Propulsion Unit and Rocket Engine

Of the many different ways of combining the principles of rocket engines and ducted propulsion units, only a few of the more interesting versions are briefly mentioned here and illustrated in Figure 1–14.

A *ducted rocket* is essentially a modified ramjet in which one or more small rockets are used to ignite the fuel or to stabilize the flame or to augment the ramjet by an ejector-like action. The mixing action of the high velocity rocket gases with the relatively

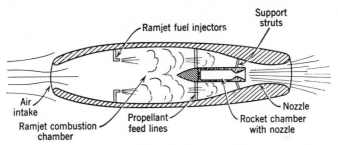

FIGURE 1–14. Simple schematic diagram of ducted rocket.

slow fluid gases of the duct permits an increase in thrust particularly at low flight velocities.

A *ducted underwater* rocket is similar but uses water for the working fluid, with the water being partly vaporized.

A *rocket turbojet* was proposed by the Germans in 1945. Here the power for driving the turbine is derived from a small rocket. The fuel-rich exhaust gases of the rocket and some additional fuel burn with the air coming from the compressor.

4 Momentum Principle

The thrust force of a rocket is the reaction experienced by its structure due to the ejection of high velocity matter. It relies on the same phenomenon which pushes a garden hose backwards or makes a gun recoil. In the latter case the forward momentum of the bullet and the powder charge is equal to the recoil or rearward momentum of the gun barrel.

Momentum is defined as the product of mass and velocity. It can be shown (Ref. 1.101) * that the momentum of a large number of uniform small particles flowing at a uniform velocity, such as

* The reference numbers refer to the titles listed in the Reference Bibliography at the end of the book.

the flow of gas, can be expressed as the momentum of an equivalent rigid body of equal mass and flow velocity.

The motion of a vehicle through a fluid medium relies on the forces imparted to it by change of momentum. About this Sänger (Ref. 2.105) writes:

> All self-propelled means of transportation within a liquid or gaseous medium obtain their driving forces on the basis of the momentum principle, since all ship propellers, airplane propellers, water wheels and oars generate their forward push at the expense of the momentum of water or air masses which are accelerated toward the rear. Rocket propulsion differs from these old devices only in the relative magnitude of the accelerated masses and the velocities. While hitherto large masses were thrown back at low velocities, in rocket propulsion only relatively small gas masses are used, which are carried within the vehicle and ejected at a very high velocity.

The force acting on a vehicle moving through a homogeneous fluid can be determined from the momentum principle of fluid

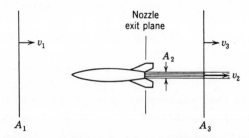

FIGURE 1–15. Vehicle flying through homogeneous fluid.

mechanics (Refs. 1.101, 3.101). It states that the net external force acting on a body which is immersed in a steadily flowing fluid must equal the difference in the momentum per unit time of the fluid and the increase in the pressure forces which are acting on the surfaces of the body. Applying this principle to rocket-propelled vehicles, imagine a fictitious box surrounding the propelled vehicles as shown in Figure 1–15.

A relative or an absolute system of coordinates can be established, depending on whether the body or the fluid is considered to be at rest. Since the coordinate system will not change the results, the first one is arbitrarily selected with the body at rest and the fluid moving toward the body with a velocity which the body actually possesses. All velocities are taken relative to the vehicle.

There is no friction or mixing between the air and the exhaust gases which flow at a uniform velocity c with respect to the vehicle, and the pressure of the exhaust gases at the nozzle exit of the vehicle is not equal to the pressure of the fluid. The surfaces A_1 and A_3 are very large and are normal to the velocities. The rocket exhaust gases flow with an exhaust velocity v_2 through the exhaust jet area A_2. According to the above definition of the momentum principle, the force on the fluid is

$$F = \int_{A_3} dM - \int_{A_1} dM + \int_{A_3} p\, dA - \int_{A_1} p\, dA \qquad (1-1)$$

where F is the external force on the body, $\int_A dM$ is the momentum integral over the area concerned, p is the fluid pressure, and A is an area. If the subscript 1 refers to a reference plane in front of the vehicle, 2 refers to the exhaust gas stream, and 3 to the air behind the vehicle, this can be expressed for a steady flow as

$$F = [\dot{m}_3 v_3 + \dot{m}_2 v_2] - [\dot{m}_1 v_1] + [p_3(A_3 - A_2) + p_2 A_2] - [p_1 A_1]$$

where $\dot{m}$ is the respective mass flow rate and v is the respective relative velocity.

For infinitely large reference areas, the mass flows, pressures, and velocities of the fluid are equal, and the external force is expressed as

$$F = \dot{m}_2 v_2 + (p_2 - p_3)A_2$$
$$= (\dot{w}/g)v_2 + (p_2 - p_3)A_2 \qquad (1-2)$$

where $\dot{w}$ is the weight flow rate of propellants and g is a conversion factor required to make the equation units consistent. The numerical value depends on the system of units chosen. In this book the English system of engineering units is used, and g is equal to 32.2 feet per second squared.

This external force, which is the thrust acting on the vehicle, is composed of two terms. The first term, the *momentum thrust*, is the product of the propellant mass flow rate and the exhaust velocity relative to the vehicle. The second term, the *pressure thrust,* consists of the product of the cross-sectional area of the exhaust jet leaving the vehicle and the difference between the exhaust pressure and the fluid pressure. If the exhaust pressure is less than the surrounding fluid pressure, the pressure thrust is negative. Since this condition gives a low thrust and is undesirable, the rocket exhaust nozzle is usually so designed that the exhaust pressure is equal to or slightly higher than the fluid pressure.

When the fluid pressure is equal to the exhaust pressure, the pressure thrust term is zero, and the thrust is expressed as

$$F = (\dot{w}/g)v_2 \tag{1-3}$$

This condition gives a maximum thrust for a given propellant and chamber pressure as will be explained in Chapter 3. The rocket

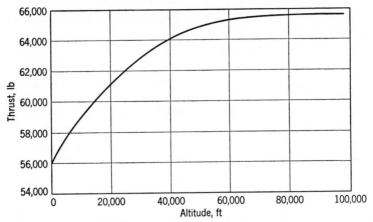

Figure 1-16. V-2 propulsion system. Variation of thrust with altitude.

nozzle design, which permits the expansion of the propellant products to the pressure that is exactly equal to the pressure of the surrounding fluid, is referred to as the rocket nozzle with *optimum expansion ratio.*

Equation 1-2 shows that the thrust of a rocket unit is independent of flight velocity. Since changes in the fluid pressure affect the pressure thrust, a variation of the rocket thrust with altitude is to be expected. Since the atmospheric pressure decreases with increasing altitudes, the thrust will increase if the vehicle is propelled at a higher altitude. The change in pressure thrust due to altitude changes amounts to 10 to 30 per cent of the overall thrust. The variation of the thrust of the V-2 rocket with altitude is shown in Figure 1–16.

The *effective exhaust velocity* is defined by the equation

$$c = \frac{F}{\dot{w}/g}$$

$$= v_2 + \frac{(p_2 - p_3)A_2 g}{\dot{w}} \tag{1–4}$$

and can be determined from thrust and propellant flow measurements. When $p_2 = p_3$, the effective exhaust velocity c is equal to the exhaust velocity of the propellant gases v_2. With this definition of effective exhaust velocity, the thrust can be defined by rewriting equation 1–4

$$F = c(\dot{w}/g) \tag{1–4a}$$

5 Efficiencies

Although efficiencies are not commonly used in designing rocket units, they permit an understanding of the energy balance of a rocket system. Their definitions are arbitrary, depending on the losses considered, and any consistent set of efficiencies, such as the one presented in this section, will be satisfactory in evaluating energy losses. The heat of reaction of the propellants at the rated chamber conditions represents the maximum energy available in the rocket energy transformation. The energy balance diagram (Figure 1–17) shows how this energy is expended. Because of imperfect mixing and incomplete combustion, the ideal value of the heat of reaction of the propellants is never fully realized.

The *combustion efficiency* expresses the ratio of the actual and the ideal heat of reaction per unit of propellant. Its value is high (approximately 94 to 99 per cent), and it is defined in Section 4–5.

The nozzle converts the available thermal energy of the hot gases into the kinetic energy of an exhaust jet. The ratio of this kinetic energy of the exhaust jet and the chemical energy of the propellants is called the *internal efficiency*. It is defined as

$$\eta_{int} = \frac{\frac{1}{2}(\dot{w}/g)c^2}{\dot{w}Q_R J}$$

$$= \frac{c^2}{2gJQ_R} \tag{1-5}$$

where η_{int} is the internal efficiency, c is the effective exhaust velocity of the jet, Q_R is the heat of reaction per unit of propellant at

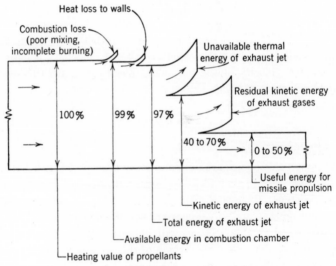

FIGURE 1-17. Energy balance diagram for rocket.

chamber conditions, and J is the conversion factor, the so-called mechanical equivalent of heat.

A large portion of the energy of the exhaust gases is unavailable for conversion into kinetic energy and leaves the nozzle as residual enthalpy. This is analogous to the energy lost in the high temperature exhaust gases of internal combustion engines.

The *propulsive efficiency* determines how much of the kinetic energy of the exhaust jet is useful for propelling a vehicle. It is shown in Figure 1-18 and defined as

$$\eta_p = \frac{\text{Vehicle energy}}{\text{Vehicle energy} + \text{Residual kinetic jet energy}}$$

$$= \frac{Fv}{Fv + \frac{1}{2}(\dot{w}/g)(c - v)^2}$$

$$= \frac{2v/c}{1 + (v/c)^2} \tag{1-6}$$

where F is the thrust in pounds, v is the absolute vehicle velocity in feet per second, c is the effective rocket exhaust velocity with respect to the vehicle in feet per second, $\dot{w}$ is the weight flow rate in

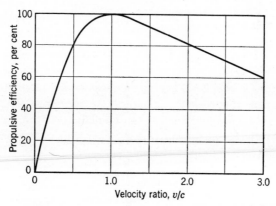

FIGURE 1-18. Propulsive efficiency at varying velocities.

pounds per second, and η_p is the propulsive efficiency. The propulsive efficiency is a maximum when the forward vehicle velocity is exactly equal to the exhaust velocity. Then the residual kinetic energy and the absolute velocity of the jet are zero and the exhaust gases stand still in space. Since the rocket exhaust velocities of present-day propellants are on the order of 5000 to 12,000 feet per second, the vehicle velocities would have to be 3400 to 6800 miles per hour for a maximum propulsive efficiency. If the vehicle velocity exceeds the magnitude of the exhaust velocity, the energy conversion into vehicle energy will be less efficient than at the condition of $v = c$.

The *total* or *overall efficiency* (sometimes called *thermal efficiency*) is the ratio of the vehicle energy to the chemical energy augmented by the kinetic energy of the propellants within a moving vehicle,

$$
\eta_t = \frac{Fv}{\dot{w}Q_R J + \dfrac{1}{2}\dfrac{\dot{w}}{g}v^2}
$$

$$
= \frac{cv}{gQ_R J + \dfrac{v^2}{2}}
$$

$$
= \frac{\dfrac{2v}{c}}{\dfrac{1}{\eta_{int}} + \left(\dfrac{v}{c}\right)^2}
\tag{1-7}
$$

6 Definitions

The *specific impulse* is one of the most important performance parameters used in rockets. The term *specific thrust* is frequently used for this same concept. It can be defined as the thrust that can be obtained from an equivalent rocket which has a propellant weight flow rate of unity. It is defined as

$$
I_s = F/\dot{w}
$$

$$
= c/g
\tag{1-8}
$$

where I_s is the specific impulse in pound of thrust per pound per second of propellant flow,* F is the thrust in pounds, $\dot{w}$ is the

---

* In equations 1-3, 1-4, and 1-8 care must be exercised to distinguish the concepts and terminology involving mass, weight, and gravity. In ordinary engineering practice gravity variations are not important, and it has become common practice to use mass and weight quantities interchangeably. Because weights change with altitude and the gravitational fields, mass units are preferred in many publications on rocketry. Because of the widely accepted practice weight units are used in this book; however, the reader is cautioned in examining and using specific quantities correctly. For example, the thrust of a rocket (equations 1-3, 1-4a) is really a function of the mass flow rate and not of the weight flow rate. Similarly specific impulse (equation 1-8) with the units of seconds is defined here as a force (lb) divided

weight flow rate in pounds per second, c is the effective exhaust velocity and g is the gravitational constant.

The *impulse* (often called *total impulse*) is the integral of the thrust F over the operating duration t. It can also be defined as a function of specific impulse

$$I_t = \int_0^t F \, dt = I_s \dot{w} \, dt \tag{1-9}$$

where I_t is the *impulse* or *total impulse* in pound-seconds, and t is the duration in seconds. For constant thrust these relations can be simplified

$$I_t = Ft = I_s W \tag{1-9a}$$

where W is the total weight of effective propellant in pounds.

In many solid propellant rockets it is difficult to measure the propellant flow rate accurately, and therefore the average specific impulse is often calculated from the thrust, time, and propellant weight relation of equations 1-9 and 1-9a. In liquid propellant units it is possible to measure the thrust and propellant flow rate and thus use equation 1-8 for the calculation of specific impulse. Equation 1-9a allows another definition for specific impulse, namely the amount of impulse imparted to a vehicle (in pound-seconds) per pound of effective propellant.

The *specific propellant consumption* is the reciprocal of the specific impulse. It is defined as the required propellant flow to produce one pound of thrust in an equivalent rocket. Its units are pounds per pound-second, and it is expressed as

$$w_s = \frac{1}{I_s}$$

$$= \frac{\dot{w}}{F} \tag{1-10}$$

In common engine practice, the specific fuel consumption is based on the horsepower output, and its units are pounds of fuel per horsepower-hour; in jet propulsion practice the specific fuel or

by a weight flow rate (lb/sec); however, it is really independent of gravity. In mass terminology the quantity I_s would have the dimension of ft/sec and would be numerically equal to the exhaust velocity c.

propellant consumption is based on the thrust and is expressed in pounds of fuel or propellant per unit time per pound of thrust. The thrust is used in preference to the power because it can readily be measured in static firing tests; in the case of a rocket it remains unchanged with respect to the flight velocity.

Problems

1. Prove that the ratio of the reaction thrust F equals twice the total dynamic pressure across the area A for an incompressible fluid as shown in Figure 1–19.

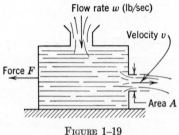

Flow rate w (lb/sec)

Velocity v

Force F

Area A

FIGURE 1–19

2. The following data are given for a certain rocket unit: Thrust, 2000 lb. Propellant consumption, 10.7 lb/sec. Velocity of vehicle, 800 mph. Energy content of propellant, 3000 Btu/lb.

Determine (a) the effective exhaust velocity, (b) the kinetic jet energy for 1 lb of propellant, (c) the internal efficiency, (d) the propulsive efficiency, (e) the overall efficiency, (f) the specific impulse, (g) the specific propellant consumption.

Answers: (a) 6030 ft/sec; (b) 5.7×10^5 ft-lb; (c) 24.2 per cent; (d) 37.5 per cent; (e) 9.36 per cent; (f) 187 sec; (g) 0.00535 sec^{-1}.

3. A certain rocket has an effective exhaust velocity of 7000 ft/sec; it consumes 280 lb/sec of propellant, each of which liberates 2400 Btu/lb. The unit operates for 65 sec. Construct a set of curves plotting the propulsive, internal, and overall efficiencies versus the velocity ratio v/c. $(0 < v/c < 1.0.)$ The flight velocity equals 5000 ft/sec. Calculate (a) the specific impulse,

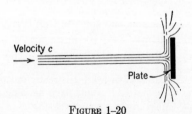

Velocity c

Plate

FIGURE 1–20

(b) the total impulse, (c) the weight of propellants required, and (d) the volume which the propellants occupy if their average specific gravity is 0.925.
Answers: (a) 217.5 sec; (b) 3,960,000 lb-sec; (c) 18,200 lb; (d) 315 ft³.
  4. A jet of fluid hits a stationary flat plate in the manner shown in Figure 1-20. (a) If there are 50 lb of fluid flowing per minute at an absolute velocity of 200 ft/sec, what will be the force on the plate? (b) What will this force be when the plate moves in the direction of flow at $v = 50$ mph?

Symbols

A	area, ft²
c	effective exhaust velocity, ft/sec
F	thrust force, lb
g	gravitational acceleration (32.2 ft/sec²)
I_s	specific impulse or specific thrust, sec or lb-sec/lb
I_t	impulse, lb-sec
J	mechanical equivalent of heat (778 ft-lb/Btu)
M	momentum, ft-lb
$\dot{m}$	mass flow rate, slugs/sec
p	pressure, lb/ft²
Q_R	heat of reaction per unit propellant weight, Btu/lb
v	vehicle velocity, ft/sec
W	total propellant weight, lb
$\dot{w}$	propellant flow weight rate, lb/sec
w_s	specific propellant consumption, sec^{-1}

Greek Letters

η_{int}	internal efficiency
η_p	propulsive efficiency
η_t	overall or total efficiency

Chapter 2

Rocket History

(With Descriptions of Various Rocket Units)

The events of rocket history are outlined briefly in this chapter. Since only a few of the many important historical facts are mentioned, guides to further study of rocket history are given in the references at the end of the book.

1 Ancient and Medieval History

The oldest known Chinese source in which rockets are mentioned dates the first use of the invention as early as 1232, as reported by historical researchers such as a certain St. Julien, who wrote about his findings in 1849. The Chinese used a weapon of warfare called "arrow of flying fire," which, since no mention was made of a bow or any other shooting instrument, leads us to suppose that those arrows were rockets. The arrow had a small package of incendiary powder which, upon being ignited, was able to furnish propulsive power.

It is believed possible that the Chinese heard, from an occasional traveler, of a Greek invention called "Wildfire." It was an inflammable mixture of varied composition. Ingredients often used were tow, pitch, turpentine, sulphur, charcoal, and occasionally naphtha, petroleum, and incense. The Greeks added salt, which made the flame hotter; the Chinese substituted saltpeter. This or a similar powder may have propelled the Chinese rocket.

The Chinese powder rocket reached the Arabs a few years later, an invention mentioned by various Arab scientists. The rockets are still called Chinese arrows (Ref. 2.210).

It is believed the rocket idea reached Europe between 1249 and 1280, because of various references to a lost Arabic original, in a book called *Liber Ignum* or *Book of Fire.*

Rockets are mentioned in the *Chronicle of Cologne* in 1258, and the Italian historian Muratori credits an important victory in the battle for the Isle of Chrossa in 1379 to a lucky hit which set afire a defending tower.

By 1400 experiments of military engineers of various countries had produced more than one type of rocket. The German military engineer, Konrad Keyser von Eichstädt, lists three types in his book of 1405, *Bellifortis:* vertically rising skyrockets, floating rockets, and rockets running along taut strings.

An Italian sketchbook of 1420, *Bellicorum Instrumentorum Liber,* by Joanes de Fontana, contains drawings of rockets, many of which were no more than rough sketches.

Later books of the first part of the sixteenth century contain ideas resulting from actual experiments. Rockets with crude parachutes are described in an unprinted manuscript of Count Reinhard von Solms. Later, in 1610, another unprinted manuscript of the Count of Nassau describes a rocket which would dive and finally explode under water. Multiple step rockets and the use of several rockets in parallel were proposed by K. Siemienowicz, a Polish artillery expert in 1650 (Ref. 2.220). A more detailed description of medieval rockets in Europe is given by Ley (Refs. 1.108, 2.201, and 2.208).

2   Nineteenth Century Developments

Many other historical sources list similar incidents, but the real boom in rockets started when the rocket projectile was revived in Great Britain by Sir William Congreve in the period around 1800. These rockets used solid propellants. A sketch of one of these projectile rockets is shown in Figure 2–1. Congreve manufactured various types of these rockets with ranges up to 3000 yards, varying in weight from 8 to 42 pounds. He firmly believed that this new weapon would replace all artillery, except in naval warfare, within a few decades. The aiming accuracy and the exact predetermination of range were poor. The Congreve rocket was stabilized by the addition of a long stick, which added to the drag (Ref. 2.112).

A further improvement of the war rocket is attributed to William Hale, who was able to spin-stabilize the projectiles, thereby eliminating the long stick. This he achieved by building three inclined vanes into the path of the jet. This idea of spin stability was also applied to artillery shells by rifling the bores, thereby improving the accuracy of guns and mortars so much that rockets could no longer compete favorably. In fact the powder war rocket became obsolete toward the end of the nineteenth century.

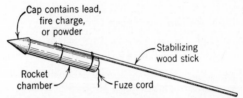

Cap contains lead, fire charge, or powder

Stabilizing wood stick

Rocket chamber

Fuze cord

FIGURE 2-1. Early rocket projectile (around 1800).

The influence of Congreve's rocket work was tremendous. All major powers attached rocket batteries to their artillery; some countries even had separate rocket corps. Rockets were used extensively in many major battles. They aided in the naval bombardment of Boulogne during the Napoleonic wars. In 1807 the British attacked Copenhagen with some 30,000 rockets. A great part of the city was set afire and burned to the ground.

One beneficial application of the early powder rocket was the life-saving flare which carried a rope. Until the advent of radio this device was credited with saving more lives at sea than any other means.

It is not yet certain when the *first liquid propellant rocket* was invented. The first practical working rocket (1895) is claimed by Pedro E. Paulet, a South American engineer from Peru (Ref. 2.111). He operated a conical motor, 10 centimeters in diameter, using nitrogen peroxide and gasoline as propellants and measuring thrust up to 90 kilograms. He apparently used spark ignition and intermittent propellant injection. The test device which he used contained elements of later test stands, such as a spring thrust-measuring device. He did not publish his work until twenty-five years later. A reconstructed Paulet rocket is shown schematically in Figure 7-4.

In 1903 K. E. Ziolkowsky, a Russian mathematics professor, made a definite proposal for a liquid propellant rocket unit in an article dealing with the possibility of rocket space travel. Up to 1930 various other papers were published by Ziolkowsky. His first manuscripts date back to 1896. He proposed oxygen and hydrogen as propellants (Ref. 2.101).

The invention of a *rocket-propelled airship* dates back to the last century. In 1882 N. I. Kibaltchitch in St. Petersburg, Russia, conceived a rocket-propelled airship. He visualized a tiltable rocket unit which was fed repeatedly with charges of solid propellant. In 1884 General Thayer of Philadelphia proposed a military airship to be propelled by expulsion of compressed air and equipped with a cannon. In 1892 Nicholas Petersen of Mexico City proposed an air vessel with a repeatable cartridge type solid propellant rocket. The chamber was fashioned like the barrel in an automatic revolver and the ignition of the new solid rocket charge was to take place automatically. The operator had only to keep the revolving chamber loaded with fresh charges and to steer the vessel by directing the exhaust from the rocket, which was mounted in a swivel. S. B. Battey, who was granted a United States patent in 1893, had a similar mechanism; the charges were smaller and worked in machine gun fashion through a loading device.

3   Modern European Developments

In Europe, Professor Hermann Oberth pioneered the cause of the rocket (Refs. 2.204, 2.205). In his 1923 publication, *By Rocket to Planetary Space,* he developed a detailed *mathematical theory* for rocket projectiles, and he also presented a number of striking new ideas on rocket construction and space ship travel. He proposed the first *self-cooled rocket thrust chamber,* that is, a chamber which had a cooling jacket through which propellants were circulated prior to injection. Oberth also considered a *two-step rocket,* pumps, a thermostatic control of cooling jacket flow, and other innovations (Refs. 2.102, 2.103). A schematic diagram of his proposed two-step missile is shown in Figure 2–2.

Oberth's publications brought forth a series of speculative rocket books in Europe. A few experimenters built rocket-powered cars and railways. Oberth tried unsuccessfully to make a rocket projectile work. In 1927 a group of German amateur enthusiasts formed the Society of Space Travel, which not only conducted many successful rocket tests but also published the

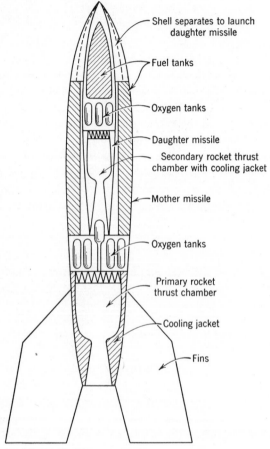

Shell separates to launch daughter missile

Fuel tanks

Oxygen tanks

Daughter missile

Secondary rocket thrust chamber with cooling jacket

Mother missile

Oxygen tanks

Primary rocket thrust chamber

Cooling jacket

Fins

FIGURE 2–2. Schematic diagram of two-step missile proposed by Oberth.

first good periodical magazine dealing with rocketry (Ref. 2.104). They used liquid oxygen in combination with gasoline or alcohol in most of their experiments. Some of their liquid propellant thrust chambers used a water cooling jacket.

A Viennese aeronautical engineer, Eugen Sänger, published a remarkable book in 1933 called *Raketenflugtechnik* (*Rocket Flight*

Technique). He pointed out the advantages of high chamber pressure and reported exhaust velocities of 9800 feet per second, using Diesel oil and liquid oxygen at a combustion pressure of 1500 pounds per square inch. Sänger perfected his ideas during the war, and he proposed rocket and missiles of 100 tons thrust. One of his ideas concerns also the use of aluminum powder suspended in oil as a new rocket fuel (Ref. 1.102). He used spherical combustion chambers as shown in Figure 7–4.

With the advent of National Socialism in Germany, the rocket society was dissolved. The work, however, was secretly continued under the auspices of the German Army. A young engineer, Wernher von Braun, was put in charge of the developments because of his outstanding ability and energy. Under him the Germans built their "A" series of rocket missiles, the most notable of which were:

A-1 and A-2	Experimental small missiles—the fuel tank surrounded the thrust chamber.
A-3	Reduced scale model of subsequent A-4. It had a good regeneratively cooled rocket of 2000-pound thrust.
A-4	This unit is better known as the V-2. Although preliminary design work was done in 1938, its detail design was not started until late in 1940, and the first experimental flight was made in 1942. Over 3000 units were produced before the end of the war. The missile is shown in Figure 1–9; the propulsion system is shown in Figure 2–3.
A-5	This was a test missile built prior to the completion of the V-2 and was intended for development of guidance equipment.
A-9	This missile was similar in size to an A-4, but was to be launched from an A-10 unit. Early version included wings.
A-10	This was a proposal for a large booster unit (200,000-kilogram thrust) for the A-9. The range of the A-9 with the booster was calculated as 3000 to 4000 kilometers. This missile was intended for bombarding the American continent.

The *German V-2* is a supersonic ground-to-ground missile, with a range of approximately 250 kilometers (Refs. 1.109, 2.202). It is propelled by liquid oxygen and a fuel consisting of 75 per cent ethyl alcohol and 25 per cent water. The thrust measures approximately 56,000 pounds at sea level, and the unit operates for a little longer than a minute. The propellant feed system utilizes a 500-horsepower turbopump assembly which is driven by a hydrogen peroxide steam generator. For safe ignition, the launching cycle requires that combustion in the thrust chamber be started in a so-called preliminary stage, which is a reduced propellant flow stage. A schematic flow diagram of this unit is explained in Chapter 8.

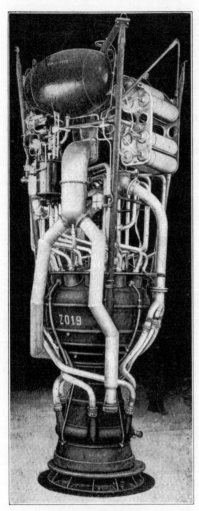

FIGURE 2-3. V-2 propulsion system.

The timing of the cut-off of the propulsion system determines the exact range of the V-2. After power cut-off, the missile follows the path of a free flight projectile. During powered flight an electronic device integrates the acceleration of the missile, which is measured by accelerometers. At a predetermined distance the electronic instrument sends out a signal which cuts off the combustion of the rocket engine. In order to achieve a more nearly accurate trajectory control, the rocket is shut off in two steps; a few seconds before cut-off, the thrust is diminished to approximately 17,000 pounds; when the integration of the acceleration equals the predetermined value, the thrust is cut off completely.

The V-2 consists of four separate sections as illustrated in Figure 1–9. The front compartment contains the explosive warhead, the next compartment contains accelerometers, gyroscopes, batteries, and other electrical instruments. The large center section contains the fuel and the oxygen tank, and the aft compartment houses the propulsion unit and mounts the tail structure. Weights and dimensions of the V-2 are given in Table 2–1, per-

TABLE 2–1. V-2 WEIGHTS AND DIMENSIONS

WEIGHTS

Warhead		2,205 lb
Explosive payload	1,650 lb	
Instrument compartment		1,060
Center section		1,635
Shell	920	
Oxygen tank	266	
Fuel tank	167	
Propulsion unit		2,050
Thrust chamber	930	
Turbopump	350	
Air supply bottles	165	
Generator	161	
Thrust frame	123	
Tail section		1,890
Structure and skin	1,050	
Vane motor	352	
Jet vanes	132	

Total net weight	8,840 lb
Fuel weight	8,400
Oxygen weight	10,800
Peroxide weight	390
Permanganate weight	30

Total loaded weight	28,500 lb

DIMENSIONS

Length overall	46 ft
Diameter—body	65 in.
Diameter—across fins	11.7 ft
Number of fins	4

TABLE 2-2. V-2 PERFORMANCE DATA

TRAJECTORY DATA (TYPICAL)

Time, sec	Altitude, miles	Distance, miles	Velocity, ft/sec	Acceleration, ft/sec^2	Remarks
0	0	0	0	32.8	launching
4	0.49	0	131	55	
52	10.1	6.3	3185	118	
66	17.4	14.3	5060	180	power cut-off
176	51.0	92	2825	0	zenith
310	0	182	3300	−147	instant before impact

PROPULSION SYSTEM DATA

Chamber pressure	220 psia
Oxygen flow	152.5 lb/sec
Fuel flow	123.5 lb/sec
Measured combustion temperature	4760°R
Sea level thrust	56,000 lb
Sea level exhaust velocity	6540 ft/sec
Ideal sea level exhaust velocity	7240 ft/sec
Average injection pressure differential	34 psi
Cooling jacket differential	63 psi
Throat diameter	15.75 in. I D
Chamber diameter	36.3 in. I D
Nozzle exit diameter	29.1 in. I D
Film cooling flow	13% of fuel
Average heat transfer	1.3 Btu/in.^{2} sec
Fuel	{75% ethyl alcoho 25% water
Oxidizer	Liquid oxygen
Characteristic chamber length	113 in.
Coolant temperature rise	63°F
Number of injection heads	18

(For feed system data see Table 8-1 and Figure 8-27.)

formance in Table 2–2 and Figures 8–16, 12–2, and 12–3. Components of this propulsion unit are shown in Figures 7–6, 8–7, 8–11, 8–14, 8–15, 8–22, and 8–27.

German war developments included a number of assisted take-off units, powder rockets, and torpedoes (Refs. 1.106, 1.107).

Various rocket-propelled missiles and fighter planes were also designed, and experimental units were built. Notable among them was the *Wasserfall* antiaircraft missile, which was a nitric acid unit. It will be discussed in more detail in Chapter 8, Section 9.

Considerable development work on hydrogen peroxide units for airplanes and submarines was also done by the Walter Works in Kiel, Germany. This work was climaxed by the production of the *Walter 109–509 rocket unit*, which was used for the propulsion of

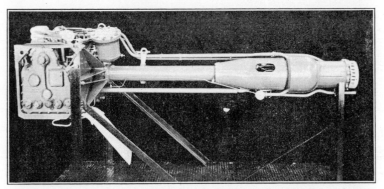

FIGURE 2–4. German 109-509A1 propulsion system for Me 163 airplane.

various fighter planes and missiles. Most important among the applications were the German Me 163 fighter, the Me 262 fighter, and the BP20 "Natter" fighter. The propulsion system is shown in Figure 2–4.

The propellants were 80 per cent hydrogen peroxide as an oxidizer and a fuel mixture consisting of 57 per cent methyl alcohol, 13 per cent water, and 30 per cent hydrazine hydrate. The hydrazine hydrate made the propellant mixture spontaneously ignitable; the water reduced the combustion temperature (about 3275° F). Data on this propulsion system can be found in Tables 2–3 and 8–2 and in Figures 3–10, 7–8, 8–9, and 8–23.

The propellants are pressurized by two centrifugal pumps, which are driven by a directly coupled turbine. The turbine is powered by steam resulting from the catalytic decomposition of hydrogen peroxide. The steam generator is a metal pot which contains porous porcelain pieces. They are impregnated with calcium permanganate and potassium chromate, which in turn cata-

TABLE 2–3. DATA ON ROCKET UNITS

Name of Unit	V-2 (German)	Walter 109–509 A1 (Me 163)	Wasserfall (German)	Aerojet 38 ALDW 1500	Cal Tech Wac Corporal	Aerojet AS 1000	RMI 1500 N4C
Application of propulsion system	Guided ground-to-ground missile	Aircraft power plant	Antiaircraft guided missile	Assisted take-off	Sounding rocket	Assisted take-off	Aircraft power plant
Total filled weight, lb	28,200	368 (empty)	7,640	....	665	160	Approx. 380
Weight of propellants, lb	19,300	....	4,100	....	Approx. 385	....	....
Thrust at sea level, lb	56,000	3,740 (max.) 440 (min.)	17,600	1,500	1,500	1,000	6,000
Average specific thrust, sec	220	175 (max.) 95 (min.)	190	Estimated 190	Estimated 195	171	192
Firing duration, sec	65	....	45	38	45	10	....
Effective sea level exhaust velocity, ft/sec	6,540	5,620 (max.)	6,070	6,120	6,250	5,600	6,200
Oxidizer	Liquid oxygen	80% hydrogen peroxide, 20% water	90% HNO$_3$, 10% H$_2$SO$_4$	Red fuming nitric acid	Red fuming nitric acid	Solid propellant	Liquid oxygen
Fuel	75% ethyl alcohol, 25% water	57% methyl alcohol, 30% hydrazine hydrate, 13% water	Vinyl isobutyl ether (called visol)	Aniline	Aniline	Solid propellant	75% ethyl alcohol
Type of feed system	Turbopump	Turbopump	Air pressure	Gas pressure	Compressed air	....	Air pressure or turbopump
Chamber pressure, psia	220	61 to 315	272	......	......	Approx. 2,000	225
Max. flight velocity, ft/sec	5,000	900	2,000	......	......	....	....
Total impulse, lb-sec	4,100,000	....	793,000	57,000	67,500	10,000	....
Useful load, lb	2,200	....	674	......	......	....	....

lytically decompose the hydrogen peroxide into steam and free oxygen.

The thrust chamber is at the extreme aft end of the unit on the end of the long thrust pipe. It has altogether twelve injector heads which are coupled into three sets of propellant manifolds. The first pair of manifolds (oxidizer and fuel) supplies propellant to three injectors, the next set is identical, and the last set supplies six injectors. This manifold arrangement permits a change in propellant flow without changing the injector pressure drop appreciably by switching various injector sets on and off.

Since the unit has a variable thrust, the amount of propellant flow to the thrust chamber, the pump speed, and the amount of gas generation are controlled.

The starting of the unit is accomplished by means of an electric motor which is connected through a gear train and a clutch to the turbine shaft.

FIGURE 2–5. The French rocket-powered airplane "Trident" in flight, powered by approximately 10,000-lb thrust. (Courtesy S.N.C.A.S.O. and S.E.P.R., Paris.)

Solid propellant rocket projectiles were perfected during the war by Great Britain, Germany, Russia, the United States, and also Japan. The adaptation of the solid rocket projectile to the airplane was pioneered by Great Britain and perfected in this country.

Recent European developments include solid and liquid propellant work in France as shown in Figures 2–5 and 8–24. The developments in Great Britain include solid propellant boosters for ramjet missiles, hydrogen peroxide liquid propellant assisted take-off units (see Figure 2–6) and aircraft rockets.

4   American Rocket Developments

In this country Professor Robert H. Goddard is hailed as the father of American rocketry. He experimented as early as 1915 with smokeless powders. His 1919 publication, *A Method of Reaching Extreme Altitude*, was given wide publicity (Ref.

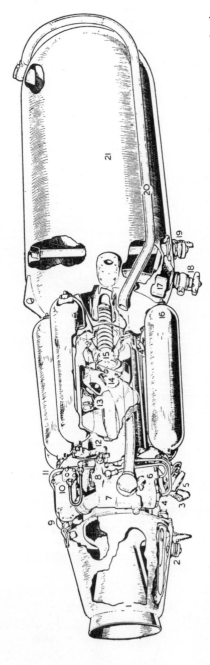

1, Catalyst tank; 2, catalyst filling point; 3, air filling point; 4, catalyst feed to injector (14); 5, air pressure gage; 6, air distributor valve for catalyst; 7, air distributor valve for hydrogen peroxide; 8, starting valve; 9, air-reducing valve; 10, check thrust valve; 11, air feed pipe to catalyst tank (1); 12, air manifold; 13, reaction chamber; 14, catalyst injector; 15, hydrogen peroxide injector; 16, compressed-air bottles, nine in number; 17, hydrogen peroxide collector pipe; 18, hydrogen peroxide dump valve; 19, hydrogen peroxide filling point; 20, air feed pipe to peroxide tank (21); 21, hydrogen peroxide tank.

Figure 2–6. Cutaway drawing of the Sprite rocket engine. (Courtesy DeHavilland Engine Company, Great Britain.)

2.106). In 1920 he began active work on a liquid oxygen–gasoline rocket unit, and on March 16, 1926, he succeeded in making the first short flight with a projectile using a liquid propellant rocket engine.

Dr. Goddard's flying missile had the rocket in the front and the tanks at the aft end as shown in Figure 2–7. Because of the drag of the tanks this missile was stable in flight. A shield protected the tanks from the flame. Oxygen gas pressurized both the liquid oxygen and the gasoline.

In 1930 Goddard rockets were flown at the Roswell, New Mexico, test site. One rocket reached a record altitude of 2000 feet and a velocity of 500 miles per hour. Goddard also tried to stabilize his missiles by pendulum and gyroscope controls.

A number of spirited amateurs formed the American Rocket Society in 1932. The society built and perfected a number of new types of rockets and carried out tests as early as 1934. See Figure 2–8. Most of these used liquid oxygen. One intesting thrust chamber was the "heat sponge" type rocket, and several others offered novel schemes for cooling (Ref. 2.107). Two of these thrust chambers are shown in Figure 7–4.

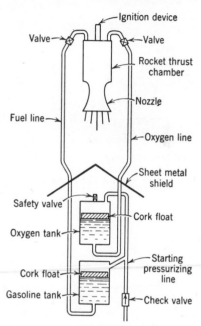

FIGURE 2–7. Schematic diagram of first flying rocket unit.

A number of prominent members of the American Rocket Society formed a company in New Jersey called Reaction Motors, Incorporated. During the war this company produced successful liquid oxygen–gasoline and liquid oxygen–alcohol units of 1000-pound and 3400-pound thrust. Recently this company has perfected a quadruple thrust chamber, 6000-pound thrust aircraft

FIGURE 2–8. Typical, crude, early test setup of small experimental rocket. Note simple protection for personnel, visual instrumentation recorded by movie camera and gas pressure cylinder in foreground. (Courtesy American Rocket Society and Reaction Motors, Inc.)

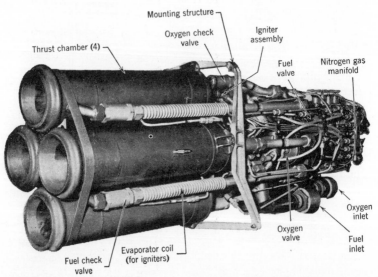

FIGURE 2–9. Model 1500 N4C rocket engine used in research rocket airplanes such as XS-1 and D-558. The rated maximum thrust of 6000 lb can be decreased in steps of 1500 lb by shutting individual thrust chambers off. This thrust chamber assembly has a dry weight of approximately 210 lb. (Courtesy Reaction Motors, Inc.)

rocket propulsion system, which is used on the XS-1 supersonic plane. Each thrust chamber has its own valves and igniters, and it is possible to adjust the thrust by a pilot throttle control. The unit is shown in Figure 2-9 and described in Table 2-3.

Another important American Rocket Group was the Jet Propulsion Laboratory of the California Institute of Technology in

FIGURE 2-10. Close-up of liquid propellant assisted take-off rocket engine which is permanently installed in an F84 fighter aircraft. This engine, manufactured by the Aerojet-General Corporation, uses external droppable propellant tanks, which are visible at lower right. The cowling has been removed to show the thrust chamber at the lower left. (Official U. S. Air Force Photograph.)

Pasadena, California (Ref. 2.203). It was officially formed at the beginning of the Second World War (1940). Research on solid propellant jet assisted take-off units was successfully completed at the laboratory. The first jet-assisted take-off with a solid unit was made at March Field in August 1941. The nitric acid–aniline liquid propellant combination was developed, and in April 1942 the first American liquid-assisted take-off unit giving 1000-pound thrust was used. Research was also carried out on underwater propulsion units (solid propellant) and various types of sounding rockets.

This development work included the *Wac Corporal*, which is a meteorological sounding rocket intended to carry meteorological instruments to high altitudes. It is shown in Figure 1–10 and described in Table 2–3. It is propelled by a nitric acid–aniline

FIGURE 2–11. The NIKE guided antiaircraft missile has a solid propellant booster rocket which drops off, and an integral sustainer rocket in the missile. (Courtesy U. S. Army.)

propellant combination. The missile is 12 inches in diameter and is approximately 16 feet long. It has a fuel-cooled 1500-pound thrust chamber, and the feed system is of the pressurized type using compressed air. The missile is launched by means of a booster rocket, which delivers some 50,000-pound thrust for about one-half second. Because of the acceleration imparted to the missile by the booster, an inertia valve in the missile is actuated, starting the flow of the compressed air in the liquid unit. When the unit fires, it separates from the booster. Fitted into the nose are a parachute and automatic devices for releasing the instru-

FIGURE 2–12. Four SPARROW guided and rocket-powered air-to-air missiles installed under the wings of their launching aircraft. (Courtesy U. S. Navy.)

ment compartment and the parachute from the missile. In 1945 the Wac Corporal attained an altitude of over 43 miles.

The Aerojet-General Corporation in California continued and perfected some of the developments of the California Institute. They have manufactured standard solid propellant JATO units, the first rocket units which had extensive commercial application for increasing airplane take-off performance. (See Figure 1–12 and Table 2–3.) They developed and manufactured several liquid propellant JATO units and one of the first successful stainless steel rocket thrust chambers. They have manufactured the rockets for the first United States rocket-powered airplane

FIGURE 2–13. The Bumper-Wac two-stage experimental rocket missile just prior to launching. In 1949 this vehicle exceeded altitudes of 250 miles and velocities of 5000 miles per hour. The modified V-2 rocket booster carries a Wac-Corporal missile as its second stage. (U. S. Air Force Photograph.)

FIGURE 2-14. High explosive infantry rocket of 3.5-in. diameter. (Courtesy U. S. Department of Defense.)

(see Figure 1–5), for take-off of bombers and fighter aircraft (see Figure 2–10), and for research missiles.

Almost all the work on rockets in this country has been originated by and conducted for the military services, and the United States Armed Forces have participated actively in the many technical developments and in creating and operating test facilities.

FIGURE 2–15. This supersonic Air Force research sled rides on rails; it is propelled by a North American 50,000-lb liquid propellant rocket. The rocket nozzle is visible on the rear (left) of the vehicle. The sled is used to test parachutes contained in the capsule on the upper left of the sled. (Courtesy North American Aviation, Inc.)

Illustration of various Government test facilities are shown in Chapter 13. A few of the many accomplishments are depicted in Figures 2–11, 2–12, 2–13, and 2–14 and in some of the illustrations of the other chapters.

Other organizations in the United States have been engaged in rocket work, including North American Aviation, Inc., Bell Aircraft Company, General Electric Company, and the Hercules Powder Company. Figures 2–15, 2–16, 7–3, 7–14, 8–8, 8–28, and 13–7 show other typical United States rocket effort. Unfortunately it is not possible in this text to mention all the many interesting rocket projects and all the important contributing organizations.

FIGURE 2-16. High thrust liquid propellant rocket engine being tested in large static test stand in vertically downward firing position. Tanks above rocket engine hold liquid propellants. (Courtesy North American Aviation, Inc.)

Chapter 3

Nozzle Theory and

Thermodynamic Relations

The thermodynamic relations of the processes inside a rocket chamber furnish the mathematical tools with which to calculate the performance and to determine design parameters of rockets. They are useful as a means for evaluating and comparing the performance of various rocket units with each other; they permit the prediction of the operational performance of any rocket unit and the determination of several necessary design parameters, such as nozzle size and shape, for any given performance requirement.

These relations, which are fundamental and important in the analysis and design of rocket units, are derived and explained in this chapter. The derivations of these equations should give the student a basic understanding of the thermodynamic processes involved in rocket combustion and gas expansion. A knowledge of elementary thermodynamics and fluid mechanics on the part of the reader is assumed.

For convenience, the significant relations are summarized at the end of this chapter.

1 Ideal Rocket

The analysis of ideal rockets assumes one-dimensional flow. The usefulness of this concept is indicated by the fact that the measured performance is usually within 10 per cent of the calculated ideal values. In designing new rocket chambers it has become accepted practice to use ideal rocket parameters which are then modified by appropriate corrections, such as those discussed in Section 4 of this chapter.

An ideal rocket unit is one in which the following assumptions are valid:

1. The working substance (propellant products) is *homogeneous* and *invariant* in composition throughout the rocket chamber.
2. The working substance obeys the *perfect gas laws.*
3. There is *no friction.*
4. There is *no heat transfer* across the rocket walls; therefore, the flow is adiabatic.
5. The *propellant flow* is *steady* and constant.
6. All the exhaust gases leaving the rocket nozzle have an *axially directed velocity.*
7. The gas *velocity* is *uniform* across any section normal to the nozzle axis.
8. *Chemical equilibrium* is established within the rocket chamber and does not shift in the nozzle.

For a liquid propellant rocket the idealized theory postulates an injection system in which the fuel and oxidizer are mixed perfectly, so that a homogeneous working substance results. Minor local variations of the mixture ratio give products whose properties are very nearly the same as those of the design mixture ratio, even though the gas composition differs slightly. A good rocket injector, therefore, can approach this condition closely and assumption 1 is, therefore, reasonable. For a solid propellant rocket unit, a homogeneous propellant grain and a uniform and steady burning rate are postulated.

Since the combustion temperatures are high (4000° to 6000° F), the product gases are well above their respective saturation condition and follow the perfect gas laws very closely.

Postulating no friction and a steady flow without heat transfer to the wall allows the use of isentropic expansion relations in the rocket nozzle, thereby permitting the assumption of a maximum conversion of heat energy into the kinetic energy of the jet. The wall friction losses are difficult to determine accurately, but they are small.

The energy transferred as heat to the walls of the rocket unit is usually less than 2 per cent of the total energy and therefore can be neglected.

Although fluctuations in the propellant flow rate of a steadily operating rocket chamber have been measured, their magnitude is so small that a steady state flow can be assumed.

The eight assumptions above permit the derivation of a simple, one-dimensional theory as explained in subsequent sections. The Reference Bibliography lists more sophisticated theories and gives some supporting test data.

2   Summary of Thermodynamic Relations *

The principle of *conservation of energy* may be written for an adiabatic flow process between any points x and y as the energy equation in which the decrease in enthalpy is equal to the increase in kinetic energy of the flowing gases.

$$c_p(T_x - T_y) = \frac{1}{2gJ}(v_y{}^2 - v_x{}^2) \tag{3-1}$$

The principle of *conservation of matter* in a steady flow process is expressed by equating the flow at any section x to the flow at section y, and is known in mathematical form as the continuity equation.

$$\dot{w}_x = \dot{w}_y = \frac{A_x v_x}{V_x} = \frac{A_y v_y}{V_y} \tag{3-2}$$

The *perfect gas law* is

$$p_x V_x = R T_x \tag{3-3}$$

where the gas constant R is defined as the universal gas constant R' ($R' = 1544$ foot-pounds per °R mole) divided by the molecular weight $\mathfrak{M}$ of the reaction gases. The specific heat at constant pressure c_p, the specific heat at constant volume c_v, and their ratio k are constant for perfect gases and are related.

$$k = c_p/c_v \tag{3-4}$$

---

* Derivations and discussions of the relations given in this section can be found in any good thermodynamics or fluid dynamics text, such as references 3.101–3.106 inclusive.

$$c_p - c_v = R/J$$

$$c_p = \frac{kR}{(k-1)J} \tag{3-5}$$

For an *isentropic flow process* the following relations hold between any points x and y:

$$T_x/T_y = (p_x/p_y)^{(k-1)/k} = (V_y/V_x)^{k-1} \tag{3-6}$$

For convenience of calculation the isentropic temperature ratio is plotted against pressure ratio in Figures 3-1 and 3-2. When the flow of a compressible fluid is stopped or stagnated isentropically, the prevailing conditions are known as the *stagnation conditions* and are designated by the subscript 0. The *stagnation temperature* or *total temperature* T_0 is defined from the energy equation as

$$T_0 = T + v^2/(2gc_pJ) \tag{3-7}$$

where T is the fluid or free stream temperature. In an adiabatic flow process the stagnation temperature remains constant. The isentropic flow relation for stagnation conditions is

$$T_0/T = (p_0/p)^{(k-1)/k} = (V/V_0)^{k-1} \tag{3-8}$$

The energy of the fluid corresponding to the stagnation condition, called the stagnation or total energy, consists of the enthalpy and the kinetic energy of the flowing fluid.

The *velocity of sound* or the *acoustic velocity* in ideal gases is independent of pressure. It is defined as

$$a = \sqrt{gkRT} \tag{3-9}$$

The *Mach number* is a dimensionless flow parameter and is defined as the ratio of the flow velocity to the acoustic velocity.

$$\cdot M = v/a$$

$$= \frac{v}{\sqrt{gkRT}} \tag{3-10}$$

The Mach number is less than one when the flow is subsonic, more than one when the flow is supersonic, and equal to one when the flow velocity is equal to the velocity of sound. It will be shown that the Mach number at the throat of a supersonic nozzle is equal to one.

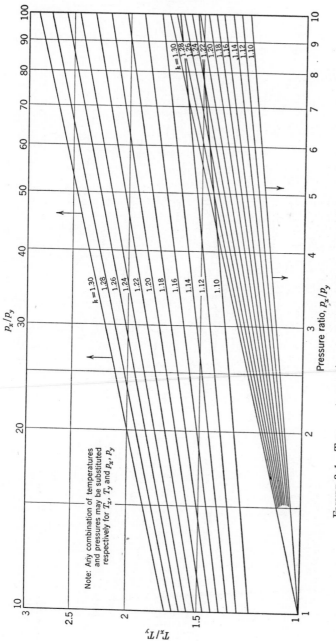

Note: Any combination of temperatures and pressures may be substituted respectively for T_x, T_y and p_x, p_y

p_x/p_y

T_x/T_y

Pressure ratio, p_x/p_y

$k = 1.30$
1.28
1.26
1.24
1.22
1.20
1.18
1.16
1.14
1.12
1.10

$k = 1.30$
1.28
1.26
1.24
1.22
1.20
1.18
1.16
1.14
1.12
1.10

FIGURE 3–1. Temperature ratio versus pressure ratio for isentropic process.

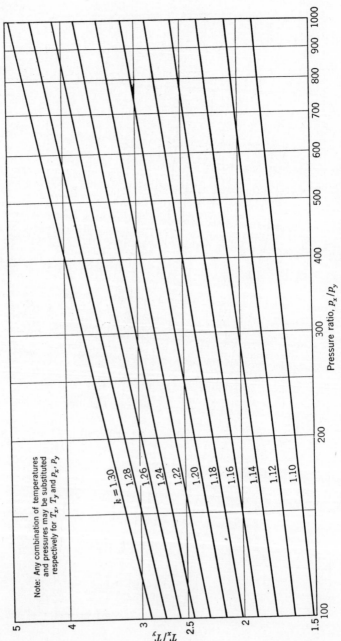

FIGURE 3-2. Temperature ratio versus pressure ratio for isentropic process.

The total temperature–Mach number relation can be written from equations 3–7 and 3–10 as

$$T_0 = T[1 + \tfrac{1}{2}(k - 1)M^2] \qquad (3\text{--}11)$$

or

$$M = \sqrt{\frac{2}{k - 1}\left(\frac{T_0}{T} - 1\right)}$$

where T_0 is the total temperature and T is the static temperature of a stream flowing at Mach number M.

The total pressure p_0 is the pressure a fluid will have when the flow energy is converted isentropically into thermal energy. It remains constant for an isentropic flow process only.

$$p_0 = p\left(1 + \frac{k - 1}{2}M^2\right)^{k/(k-1)} \qquad (3\text{--}12)$$

The area ratio for an isentropic nozzle can be expressed in terms of Mach numbers for any points x and y within the nozzle (Ref. 3.106). This relation is plotted in Figure 3–3 for $A_x = A_t$ and $M_x = M_t = 1.0$.

$$\frac{A_y}{A_x} = \frac{M_x}{M_y}\sqrt{\left[\frac{1 + \dfrac{k - 1}{2}M_y^{\,2}}{1 + \dfrac{k - 1}{2}M_x^{\,2}}\right]^{(k+1)/(k-1)}} \qquad (3\text{--}13)$$

Example 3–1. An ideal rocket chamber is to operate at sea level using propellants whose combustion products have a specific heat ratio of 1.30. Determine the required chamber pressure and nozzle area ratio between throat and exit if the nozzle exit Mach number is 2.40. The nozzle inlet Mach number may be considered to be zero.

Solution. For optimum expansion the exit pressure should be equal to the atmospheric pressure of 14.7 psia. If the chamber velocity is small, the chamber pressure is equal to the total pressure and is from equation 3–12:

$$p_0 = p\left(1 + \frac{k - 1}{2}M^2\right)^{k/(k-1)}$$

$$= 14.7\left(1 + \frac{0.30}{2}2.4^2\right)^{1.3/0.3}$$

$$= 132 \text{ psia}$$

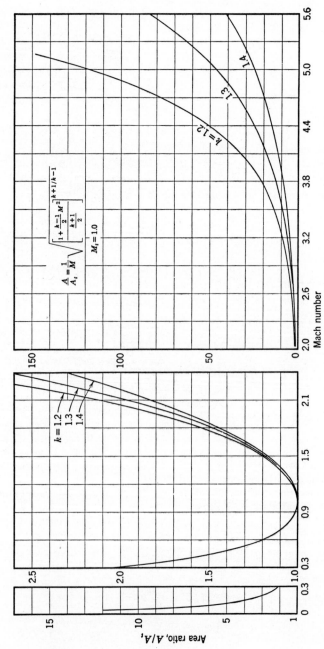

FIGURE 3–3. Relation of area ratio to Mach number for isentropic flow in De Laval nozzle.

The area ratio is determined from equation 3–13 with $M_t = 1.0$ at the throat (see also Figure 3–3).

$$\epsilon = \frac{A_2}{A_t} = \frac{1.0}{2.4} \sqrt{\left(\frac{1 + 0.15 \times 2.4^2}{1 + 0.15}\right)^{2.3/0.3}}$$

$$= 2.64$$

3   Isentropic Flow through Nozzles *

From equations 3–1, 3–5, and 3–6 an expression for the *nozzle exhaust velocity* v_2 can be obtained in terms of the nozzle inlet conditions and the exit conditions. The subscripts 1 and 2 apply to inlet and exit conditions, respectively.

$$v_2 = \sqrt{\frac{2gk}{k-1} RT_1 \left[1 - \left(\frac{p_2}{p_1}\right)^{(k-1)/k}\right] + v_1^2} \qquad (3\text{–}14)$$

This equation also holds for any two points within the nozzle. When the chamber cross section is large compared to the nozzle section, the chamber velocity is comparatively small, and the term v_1^2 can be neglected. The chamber temperature T_1 is equal to the nozzle inlet temperature; for an isentropic nozzle flow process it is also equal to the stagnation temperature.

$$v_2 = \sqrt{\frac{2gk}{k-1} RT_1 \left[1 - \left(\frac{p_2}{p_1}\right)^{(k-1)/k}\right]} \qquad (3\text{–}15)$$

$$= \sqrt{\frac{2gk}{k-1} RT_0 \left[1 - \left(\frac{p_2}{p_0}\right)^{(k-1)/k}\right]}$$

$$= \sqrt{\frac{2gkR'T_0\eta}{(k-1)\mathfrak{M}}}$$

where the subscript 0 refers to stagnation conditions and η is defined as

$$\eta = 1 - \left(\frac{p_2}{p_1}\right)^{(k-1)/k} \qquad (3\text{–}16)$$

and is equivalent to the *ideal cycle efficiency* of a constant pressure engine cycle operating between the pressures p_2 and p_1.

* For additional and more detailed discussion see Section 3.2 of Reference Bibliography.

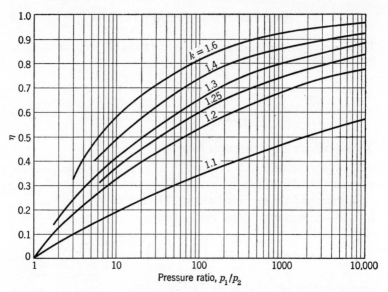

FIGURE 3–4. Change of ideal constant pressure cycle efficiency η with pressure ratio p_1/p_2.

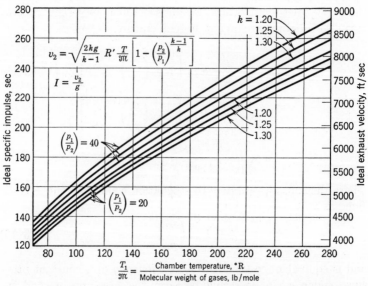

$$v_2 = \sqrt{\frac{2kg}{k-1} \, R' \, \frac{T}{\mathfrak{M}} \left[1 - \left(\frac{p_2}{p_1} \right)^{\frac{k-1}{k}} \right]}$$

$$I = \frac{v_2}{g}$$

$k = 1.20$
1.25
1.30

1.20
1.25
1.30

$\left(\dfrac{p_1}{p_2} \right) = 40$

$\left(\dfrac{p_1}{p_2} \right) = 20$

$$\frac{T_1}{\mathfrak{M}} = \frac{\text{Chamber temperature, } °R}{\text{Molecular weight of gases, lb/mole}}$$

FIGURE 3–5. Specific impulse and exhaust velocity as functions of the chamber temperature and the molecular weight for various values of k and p_1/p_2.

54

Values of η for different specific heat ratios and pressure ratios are shown in Figure 3–4.

It can be seen that the exhaust velocity of a nozzle is a function of the pressure ratio p_1/p_2, the specific heat ratio k, and is proportional to the square root of the absolute temperature at the nozzle inlet (combustion temperature) T_1 and the gas constant R. Since the gas constant for any particular gas is inversely proportional to the molecular weight, the exhaust velocity is proportional to the square root of the absolute combustion temperature T_1 divided by the molecular weight $\mathfrak{M}$ as shown in Figure 3–5.

The relations between the exhaust velocity v_2, the thrust F, and the specific impulse I_s are given by equations 1–3, 1–4, and 1–8.

For convenience of calculation, values of $\sqrt{2gk/(k-1)}$ are given for various values of k in Table 3–1.

TABLE 3–1. VALUES OF FUNCTIONS OF THE SPECIFIC HEAT RATIO k

k	$\sqrt{\dfrac{2gk}{k-1}}$	$\dfrac{k-1}{k}$	$\left(\dfrac{2}{k+1}\right)^{k/(k-1)}$	$k\sqrt{\left(\dfrac{2}{k+1}\right)^{(k+1)/(k-1)}}$
1.10	26.61	0.0909	0.5847	0.6590
1.15	22.21	0.1304	0.5744	0.6848
1.20	19.65	0.1667	0.5645	0.7104
1.21	19.26	0.1736	0.5626	0.7155
1.22	18.89	0.1803	0.5607	0.7205
1.23	18.55	0.1870	0.5588	0.7257
1.24	18.23	0.1936	0.5569	0.7307
1.25	17.94	0.2000	0.5549	0.7356
1.26	17.66	0.2064	0.5532	0.7408
1.27	17.40	0.2126	0.5513	0.7457
1.28	17.15	0.2188	0.5494	0.7508
1.29	16.92	0.2248	0.5475	0.7558
1.30	16.70	0.2308	0.5457	0.7608
1.33	16.10	0.2481	0.5405	0.7757
1.36	15.59	0.2647	0.5352	0.7906
1.40	15.01	0.2857	0.5283	0.8102
1.50	13.89	0.3333	0.5120	0.8586
1.60	13.10	0.3750	0.4968	0.9062

The maximum value of the nozzle outlet velocity is reached at an infinite pressure ratio p_1/p_2. This maximum value equals

$$(v_2)_{max} = \sqrt{\frac{2gk}{k-1} RT_0} \qquad (3\text{--}17)$$

It is interesting to note that the exhaust velocity has a finite value at infinite pressure ratios, such as when exhausting into a vacuum.

Example 3–2. A rocket operates at sea level ($p_2 = 14.7$ psia) with a chamber pressure of $p_1 = 300$ psia (43,200 lb/ft²), a chamber temperature of $T_1 = 4000°$ R, and a propellant consumption of $\dot{w} = 2.2$ lb/sec. (Let $k = 1.30$, $c_p = 0.359$ Btu/lb °R, and $R = 64.4$.) Show graphically the variation of A, v, V, and M with respect to pressure in the nozzle. Calculate the ideal thrust and the ideal specific impulse.

Solution. Select a series of pressure values and calculate for each pressure the corresponding values of v, V, and A. A sample calculation is given below. The initial specific volume V_1 is calculated from the equation of state of a perfect gas, equation 3–3:

$$V_1 = \frac{RT_1}{p_1} = \frac{64.4 \times 4000}{43,200} = 5.96 \text{ ft}^3/\text{lb}$$

In an isentropic flow at a point of intermediate pressure, say at $p_x = 200$ psi, the specific volume is, from equation 3–6,

$$V_x = V_1 \left(\frac{p_1}{p_x}\right)^{1/k} = 5.96 \left(\frac{300}{200}\right)^{1/1.3} = 8.14 \text{ ft}^3/\text{lb}$$

and the temperature is

$$T_x = T_1 \left(\frac{p_x}{p_1}\right)^{(k-1)/k} = 4000 \left(\frac{200}{300}\right)^{0.3/1.3} = 3640°\text{R}$$

which permits the calculation of the velocity from equation 3–15.

$$v_2 = \sqrt{\frac{2gk}{k-1} RT_1 \eta}$$

$$= \sqrt{\frac{2 \times 32.2 \times 1.30}{0.30} 64.4 \times 4000(0.09)}$$

$$= 2540 \text{ ft/sec}$$

The cross-sectional area is found from equation 3–2:

$$A_x = \frac{\dot{w}_x V_x}{v_x} = \frac{2.2 \times 8.14}{2540} = 0.00704 \text{ ft}^2$$

The Mach number M is from equation 3–10:

$$M = \frac{v}{\sqrt{gkRT}} = \frac{2540}{\sqrt{32.2 \times 1.30 \times 64.4 \times 3640}} = 0.81$$

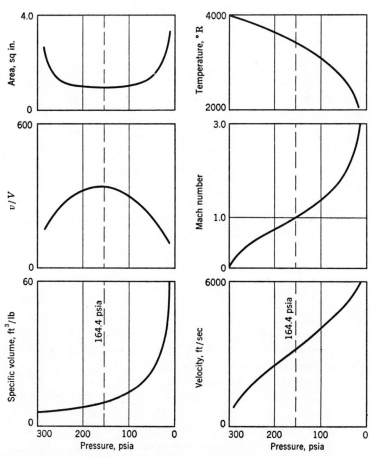

FIGURE 3–6. Typical variation of velocity, area, temperature, specific volume, and Mach number with pressure in a rocket nozzle.

Figure 3–6 shows a plot of the variation of the velocity, the specific volume, the area, the Mach number, and the pressure in this nozzle; Table 3–2 shows the calculated results.

TABLE 3–2.   TABULATION OF NOZZLE DATA FOR EXAMPLE 3–2

p_x, psi	T_x, °R	V_x, ft³/lb	v, ft/sec	A, in.²	v/V	M
300	4000	5.96	0		0	0
250	3790	6.90	1730	1.26	250	.53
200	3640	8.14	2540	1.02	310	.80
164	3480	9.48	3050	.98	322	1.00
100	3100	13.9	4010	1.10	288	1.42
60	2750	20.6	4720	1.37	231	1.79
14.7	1990	60.8	6000	3.12	99	2.59

At optimum expansion the ideal exhaust velocity v_2 is equal to the effective exhaust velocity c and, from equation 3–15, it is calculated to be 6000 ft/sec. Therefore, the thrust F and specific impulse can be determined from equations 1–3 and 1–8.

$$F = v_2 \dot{w}/g = 6000 \times 2.2/32.2 = 410 \text{ lb}$$

$$I_s = c/g = 6000/32.2 = 186 \text{ sec}$$

A number of interesting deductions can be made from the example above.

Very *high gas velocities* (over a mile per second) can be obtained in rocket nozzles.

The *temperature drop* of the combustion gases through a rocket nozzle is appreciable. In the example above the temperature changed through 2010° F in a relatively short distance. This is not surprising, since the increase in the kinetic energy of the gases is derived from a decrease of the enthalpy, which in turn is roughly proportional to the decrease in temperature. Since the exhaust gases are still very hot (1990° R) when leaving the nozzle, they contain considerable energy not available for conversion into kinetic energy of the jet.

The required nozzle area decreases to a *minimum* (at 164 pounds per square inch pressure) and then increases again. Nozzles of this type (often called De Laval nozzles after their inventor) consist of a convergent and a divergent section. From the continuity equation the area is inversely proportional to the ratio v/V. This quantity is also plotted in Figure 3–6. There is a maximum in the curve v/V, because at first the velocity increases at a greater rate than the specific volume; however, in the divergent section, the specific volume increases at a greater rate. The minimum nozzle area is called the *throat area*. The ratio of the nozzle exit area A_2 to the throat area A_t is called the *nozzle area expansion ratio* and is designated by the letter ϵ.

$$\epsilon = A_2/A_1 \tag{3-18}$$

For any isentropic steady flow process, such as occurs in rocket nozzles, the weight flow can be computed from the continuity equation, the isentropic relations, and the nozzle gas velocity (equations 3–2, 3–6, and 3–15) between any section x and the nozzle inlet section 1.

$$\dot{w} = \frac{A_x p_1}{R} \sqrt{2gJ} \left\{ \frac{c_p}{T_1} \left[\left(\frac{p_x}{p_1} \right)^{2/k} - \left(\frac{p_x}{p_1} \right)^{(k+1)/k} \right] \right\}^{1/2} \tag{3-19}$$

The maximum gas flow per unit area occurs at the throat, and a unique gas pressure corresponding to this maximum flow will exist. This throat pressure p_t for a maximum flow in an isentropic expansion nozzle can be found by differentiating equation 3–19 and setting the derivative equal to zero.

$$\frac{p_t}{p_1} = \left(\frac{2}{k+1} \right)^{k/(k-1)} \tag{3-20}$$

The throat pressure for which the isentropic weight flow is a maximum is called the *critical pressure*. The flow through a given rocket nozzle with given inlet condition is less than the maximum possible, if the pressure ratio is larger than that defined by equation 3–20. All rocket thrust chambers have sufficient combustion chamber pressure to attain the critical pressure at the throat. Various values of the critical pressure ratio for different values of k are shown in Table 3–1.

At the point of critical pressure, the values of specific volume and the temperature can be obtained from the isentropic relations and equation 3–20:

$$V_t = V_1 \left(\frac{k+1}{2} \right)^{1/(k-1)} \tag{3-21}$$

$$T_t = T_1 \left(\frac{2}{k+1} \right) \tag{3-22}$$

From equations 3–15, 3–20, and 3–22, the *critical velocity* or *throat velocity* v_t is obtained.

$$v_t = \sqrt{\frac{2gk}{k+1} RT_1}$$

$$= \sqrt{gkRT_t} \tag{3-23}$$

The first version of this equation permits the throat velocity to be calculated directly from the nozzle inlet conditions without any of the throat conditions being known.

At the nozzle throat the temperature is T_t and equations 3–9 and 3–23 are identical. Therefore, the critical throat velocity v_t is always equal to the local acoustic velocity a for ideal nozzles in which critical conditions prevail; the Mach number at the throat is unity. The divergent portion of a nozzle permits a further decrease in pressure and an increase in velocity above the velocity of sound. If the nozzle is cut off at the throat section, the exit gas velocity will be sonic. The sonic and supersonic flow condition can be attained only if the critical pressure prevails at the throat, that is, if p_2/p_1 is equal or less than the quantity defined by equation 3–20. There are, therefore, essentially three types of nozzles: subsonic, sonic, and supersonic nozzles. They are described in Table 3–3.

TABLE 3–3.   NOZZLE TYPES

Nozzle Types	Subsonic	Sonic	Supersonic
Throat velocity	$v_t < a_t$	$v_t = a_t$	$v_t = a_t$
Exit velocity	$v_2 < a_2$	$v_2 = v_t$	$v_2 > v_t$
Pressure ratio	$\dfrac{p_1}{p_2} < \left(\dfrac{k+1}{2}\right)^{k/(k-1)}$	$\dfrac{p_1}{p_2} = \dfrac{p_1}{p_t} = \left(\dfrac{k+1}{2}\right)^{k/(k-1)}$	$\dfrac{p_1}{p_2} > \left(\dfrac{k+1}{2}\right)^{k/(k-1)}$
Shape			

The supersonic nozzle is the one which is of interest to the rocket engineer. The ratio between the inlet and exit pressures in all rockets is sufficiently large to induce supersonic flow. Only if the chamber pressure drops below approximately 32 pounds per square inch absolute is there any danger of not producing super-sonic flow in the divergent portion of the nozzle.

The velocity of sound is equal to the velocity of propagation of a pressure wave within the medium, sound being essentially a type of pressure wave. If, therefore, sonic velocity is reached at any one point within a steady flow system, it will be impossible for a pressure disturbance to travel upstream past the location of sonic or supersonic velocity. Therefore, any partial obstruction or disturbance of the flow downstream of the nozzle throat section will have no influence on the flow at the throat section or upstream of the throat section, provided that this disturbance does not raise the downstream pressure above its critical value. It will not be possible to increase the throat velocity or the flow rate in the nozzle by lowering the exit pressure or evacuating the exhaust section.

The *flow* through the critical section of a supersonic nozzle may be derived from equations 3-2, 3-21, and 3-23.

$$\dot{w} = \frac{A_t v_t}{V_t}$$

$$= A_t p_1 g \frac{k \sqrt{[2/(k+1)]^{(k+1)/(k-1)}}}{\sqrt{gkRT_1}} \tag{3-24}$$

Values of $k \sqrt{[2/(k+1)]^{(k+1)/(k-1)}}$ are given in Table 3-1. The weight flow through a rocket nozzle is therefore proportional to the throat area A_t, the upstream pressure p_1, inversely proportional to the square root of the absolute nozzle inlet temperature T_1, and a function of the gas properties.

For a supersonic nozzle the *ratio between the throat area and any downstream area* at which the pressure p_x prevails can be expressed as a function of the pressure ratio and the specific heat ratio as follows, by using equations 3-21, 3-15, 3-3, and 3-23:

$$\frac{A_t}{A_x} = \frac{V_t v_x}{V_x v_t}$$

$$= \left(\frac{k+1}{2}\right)^{1/(k-1)} \left(\frac{p_x}{p_1}\right)^{1/k} \sqrt{\frac{k+1}{k-1} \left[1 - \left(\frac{p_x}{p_1}\right)^{(k-1)/k}\right]} \tag{3-25}$$

When $p_x = p_2$, $A_x/A_t = \epsilon$ in the equation above.

Similarly, an expression for the ratio of the velocity at any point downstream of the throat with pressure p_x and the throat velocity may be written from equations 3–15 and 3–23.

$$\frac{v_x}{v_t} = \sqrt{\frac{k+1}{k-1}\left[1 - \left(\frac{p_x}{p_1}\right)^{(k-1)/k}\right]}$$

$$= \sqrt{\frac{k+1}{k-1}}\,\eta \tag{3–26}$$

These equations permit the immediate determination of velocity ratio or of area ratio for any given pressure ratio and vice versa in ideal rocket nozzles. They are plotted in Figures 3–7 and 3–8. When the exit pressure coincides with the atmospheric pres-

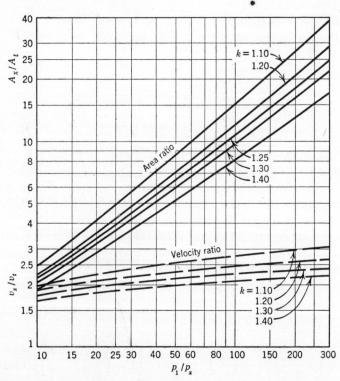

FIGURE 3–7. Area and velocity ratios as functions of pressure ratio for the diverging section of a supersonic nozzle.

sure $(p_x = p_2)$, these equations apply for optimum expansion conditions. It is interesting to note that the velocity ratio has a definite value in a vacuum when both the pressure ratio and the area ratio are infinitely large. For rockets which operate at high

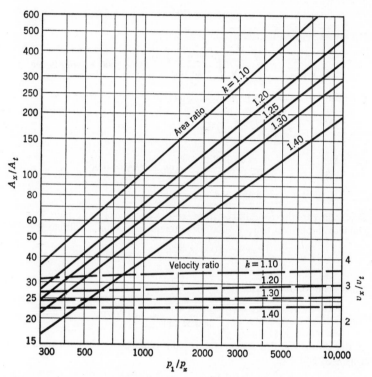

FIGURE 3–8. Area and velocity ratios as functions of pressure ratio for the diverging section of a supersonic nozzle.

altitudes, not too much additional exhaust velocity can be gained by increasing the exit area ratio above 1000. In addition the design difficulties and the weight of nozzles with large area ratios make their application impractical.

Example 3–3. Design a nozzle for an ideal rocket which has to operate at 40,000 ft altitude and give 1000-lb thrust at a chamber pressure of 300 psia and a chamber temperature of 5000° R. Assuming that $k = 1.30$ and $R = 66$, determine the throat area, and exit area, the throat velocity, the exit velocity, and the exit temperature.

Solution. At 40,000 ft altitude, the atmosphere pressure equals 2.72 psia. The pressure ratio is

$$p_2/p_1 = 2.72/300 = 0.00907 = 1/110.2$$

The critical pressure from equation 3–20 and Table 3–1 is

$$p_t = 0.546 \times 300 = 164 \text{ psi}$$

The throat velocity from equation 3–23 is

$$v_t = \sqrt{\frac{2gk}{k+1} RT_1} = \sqrt{\frac{2 \times 32.2 \times 1.30}{1.30 + 1} 66 \times 5000} = 3460 \text{ ft/sec}$$

The ideal exit velocity is found from equation 3–15 and Figure 3–4:

$$v_2 = \sqrt{\frac{2gk}{k-1} RT_1 \eta}$$

$$= \sqrt{\frac{2 \times 32.2 \times 1.30}{1.30 - 1} 66 \times 5000 \times 0.665}$$

$$= 7810 \text{ ft/sec}$$

This value can also be obtained from the throat velocity and Figure 3–7. The ideal propellant consumption for optimum expansion conditions is

$$\dot{w} = \frac{Fg}{c} = \frac{1000 \times 32.2}{7810} = 4.12 \text{ lb/sec}$$

The specific volume at the entrance to the nozzle equals

$$V_1 = \frac{RT_1}{p_1} = \frac{66 \times 5000}{300 \times 144} = 7.64 \text{ ft}^3/\text{lb}$$

At the throat and exit section the specific volumes are obtained from equations 3–21 and 3–6.

$$V_t = V_1 \left(\frac{k+1}{2}\right)^{1/(k-1)} = 7.64 \left(\frac{2.3}{2}\right)^{1/0.3} = 12.17 \text{ ft}^3/\text{lb}$$

$$V_2 = V_1(p_1/p_2)^{1/k} = 7.64(300/2.72)^{1/1.3} = 285 \text{ ft}^3/\text{lb}$$

The areas at the throat and exit sections are

$$A_t = \frac{\dot{w}V_t}{v_t} = \frac{4.12 \times 12.17}{3460} = 0.0145 \text{ ft}^2$$

$$A_2 = \frac{\dot{w}V_2}{v_2} = \frac{4.12 \times 285}{7810} = 0.1485 \text{ ft}^2$$

The area ratio ϵ is therefore

$$\epsilon = A_2/A_1 = 0.1485/0.0145 = 10.4$$

This result can also be obtained directly from Figure 3–7 for $k = 1.30$ and $p_1/p_2 = 110.2$.

The exit temperature equals

$$T_2 = T_1(p_2/p_1)^{(k-1)/k} = 5000(2.72/300)^{0.231}$$
$$= 1680° \text{ R}$$

The *thrust* or *reaction force* on the rocket unit structure is caused by the action of the pressure of the combustion gases against the rocket chamber, injector, and nozzle surfaces.

The axial thrust F can be determined by summing up all the pressures acting on all the area elements dA, which are projected into a plane normal to the nozzle axis. The pressure components normal to the nozzle axis are appreciable, but do not contribute to the axial thrust, because the rocket is symmetrical in construction.

$$F = \int p \, dA \qquad (3\text{--}27)$$

Both the external and internal pressures are to be considered. The summation of all axial forces caused by cooling coil pressures are internally balanced and usually very close to zero. As shown in the free body diagram of Figure 3–9, the internal pressure in the

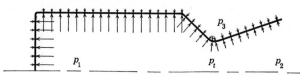

FIGURE 3–9. Free body diagram of pressure forces acting on rocket chamber and nozzle walls.

chamber is high and decreases steadily in the nozzle, while the external pressure is equal to atmospheric pressure and is constant over the external chamber and nozzle surface. It can be shown that the force obtained by summing up these pressures equals that obtained by the momentum principle, equation 1–2, namely,

$$F = v_2\dot{w}/g + (p_2 - p_3)A_2 \qquad (3\text{--}28)$$

The pressure thrust term consists of the pressure difference between exit pressure and atmospheric pressure, multiplied by the nozzle exit area, and can be considered as a force acting on a fictitious exit plane.

This equation gives accurate values of the thrust variations of rockets with altitude. For convenience the pressure and other properties of the atmosphere are listed in Table 3–4. Figure 1–15 shows a typical variation of thrust with altitude.

TABLE 3–4.. PROPERTIES OF THE ATMOSPHERE *

Altitude, ft	Altitude, miles	Absolute Temperature, °R	Absolute Pressure, lb/ft²	Pressure Ratio	Density, slugs/ft³	Density Ratio	Speed of Sound, ft/sec
0	0	518	2,116	1.00	2.38×10^{-3}	1.00	1,120
5,000	0.947	500	1,758	8.32×10^{-1}	2.05×10^{-3}	8.61×10^{-1}	1,100
10,000	1.894	483	1,456	6.87×10^{-1}	1.76×10^{-3}	7.38×10^{-1}	1,080
20,000	3.788	447	972	4.59×10^{-1}	1.27×10^{-3}	5.33×10^{-1}	1,040
30,000	5.682	411	628	2.97×10^{-1}	8.93×10^{-4}	3.76×10^{-1}	997
40,000	7.576	392	392	1.85×10^{-1}	5.83×10^{-4}	2.45×10^{-1}	973
50,000	9.470	392	243	1.15×10^{-1}	3.62×10^{-4}	1.52×10^{-1}	973
60,000	11.364	392	151	7.13×10^{-2}	2.25×10^{-4}	9.45×10^{-2}	973
70,000	13.258	392	94.5	4.47×10^{-2}	1.40×10^{-4}	5.90×10^{-2}	974
80,000	15.152	392	58.8	2.78×10^{-2}	8.73×10^{-5}	3.67×10^{-2}	974
90,000	17.045	392	36.6	1.73×10^{-2}	5.4×10^{-5}	2.28×10^{-2}	974
100,000	18.939	392	22.8	1.08×10^{-3}	3.4×10^{-5}	1.4×10^{-2}	975
150,000	28.409	575	3.2	1.5×10^{-3}	3.6×10^{-6}	1.5×10^{-3}	1,190
200,000	37.879	623	0.73	3.6×10^{-4}	6.9×10^{-7}	2.9×10^{-4}	1,240
300,000	56.818	487	0.017	9.0×10^{-6}	2.1×10^{-8}	9.0×10^{-6}	1,110
400,000	75.758	695	0.0011	5.2×10^{-7}	0.83×10^{-9}	3.5×10^{-7}	1,430
500,000	94.697	910	1.2×10^{-4}	8.5×10^{-8}	9.8×10^{-11}	4.1×10^{-8}	.....
600,000	113.64	1,130	4.1×10^{-5}	1.9×10^{-8}	1.8×10^{-11}	7.5×10^{-9}	.....
700,000	132.58	1,350	1.3×10^{-5}	6.2×10^{-9}	4.5×10^{-12}	1.9×10^{-9}	.....
800,000	151.52	1,570	4.6×10^{-6}	2.2×10^{-9}	1.4×10^{-12}	6.0×10^{-10}	.....
900,000	170.45	1,800	1.9×10^{-6}	9.0×10^{-10}	5.3×10^{-13}	2.2×10^{-10}	.....

* Data taken from references in Section 8.5 of the Reference Bibliography.

Equation 3–28 can be expanded by modifying it and substituting v_2, v_t, and V_t from equations 3–15, 3–23, and 3–21.

$$F = \frac{A_t v_t v_2}{g V_t} + (p_2 - p_3)A_2$$

$$= A_t p_1 \sqrt{\frac{2k^2}{k-1}\left(\frac{2}{k+1}\right)^{(k+1)/(k-1)}}\left[1 - \left(\frac{p_2}{p_1}\right)^{(k-1)/k}\right]$$

$$+ (p_2 - p_3)A_2 \tag{3-29}$$

This equation shows that the thrust is proportional to the throat area A_t, the nozzle inlet pressure p_1, and is a function of the pressure ratio across the nozzle p_1/p_2, the specific heat ratio k, and the pressure thrust. It is called the *ideal thrust equation.* If the *thrust coefficient* C_F is defined as

$$C_F = \sqrt{\frac{2k^2}{k-1}\left(\frac{2}{k+1}\right)^{(k+1)/(k-1)}\left[1-\left(\frac{p_2}{p_1}\right)^{(k-1)/k}\right]}$$
$$+ \frac{p_2 - p_3}{p_1}\frac{A_2}{A_t} \quad (3\text{-}30)$$

the ideal thrust equation is simplified.

$$F = C_F A_t p_1 \quad (3\text{-}31)$$

For optimum expansion, when $p_2 = p_3$, the last term of the thrust coefficient equals zero. Since the thrust coefficient is a function of chamber pressures, the thrust is not quite proportional to p_1 as confirmed by experimental data plotted in Figure 3–10.

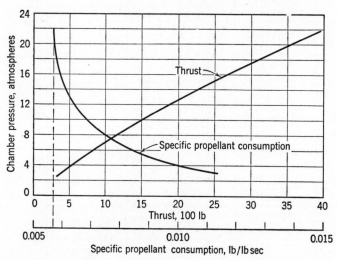

FIGURE 3–10. Static test performance of Walter 109–509 propulsion system.

The thrust coefficient determines the amplification of thrust due to the gas expansion in the rocket nozzle as compared to the thrust that would be exerted if the chamber pressure acted over the throat area.

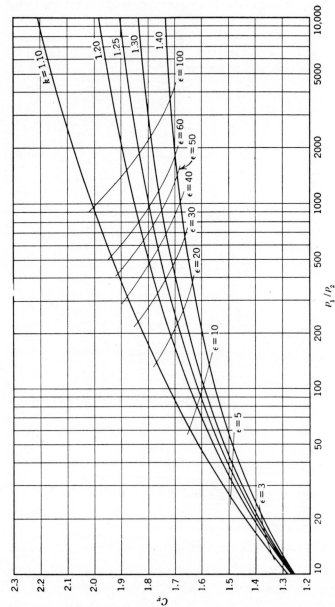

FIGURE 3-11. Thrust coefficient C_F as a function of pressure ratio, area ratio, and specific heat ratio for optimum expansion conditions.

Figure 3–11 shows the variation of the *optimum expansion* thrust coefficient at sea level for different chamber pressures and area ratios ($p_2 = p_3$).

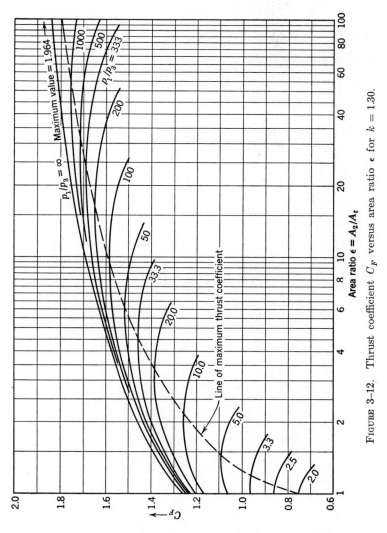

FIGURE 3-12.   Thrust coefficient C_F versus area ratio ϵ for $k = 1.30$.

The thrust coefficient is plotted in Figures 3–12 and 3–13 as functions of pressure ratio and the area ratio for $k = 1.30$ and 1.20 (Ref. 3.107). These two sets of curves are useful in solving various nozzle problems, for they permit an evaluation of under- and overexpansion as explained in the next paragraphs.

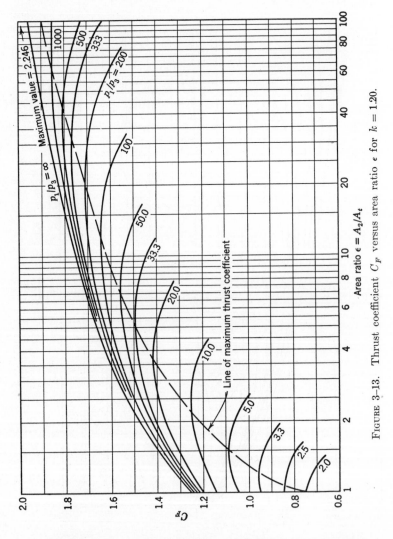

FIGURE 3–13.   Thrust coefficient C_F versus area ratio ϵ for $k = 1.20$.

Example 3–4. What is the percentage variation in thrust between sea level and 40,000 ft for a rocket having a chamber pressure of 350 psia and an expansion ratio of 3.5? (Use $k = 1.30$.)

Solution.

At sea level:

$$p_1/p_3 = 350/14.7 = 23.8$$

At 40,000 ft:

$$p_1/p_3 = 350/2.72 = 128.7$$

Use Figure 3–12 to determine thrust coefficient for $A_2/A_t = 3.5$.

At sea level:

$$C_F = 1.402$$

At 40,000 ft:

$$C_F = 1.525$$

Thrust increase $= (1.525 - 1.402)/1.402 = 8.8$ per cent

An *underexpanding nozzle* is one which discharges the fluid at a pressure greater than the external pressure, because the exit area is too small. The expansion of the fluid is, therefore, incomplete within the nozzle and continues outside. The nozzle exit pressure is higher than the atmospheric pressure.

An *overexpanding nozzle* is one in which the fluid is expanded to a lower pressure than the external pressure; it has an exit area which is too large.

The phenomenon of overexpansion can perhaps be better explained by referring to Figure 3–14, which shows typical pressure measurements along a nozzle axis with different back pressures. Curve AB shows the variation of pressure with the correct back pressure corresponding to the area ratio. Curves AC, AD, etc., show the variation of pressure along the nozzle axis for increasingly higher external pressures. The expansion within the nozzle proceeds normally for the initial portion of the nozzle. At point I, on curve AD, for example, the pressure is lower than the exit pressure, and a sudden rise in pressure or a pressure shock takes place; this is accompanied by the separation of the jet from the walls.

The different possible flow conditions in an overexpanding nozzle are:

1. When the external pressure p_3 is below the nozzle exit pressure p_2, the nozzle will flow full, but will have expansion shock waves at its exit.

2. For external pressures p_3 slightly higher than the nozzle exit pressure p_2, the nozzle will continue to flow full ($p_2 \geqq 0.4p_3$). Oblique shock waves will exist outside of the exit section.

3. For higher external pressures, a separation of the jet will take place in the divergent section of the nozzle. The flow

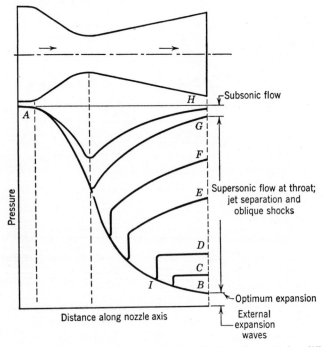

FIGURE 3–14. Distribution of pressures in a De Laval nozzle for different flow conditions.

separation is axially symmetrical and is believed to be accompanied by oblique shock waves. The point of separation travels upstream with increasing external pressure. The flow at the nozzle exit is supersonic. Experimental results on nitric acid–anile liquid propellant units with overexpanded nozzles have shown good agreement with a theory postulating oblique shock (Ref. 3.107). The nozzle portion of supersonic flow between the throat and the location of the separation diminishes in length with increasing back pressure until the shock wave and the point of separation reach the throat.

4. For nozzles in which the exit pressure is very close in value to the inlet pressure, subsonic flow prevails throughout the nozzle.

The axial thrust direction is not usually altered by separation, since the flow separates uniformly over one cross section of the divergent nozzle cone of conventional rocket designs.

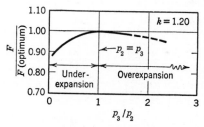

FIGURE 3–15. Theoretical reduction of thrust due to under- or overexpansion.

The phenomenon of pressure shock has been treated analytically. Experiments indicate that because of boundary layer effects the shock wave in overexpanding nozzles is not fixed in location, but oscillates over a finite length within the nozzle, giving rise to vibration (Ref. 3.201).

The loss of thrust due to over- or underexpansion can be determined from the thrust coefficient C_F of equation 3–30 or from Figures 3–12 and 3–13. This simplified theory assumes that the nozzle is flowing full and that the pressure thrust is positive for underexpansion and negative for overexpansion. A typical variation of thrust is shown in Figure 3–15. For underexpansion the simple theory is in accurate agreement with measured results. For overexpansion the simple theory gives slightly conservative thrust values. The dotted line of Figure 3–15 indicates the region where flow separation takes place.

The effect of either overexpansion or underexpansion is a slight reduction in the exhaust velocity and, therefore, a loss of energy.

The jet separates from the nozzle wall with considerable overexpansion, and the nozzle does not flow full. Thus a large and usually heavy portion of the nozzle is not utilized, and the nozzle is bulkier and longer than necessary. Added engine weight and size decrease the flight performance.

The tendency in rocket design is, therefore, to obtain either a nozzle with a correct (optimum) expansion ratio or one that underexpands the jet slightly. Nozzles of rocket units which operate over a range of different altitudes are, therefore, so proportioned that the correct expansion ratio is attained at or near sea level or at relatively low altitudes. The German V-2, which has reached altitudes well over 100 miles, attains an optimum expansion ratio at approximately one mile of altitude.

The *characteristic exhaust velocity* has frequently been used in the rocket literature. It is defined as $c^* = c/C_F$. Using equations 1–4, 3–24, and 3–29, the characteristic exhaust velocity can be expressed as a function of the combustion product gas properties in the combustion chamber.

$$c^* = \frac{p_1 A_t g}{\dot{w}} = \frac{I_s g}{C_F}$$

$$= \frac{\sqrt{gkRT_1}}{k\sqrt{[2/(k+1)]^{(k+1)/(k-1)}}} \tag{3-32}$$

The function of k in the denominator is given in Table 3–1.

4 Real Nozzles

This section considers the real nozzles, their shape, and the losses and corrections necessary to adapt the ideal nozzle theory to actual operating conditions.

The *optimum nozzle angle* and *nozzle shape* are based on a number of practical considerations. Since the kinetic energy of the gases in the convergent section of a rocket nozzle is relatively small, almost any symmetrical and well-rounded convergent nozzle shape will have very low losses. Various convergent shapes are shown in Chapters 7 and 9.

The selection of a suitable divergence shape and angle for a given area ratio is considerably more critical because:

1. *Wall friction losses* are low for large divergence angles and short nozzles.

2. The external *aerodynamic drag* and the *structure weight* of missiles decrease if the nozzle is short.
3. *Heat transfer* to the coolant usually decreases when the exposed internal nozzle surface area becomes smaller with larger divergence angles.
4. The *radial velocity* component, which is not useful in producing thrust, becomes larger with increased nozzle divergence.
5. The rocket *installation weight* and *design complications* increase with decreasing divergence angles.
6. *Separation* and *turbulence* losses become prohibitive if the divergence angle is too large at any one point.

A divergent cone half angle between 12 to 18 degrees has been found experimentally to be the optimum. For convenience of manufacture the shapes of the converging and diverging nozzle sections are often made a straight cone, but it is not fully established that a straight cone is the optimum configuration. Since nozzles with discontinuities in the wall contour are likely to cause shock waves, all nozzle sections, particularly the entrance and throat sections, are well rounded. The nozzle exit section usually has a sharp edge because a rounded edge would permit overexpansion and flow separation. Typical nozzle contours are shown in Figures 3–9 and 7–1.

Although a single factor is used to correct the ideal performance to actual operating conditions, it has been possible to evaluate analytically several of the individual minor effects.

In order to correct for the non-axial component of the gas velocity, a theoretical correction factor λ can be applied to the nozzle exit momentum of an ideal rocket. This factor is the ratio between the momentum of the gases in a nozzle with a finite nozzle angle 2α and the ideal momentum of a nozzle with all gases flowing in an axial direction.

$$\lambda = \tfrac{1}{2}(1 + \cos \alpha)$$

The variation of λ with different values of α is shown in Table 3–5. For ideal rockets $\lambda = 1.0$.

For a rocket nozzle with a divergence cone angle of 30 degrees (half angle $\alpha = 15$ degrees) the exit momentum and, therefore,

TABLE 3–5. NOZZLE ANGLE CORRECTION FACTOR

Nozzle Cone Divergence Half Angle α, Degrees	Correction Factor λ
0	1.0000
2	0.9997
4	0.9988
6	0.9972
8	0.9951
10	0.9924
12	0.9890
14	0.9851
16	0.9806
18	0.9755
20	0.9698
22	0.9636
24	0.9567

the exhaust velocity will be 98.3 per cent of the velocity calculated by equation 3–15.

The flow in a real nozzle differs from that of an ideal nozzle because of friction effects, heat transfer, imperfect gases, non-axial flow, and non-uniformity of working substance and flow distribution. The degree of departure is indicated by the *energy conversion efficiency* of a nozzle, which is defined as the ratio of the kinetic energy per unit of flow of the jet leaving the nozzle to the kinetic energy per unit of flow of a hypothetical ideal jet leaving an ideal nozzle that is supplied with the same working substance at the same initial state and velocity and expands to the same exit pressure as the real nozzle. This relationship is expressed as

$$e = \frac{(v_2)_a^2}{(v_2)_i^2}$$

$$= \frac{(v_2)_a^2}{(v_1)_a^2 + c_p(T_1 - T_2)} \tag{3–33}$$

where e denotes the energy conversion efficiency, v_1 and v_2 the velocities at the nozzle inlet and exit, and $c_p T_1$ and $c_p T_2$ the respective enthalpies for an ideal isentropic expansion. The subscripts a and i refer to actual and ideal conditions respectively. For many practical applications $v_1 \to 0$, and the square of the expression given in equation 3–15 can be used for the denominator.

The *velocity correction factor* ζ_v is defined as the square root of the energy conversion efficiency $\sqrt{e}$. Its value ranges between 0.85 and 0.98, with an average near 0.92. This factor is also approximately the ratio of the actual specific impulse to the ideal or theoretical specific impulse.

The *discharge correction factor* ζ_d is defined as the ratio of the mass flow rate in a real nozzle to that of an ideal nozzle which expands an identical working fluid from the same initial conditions to the same exit pressure.

$$\zeta_d = \frac{\dot{w}_a}{\dot{w}_i} = \frac{\dot{w}_a c}{Fg} \qquad (3\text{--}34)$$

And from equation 3–24,

$$\zeta_d = \frac{\dot{w}_a \sqrt{gkRT_1}}{A_t p_1 g k \sqrt{[2/(k+1)]^{(k+1)/(k-1)}}}$$

The value of this discharge correction factor is usually larger than one (0.98 to 1.15); the actual flow is larger than the theoretical flow because:

1. The molecular weight of the gases increases slightly when flowing through a nozzle, thereby changing their density.
2. Some heat is transferred to the nozzle walls. This will lower the temperature in the nozzle and increase the density and weight flow slightly.
3. The specific heat ratio changes in an actual nozzle in such a manner as to slightly increase the value of the discharge correction factor.
4. Incomplete combustion increases the density of the exhaust gases.

The actual thrust is lower than the thrust calculated for an ideal rocket and can be found by an empirical *thrust correction factor* ζ_F by

$$F_a = \zeta_F F_i = \zeta_F C_F p_1 A_t$$

$$= \zeta_F c \frac{\dot{w}}{g} \qquad (3\text{--}35)$$

where

$$\zeta_F = \zeta_v \zeta_d = \frac{F_a}{F_i} \qquad (3\text{--}36)$$

and has values between 0.92 and 1.00. See equations 1–8 and 3–31.

Since the thrust correction factor is equal to the product of the discharge correction factor and the velocity correction factor, any one can be determined if the other two are known. The variation of these three correction factors with the degree of completeness of combustion for liquid oxygen and alcohol propellants is shown in Figure 3–16.

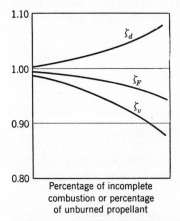

It was assumed that the velocity of the combustion gases is uniform across an ideal nozzle. In actual rocket nozzles the gas velocity is lower near the walls than in the middle and is a function of the nozzle shape, injection method, and mixing of fuel and oxidizer. The calculated velocity is, therefore, only a mean value. The chemical composition and the temperature of the gases in a real nozzle are usually also not uniform over the cross section. Therefore, the properties of the gases c_p, c_v, R, and k for any one section of the nozzle are average properties only.

Figure 3–16. Thrust, discharge, and velocity correction factors as functions of the completeness of combustion.

When accurate nozzle calculations are required, the variation of the gas properties with respect to temperature and pressure must also be considered. Since these quantities change from point to point in a nozzle, the gas properties change continuously. This effect will be considered further in the next chapter.

Example 3–5. Design a rocket nozzle to conform to the following conditions:

Chamber pressure	20.4 atm = 300 psia
Atmospheric pressure	1.0 atm = 14.7 psia
Chamber temperature	5150° R
Mean molecular weight of gases	21.87 lb/mole
Ideal specific impulse	230 sec
Specific heat ratio	1.229
Desired thrust	300 lb

Determine the following: nozzle throat and exit areas, the respective diameters, the actual exhaust velocity, and actual specific impulse.

Solution. The theoretical thrust coefficient is found from equation 3–30. For optimum conditions $p_2 = p_3$. By substituting $k = 1.229$, $p_2 = 14.7$ psia, $p_1 = 300$ psia, the thrust coefficient is $C_F = 1.405$. This value can also be obtained by interpolation between the values of c_F obtained from Figures 3–12 and 3–13.

The throat area is found using $\zeta_F = 0.96$

$$A_t = \frac{F}{\zeta_F C_F p_1} = \frac{300}{0.960 \times 1.405 \times 300} = 0.741 \text{ in.}^2$$

The throat diameter is then 0.973 in. The area expansion ratio can be determined from Figure 3–7 as $\epsilon = 3.52$. The exit area is

$$A_2 = 0.741 \times 3.52 = 2.61 \text{ in.}^2$$

The exit diameter is, therefore, 1.825 in. The theoretical exhaust velocity is

$$v_2 = I_s g = 230 \times 32.2 = 7410 \text{ ft/sec}$$

By selecting a proper velocity correction factor ζ_v such as 0.92, the actual exhaust velocity will be equal to:

$$(v_2)_a = 7410 \times 0.92 = 6820 \text{ ft/sec}$$

Since the specific impulse is proportional to the exhaust velocity, its actual value can be found by multiplying the theoretical value by the velocity correction factor ζ_v.

$$(I_s)_a = 230 \times 0.92 = 212 \text{ sec}$$

5 Flow through a Combustion Zone

Although the complex mechanism of combustion and chemical energy release in liquid propellant rocket thrust chambers is not fully understood, the flow of propellants through a rocket combustion chamber can be subjected to simple analysis by considering only the initial and final conditions ahead and behind the combustion region.

The analysis shows that high chamber gas velocities (chamber Mach number $M_1 \geq 0.2$) cause energy losses, the magnitude of which is not negligible. This section therefore applies mainly to high gas velocity combustion chambers whose cross-sectional area A_1 approaches in magnitude the throat area A_t, i.e., $A_1/A_t \leq 3$.

The burning gases expand and accelerate as heat in a combustion chamber of constant cross section is added and a pressure force must act on the gases. This implies that all heat is not added at constant pressure and the energy available for producing nozzle exit velocities is less than the maximum which exists under ideal conditions of negligible chamber velocity. The performance of the rocket is therefore impaired.

The three rocket thrust chamber shapes of Figure 3–17 illustrate the range of possible combustion chamber sizes. The process is adiabatic because no heat is transferred to the walls. However, the process is not isentropic since energy has to be expended

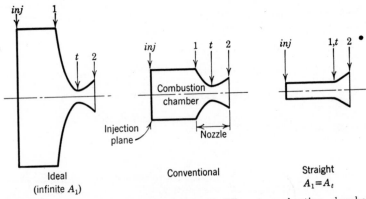

Figure 3–17. Rocket thrust chambers of different combustion chamber cross sections.

on accelerating the gases and since this energy becomes unavailable. The total pressure will decrease as the fluid flows through a combustion zone. The liquid propellants are injected into the tubular chamber at section *inj* with a small axial velocity. In solid propellant rocket units the plane *inj* would correspond to the burning surface. Between sections *inj* and 1 the chemical process of combustion occurs and is completed at section 1. As heat is liberated between sections *inj* and 1 the volume of the gas is increased and the gas must be accelerated to satisfy the conditions of constant mass flow.

The walls of the chamber are assumed to be parallel (tubular), and consequently the only force in an axial direction available for accelerating the gas is the force corresponding to the pressure difference $p_{inj} - p_1$. For dynamic equilibrium of the flow the pressure force must equal the inertia force of the gas associated with the time rate of change of momentum of the flow between sections inj and 1 or

$$p_{inj} - p_1 = \frac{\dot{w}}{A_1 g}(v_1 - v_{inj}) = \frac{v_1^2}{g V_1} - \frac{v_{inj}^2}{g V_{inj}} \qquad (3\text{–}37)$$

This relation can be expressed in terms of the Mach number according to equations 3–3 and 3–10 at sections inj and 1 so that the pressure ratio for the combustion chamber is

$$\frac{p_{inj}}{p_1} = \frac{1 + k M_1^2}{1 + k M_{inj}^2} \qquad (3\text{–}38)$$

By using equation 3–12 the ratio of the total pressure at the injection point to the total pressure at the nozzle inlet will be

$$\left(\frac{p_{inj}}{p_1}\right)_0 = \left(\frac{1 + k M_1^2}{1 + k M_{inj}^2}\right)\left[\frac{1 + \dfrac{k-1}{2}M_{inj}^2}{1 + \dfrac{k-1}{2}M_1^2}\right]^{k/(k-1)} \qquad (3\text{–}39)$$

From this equation it is evident that for a large (ideal) chamber where $M_{inj} = M_1 = 0$, the pressure ratio $(p_{inj}/p_1)_0$ is unity and there is no loss in thermodynamic availability. If the injection velocity is small ($M_{inj} \to 0$), the ratio of the static pressures (equation 3–38) becomes

$$p_{inj}/p_1 = 1 + k M_1^2 \qquad (3\text{–}40)$$

For a straight tubular chamber ($M_1 = 1.0$) the equation above shows that the pressure loss in the chamber gives a ratio of chamber inlet pressure to nozzle throat pressure equal to $1 + k$. For $M_{inj} = 0$ the total pressure ratio becomes

$$\left(\frac{p_{inj}}{p_1}\right)_0 = \frac{1 + k M_1^2}{\left(1 + \dfrac{k-1}{2}M_1^2\right)^{k/(k-1)}} \qquad (3\text{–}41)$$

This last relation gives also the ratio of the chamber to throat pressure in a tubular chamber $(p_1/p_t)_{tu}$ to the ratio of the chamber to throat pressure in a chamber of an infinitely large cross section $(p_1/p_t)_i$; the relation is shown in Figure 3–18 as a function of area ratio as determined from equation 3–13.

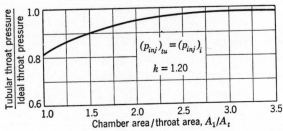

FIGURE 3–18. Decrease in throat pressure of rocket motors as a function of the chamber to throat area ratio.

The special case of the *straight thrust chamber* is interesting ($M_1 = 1.0$ in equation 3–41) because it shows the magnitude of loss compared to an ideal chamber.

$$\frac{\left(\dfrac{p_{inj}}{p_t}\right)_i}{\left(\dfrac{p_{inj}}{p_t}\right)_s} = 2\left(\frac{2}{k+1}\right)^{1/(k-1)} \tag{3–42}$$

Values of this ratio are given in Table 3–6.

By definition of an adiabatic combustion process, the total temperature after completion of combustion at section 1, $(T_1)_0$, is the

TABLE 3–6. CALCULATED RESULTS FOR STRAIGHT TUBULAR CHAMBER

k	$\dfrac{\left(\dfrac{p_{inj}}{p_t}\right)_s}{\left(\dfrac{p_{inj}}{p_t}\right)_i}$	$\dfrac{\dot{w}_s}{\dot{w}_i}$	$\dfrac{(v_2)_s}{(v_2)_i}$			$\dfrac{F_s}{F_i}$		
			$\dfrac{p_{inj}}{p_2}=10$	100	1000	$\dfrac{p_{inj}}{p_2}=10$	100	1000
1.10	1.230	0.812	0.958	0.982	0.990	0.780	0.798	0.804
1.20	1.246	0.802	0.960	0.984	0.991	0.769	0.788	0.795
1.30	1.258	0.795	0.961	0.986	0.992	0.764	0.784	0.789
1.40	1.272	0.785	0.963	0.988	0.993	0.757	0.776	0.780

same irrespective of the area of the combustion chamber. The total kinetic energy increase must equal the change in enthalpy

$$\frac{v_2^2 - v_1^2}{2gc_pJ} = (T_{inj})_0 - T_2 = (T_{inj})_0 \left(1 - \frac{T_1}{(T_{inj})_0}\frac{T_2}{T_1}\right)$$

where $(T_{inj})_0/T_1$ is the temperature ratio for the acceleration within the tubular chamber as given by equation 3–11 and T_2/T_1 is the temperature ratio for the ideal isentropic expansion in the convergent-divergent nozzle given by the isentropic relation, equation 3–6.

$$\frac{T_2}{T_1} = \left(\frac{p_2}{p_1}\right)^{(k-1)/k} = \left[\frac{(p_{inj})_0}{p_1}\frac{p_2}{(p_{inj})_0}\right]^{(k-1)/k}$$

$(p_{inj})_0/p_2$ is the overall or complete expansion ratio and $(p_{inj})_0/p_1$ is the expansion ratio for the tubular chamber as given by equation 3–38. If $v_{inj}(M_{inj} \to 0)$ is neglected the energy relation becomes $[(p_{inj})_0 = p_{inj}, \text{ when } M_{inj} = 0]$.

$$\left(\frac{1}{T_{inj}}\right)_0 \frac{v_2^2}{2gc_pJ} = 1 - \frac{\left[(1 + kM_1^2)\dfrac{p_2}{(p_{inj})_0}\right]^{(k-1)/k}}{1 + \dfrac{k-1}{2}M_1^2}$$

For the ideal conditions of negligible velocity at section inj and 1 ($M_1 = 0$) the relation above reduces to

$$1 - \left[\frac{p_2}{(p_1)_0}\right]^{(k-1)/k}$$

The *energy utilization efficiency* of the tubular thrust chamber is defined as the ratio of the two relations above. It expresses the ratio of the kinetic jet energies of tubular motors and equivalent ideal chambers with infinite chamber cross section.

$$\nu = \frac{(v_2)_{tu}^2}{(v_2)_i^2} = \frac{1 - \dfrac{\left[(1 + kM_1^2)\dfrac{p_2}{p_{inj}}\right]^{(k-1)/k}}{1 + \dfrac{k-1}{2}M_1^2}}{1 - \left[\dfrac{p_2}{(p_i)_0}\right]^{(k-1)/k}} \tag{3–43}$$

It is not convenient to use Mach number as a design criterion; the ratio of chamber area to throat area A_1/A_t gives a much more direct description of the layout of the thrust chamber. The relation between M_1 and A_1/A_t can be obtained by using equation 3–13 for $M_t = 1.0$. By combining equations 3–13 and 3–43 the *loss in energy utilization efficiency* can be expressed as a function of the chamber area ratio A_1/A_t as shown in Figure 3–19.

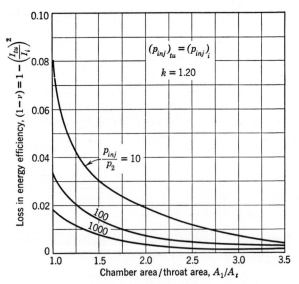

FIGURE 3–19.   Loss in energy utilization efficiency versus area ratio.

Exhaust velocity, propellant flow, and thrust are parameters important to the rocket designer. Their magnitude can now be determined for tubular chambers and compared with the same quantities in ideal rockets. The ratio of the nozzle exhaust velocities of tubular chambers and ideal chambers (specific impulse ratio) equals the square root of the energy utilization efficiency $\sqrt{\nu}$.

The throat condition in tubular chambers is unique, inasmuch as only the throat pressure and density change with variable area ratio. For the same available energy, the Mach number, static temperature, total temperature, and, therefore, also the velocity of the throat are independent of the area ratio A_1/A_t. The ideal propellant flow passing the nozzle section changes only with the throat density (or throat pressure). The ratio of the *propellant flow* for different area ratios is, therefore, the reciprocal of the pressure ratio given by equation 3–41 and is shown in Figure 3–20.

The *loss in thrust* is proportional to the loss in exit velocity and the loss of propellant flow. It is expressed as the product of both and is shown in Figure 3–21.

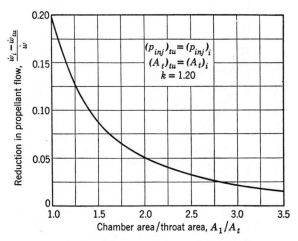

FIGURE 3–20. Propellant flow versus area ratio.

From this analysis it can be seen that rocket combustion chambers with cross-sectional areas which approach the magnitude of their nozzle cross section areas are inherently less efficient in converting thermal energy to kinetic energy of the jet than chambers with comparatively large cross sections. The losses in available energy occur only in the tubular chamber, while the conversion of thermal to kinetic energy in the nozzle proceeds without loss. As the relative amount of energy converted in the nozzle increases with larger ratios of chamber inlet pressure to nozzle exit pressure, the energy loss in the chamber will be a smaller percentage of the total available energy. The losses are due to the non-isentropic expansion within the combustion chamber and are larger for successively smaller ratios of chamber to throat cross sections and successively lower pressure ratios p_0/p_2, as shown in Figure 3–19.

For example, with a chamber to throat area ratio of unity and $p_0/p_2 = 10$, the loss in energy is 8 per cent; but for a chamber to throat area ratio of 2, the loss is only 1.7 per cent.

For equal chamber inlet pressures and throat areas, a straight tubular chamber (area ratio $A_1/A_t = 1.0$) has an exhaust velocity 1 to 4 per cent lower than an ideal infinite area chamber. The

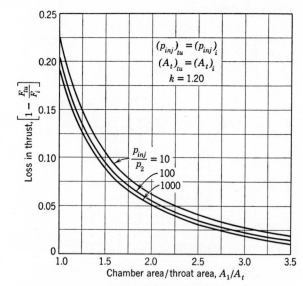

FIGURE 3–21. Loss in thrust versus area ratio.

flow of propellant is also appreciably lower (Figure 3–20). A straight chamber has approximately 21 per cent less thrust, while a tubular chamber with an area ratio of 2 has only 5 per cent less thrust (Figure 3–21).

For a straight tubular chamber ($A_1/A_t = 1$) the chamber inlet pressure is approximately 23 per cent higher, while at a chamber to throat area ratio of 2 this increase is only 5 per cent.

A variation of the thermodynamic properties of the propellants, such as a variation of the specific heat ratio between 1.1 and 1.4 as shown in Table 3–6, has only a negligible influence on the results.

Example 3–6. What percentage loss in performance is to be anticipated in a thrust chamber at sea level with a chamber cross section 1.5 times its throat area at a chamber pressure of 150 psi ($k = 1.20$) if compared with an ideal thrust chamber?

$$\text{Pressure ratio} = \frac{p_{inj}}{p_3} = \frac{150}{14.7} = 10.2$$

Energy loss from equation 3–43 or Figure 3–19,

$$1 - \nu = 0.03 \text{ or } 3 \text{ per cent } (\nu = 0.97)$$

The velocity ratio is proportional to $\sqrt{\nu}$ and the velocity decrease is

$$1 - \frac{(v_2)_{tu}}{(v_2)_i} = 1 - \sqrt{\nu} = 1.66 \text{ per cent}$$

Loss in thrust from Figure 3–21,

$$1 - \frac{(F)_{tu}}{(F)_i} = 10.6 \text{ per cent}$$

Pressure ratio in combustion chamber from equation 3–41 or Figure 3–18,

$$\frac{(p_0/p_1)_{tu}}{(p_0/p_1)_i} = \frac{(p_1)_i}{(p_1)_{tu}} = 1.10$$

The pressure at the nozzle inlet in the tubular thrust chamber is

$$(p_1)_{tu} = \frac{150}{1.10} = 136.5 \text{ psia}$$

Compared to 150 psi for a chamber with large cross section, the pressure loss in the combustion chamber of the tubular chamber is

$$(p_0 - p_1)_{tu} = 150 - 136.5 = 14.5 \text{ psi}$$

6 Summary of Equations

The equations frequently used in design of rocket nozzles are summarized for convenience of the reader.

Ideal Exhaust Velocity

$$v_2 = \sqrt{\frac{2gk}{k-1} \frac{R'T_1}{\mathfrak{M}} \left[1 - \left(\frac{p_2}{p_1}\right)^{(k-1)/k}\right]}$$

$$= \sqrt{\frac{2gk}{k-1} RT_1 \eta}$$

$$= \sqrt{gk \frac{R'T_0}{\mathfrak{M}} \left(\frac{v_2}{v_t}\right)}$$

The variation of exhaust velocity with $T_1/\mathfrak{M}$ is shown in Figure 3–5, values of $\sqrt{2gk/(k-1)}$ are given in Table 3–1, and values of η can be found from Figure 3–4. The ratio of v_2/v_t is plotted in Figures 3–7 and 3–8 for different pressure ratios.

Effective Exhaust Velocity

$$c_a = \zeta_v c$$

$$= \zeta_v c^* C_F$$

$$= \frac{F_a g}{\dot{w}_a} = \zeta_v \frac{Fg}{\dot{w}}$$

$$= \zeta_v \left(v_2 + \frac{(p_2 - p_3)A_2 g}{\dot{w}} \right)$$

$$c = v_2, \text{ when } p_2 = p_3$$

$$c = \frac{C_F p_1 A_t g}{\dot{w}}$$

$$= I_s g$$

Thrust

$$F_a = \zeta_F F = \zeta_v \zeta_d F$$

$$= \frac{\dot{w}_a c_a}{g}$$

$$F = \frac{\dot{w} c}{g}$$

$$= C_F p_1 A_t$$

$$= v_2 \dot{w}/g + (p_2 - p_3)A_2$$

The thrust coefficient C_F is defined by equation 3–30, and shown as functions of the area ratio and pressure ratio in Figures 3–11, 3–12, and 3–13. The effective exhaust velocity c is given by equation 1–4. The velocity correction factor ζ_v is defined as $\sqrt{e}$ (where e is given by equation 3–33) and has an average value near 0.92. For optimum expansion $p_2 = p_3$. The thrust correction factor ζ_F is defined by equation 3–36, and for good thrust chambers has an average value near 0.96.

Specific Impulse and Specific Propellant Consumption

$$(I_s)_a = \zeta_v I_s = \zeta_v \frac{c}{g} = \frac{c_a}{g} = \frac{F}{\dot{w}}$$

$$= \frac{1}{(w_s)_a} = \zeta_v \frac{1}{w_s}$$

Propellant Flow

$$\dot{w}_a = \zeta_d \dot{w}$$

$$\dot{w} = \frac{p_1 A_t kg \sqrt{[2/(k+1)]^{(k+1)/(k-1)}}}{\sqrt{kg \dfrac{R'T}{\mathfrak{M}}}}$$

$$\dot{w} = \frac{v_x A_x}{V_x} = \frac{v_2 A_2}{V_2} = \frac{v_t A_t}{V_t}$$

The function $k\sqrt{[2/(k+1)]^{(k+1)/(k-1)}}$ is given in Table 3–1. The discharge correction factor ζ_d is defined by equation 3–34 and has an average value of 1.04.

Area Ratio

$$\epsilon = A_2/A_t$$

The area ratio for optimum expansion is defined by equation 3–25 and is plotted for various values of p_1/p_2 and k in Figures 3–7 and 3–8.

Problems

1. Certain experimental results indicate that the propellant gases of a liquid oxygen–gasoline reaction have a mean molecular weight of 23.2 lb/mole and a specific heat ratio of 1.22. Compute the specific heat at constant pressure and at constant volume.

2. Sänger in his book *Raketenflugtechnik* reports that several propellants have theoretical exhaust velocities of 10,000 ft/sec. Assuming that the initial enthalpy of the propellants equals zero, what amount of chemical energy (in Btu/lb) has to be added to the propellant to attain this velocity?

3. A certain nozzle expands a gas under isentropic conditions. Its initial velocity equals 230 ft/sec, its final velocity 3200 ft/sec. What is the change in enthalpy of the gas in Btu/lb? What percentage of error is introduced if the initial velocity is neglected?

4. Nitrogen at 700° F ($k = 1.38$, $R = 55.1$) flows at a Mach number of 2.73. What is its actual and its acoustic velocity?

5. The following data are given for an ideal rocket thrust chamber:

$$k = 1.3, \quad R = 66$$

Chamber pressure	375 psia
External pressure	13 psia
Chamber temperature	5300° F
Throat area	2.07 in.^{2}

Determine (a) throat velocity, (b) specific volume at throat, (c) propellant flow and specific impulse, (d) thrust, (e) Mach number at throat.

6. Compute the ideal thrust coefficient for problem 5 by two methods.

7. A certain ideal rocket with an area ratio of 2.3 and a throat area of 5 in.^{2} delivers gases at $k = 1.30$ and $R = 66$ at a design chamber pressure of 300 psia and a constant chamber temperature of 5300° R against a back pressure of 10 psia. By means of an appropriate valve arrangement, it is possible to throttle the propellant flow to the thrust chamber. Calculate and plot against pressure the following quantities for 300 psia, 200 psia, and 100 psia chamber pressure: (a) pressure ratio between chamber and atmosphere, (b) effective exhaust velocity for area ratio involved, (c) ideal exhaust velocity for ideal area ratio, (d) propellant flow, (e) thrust, (f) specific impulse, (g) exit pressure, (h) exit temperature.

8. In a rocket chamber, combustion gases ($k = 1.30$, $R = 66$) at 5000° R and 20 atm pressure travel at a velocity of 250 ft/sec. What is the Mach number? For a flow of 21.6 lb/sec determine the cross-sectional area of the combustion chamber.

9. For the rocket unit given in Example 3–2 compute the exhaust velocity if the nozzle is cut off and the exit area is arbitrarily decreased by 50 per cent. Compute the losses in kinetic energy and thrust and express them as a percentage of the original kinetic energy and the original thrust.

10. In order to make the operation of a rocket thrust chamber take place at the optimum expansion ratio at any altitude, building a variable area nozzle has often been considered. Because of the enormous design difficulties of such a device, it has never been successfully realized. Assuming that such a mechanism can eventually be constructed, what would have to be the variation of the area ratio with altitude (plot up to 30,000 ft) if such a rocket had a chamber pressure of 300 psia? Assume $k = 1.20$.

11. (a) Compute the ideal nozzle efficiency η for $k = 1.22$ and a pressure ratio of 22. (b) What percentage change in this efficiency occurs when the pressure ratio is increased 10 per cent? (c) Same as (b), but the specific heat ratio is increased 10 per cent.

12. What is the maximum velocity if the nozzle in Example 3–2 was designed to expand into a vacuum? If the expansion area ratio was 2000?

13. By using Mach number relations determine the following quantities for a rocket thrust chamber which has a static and total combustion chamber

temperature of 4500° R, a total pressure of 400 psia, and a nozzle inlet Mach number 0.070. The exit Mach number is 3.00 and $k = 1.25$. Determine (a) total pressure at throat, (b) total pressure at exit, (c) area ratio between throat and exit, (d) pressure ratio between chamber and exit, (e) area ratio between chamber and throat.

14. The German A-4 propulsion system has a sea level thrust of 25,400 kg and a chamber pressure of 220 psia. If the exit pressure is 12.2 psia and the exit diameter 740 mm, what is the thrust at 40,000 ft?

15. Calculate the nozzle angle correction factor for a conical nozzle whose divergence half angle is 13 degrees.

16. For Example 3–2 determine (a) actual thrust, (b) actual exhaust velocity, (c) actual specific impulse, and (d) velocity correction factor. Assume that the thrust correction factor is 0.985 and the discharge correction factor is 1.050.

17. A fighter plane has a rocket system which provides 7.00 lb/sec of propellant for a combustion chamber operating at 300 psia and 5200° R. Assume $k = 1.20$ and $R = 67$. The nozzle is to be so designed that its fixed area ratio will be an optimum between 20,000 and 35,000 ft altitude. What is the value of this area ratio and of the mean thrust coefficient? Assume $\zeta_v = 0.94$ and $\zeta_F = 0.99$. Assume that the plane spends an equal amount of time at each altitude. Neglect overexpansion losses.

18. For a velocity correction factor of 0.93 determine the enthalpy percentage which is lost in the expansion through a nozzle.

19. An ideal rocket has the following characteristics:

Chamber pressure	27.2 atmospheres
Nozzle exit pressure	3 psia
Specific heat ratio	1.20
Average molecular weight	21.0 lb/mole
Chamber temperature	4200° F

Determine the critical pressure ratio, the gas velocity at the throat, the expansion area ratio, and the theoretical nozzle exit velocity.

Answers: 1.77; 3470 ft/sec; 11.2; and 8570 ft/sec.

20. For an ideal rocket with a characteristic exhaust velocity c^* of 4000 ft/sec, a mass flow rate of 5 slugs/sec, a thrust coefficient of 1.50, and a nozzle throat area of 40.0 in.^{2}, compute the effective exhaust velocity, the thrust, the chamber pressure, and the specific impulse.

Answers: 6000 ft/sec; 30,000 lb; 500 psia; and 186 sec.

21. In the testing of rocket thrust chambers, it is often impossible to measure thrust directly. The effective exhaust velocity is then computed from the equation:

$$c = C_F \, c^*$$

where c^* is determined from the measured values of chamber pressure, propellant flow rate, and throat area according to equation 3–32. The following data are measured or given:

Measured chamber pressure near injector	200 psia
Atmospheric pressure (sea level)	14.7 psia
Nozzle exit to throat area ratio	3.0
Chamber to throat area ratio	1.5
Throat area	100 in.^{2}
Propellant flow	129 lb/sec
Specific heat ratio	1.20
Friction and divergence correction factor to theoretical thrust coefficient	0.97

The measured chamber pressure must be corrected for the acceleration of flow in the combustion chamber to determine the effective or nozzle inlet stagnation pressure. Determine (*a*) the effective chamber pressure, (*b*) the characteristic exhaust velocity, (*c*) the effective exhaust velocity, and (*d*) the per cent error in effective exhaust velocity if the chamber pressure measurement had not been corrected.

Answers: (*a*) 180 psia; (*b*) 4500 ft/sec; (*c*) 5660 ft/sec; (*d*) 13 per cent.

Symbols

A	area, ft^2
c	effective exhaust velocity, ft/sec
C_F	thrust coefficient
c_p	specific heat at constant pressure, Btu/lb °F
c_v	specific heat at constant volume, Btu/lb °F
d	total derivative
e	energy conversion efficiency
F	thrust, lb
g	gravitational acceleration, 32.2 ft/sec^2
h	enthalpy per unit weight, Btu/lb
I_s	specific impulse, sec
J	mechanical equivalent of heat, 778 ft-lb/Btu
k	specific heat ratio
p	pressure, lb/ft^2
M	Mach number
$\mathfrak{M}$	molecular weight, lb/mole
R	gas constant per unit weight, ft-lb/lb °R ($R = R'/\mathfrak{M}$)
R'	universal gas constant (1544 ft-lb/mole °F)
T	absolute temperature, °R
V	specific volume, ft^3/lb
v	velocity, ft/sec
$\dot{w}$	propellant weight flow rate, lb/sec

Greek Letters

α	half angle of divergent nozzle section
ϵ	area ratio
ζ_d	discharge correction factor
ζ_F	thrust correction factor
ζ_v	velocity correction factor
η	rocket cycle efficiency
λ	nozzle angle correction factor
ν	energy utilization efficiency

Subscripts

a	actual
i	ideal
inj	injection plane
max	maximum
s	straight combustion chamber
t	throat
tu	tubular combustion chamber
x	any plane within rocket nozzle
y	any plane within rocket nozzle
0	stagnation or impact condition
1	nozzle inlet
2	nozzle exit
3	atmospheric

Chapter 4

Rocket Propellant

Performance Calculations

Rockets utilize the heat liberated in the combustion of chemical propellants as a source of energy. As performance and weight considerations are of prime importance in designing rockets, it is desirable to consider the relative merits of rocket propellant combinations by comparing their specific impulses and other properties, such as density or storage qualities. A high specific impulse means a saving in the weight of propellant carried and a reduction in the necessary tank size. Other important factors to be considered in the choice of rocket propellants, such as availability, density, and ease of handling, are discussed in Chapters 6 and 10.

The ideal specific impulse and the exhaust velocity of a rocket propellant system can be calculated for optimum expansion from equation 1–8 and 3–15 as

$$v = \sqrt{\frac{2gk}{k-1} \frac{R'}{\mathfrak{M}} T_1 \left[1 - \left(\frac{p_2}{p_1}\right)^{(k-1)/k} \right]} \qquad (4\text{--}1)$$

$$I_s = \frac{v}{g} \qquad (4\text{--}2)$$

The calculation of v or I_s from the equation above requires the evaluation of the flame temperature T_1, the mean molecular weight of the product gases $\mathfrak{M}$, and the specific heat ratio of the hot gases k. This chapter describes the commonly accepted method for the calculation of these quantities for any given propellant combination at any given chamber pressure and mixture ratio and gives results for a number of propellant combinations.

Since equation 4–1 assumes ideal rocket chamber conditions as explained in Section 1 of Chapter 3, it may be expected that the values of v or I_s so calculated will be higher than those obtained from firing actual propellants in rocket units. In practice it has been found that the experimental values are, in general, 5 to 12 per cent lower than those calculated by the method explained in this chapter. Since the nozzle inefficiencies explained in the previous chapter must be considered, only a portion of this correction (perhaps 1 to 4 per cent) are due to combustion inefficiencies.

Although the evaluation of the exhaust velocity or the specific impulse is not complicated in principle, it involves a lengthy trial and error calculation, which is only warranted if accurate results are required. Often an approximate answer can be obtained by comparing a given propellant combination with combinations whose performance has been accurately evaluated and by thus estimating the performance values.

The quantity of energy available from a given rocket propellant, either liquid or solid, is determined by the chemical nature of the oxidizer and fuel molecules or groups as well as by the chemical nature of the reaction gas products. The propellant molecules should be as weakly valence-bonded as is compatible with stability and good physical properties. Compounds whose formation is characterized by an absorption of energy will generally liberate this additional energy on combustion and so provide increased performance. For example, hydrazine is such a compound. Since combustion reactions are essentially oxidation processes, representing a transfer of electrons from fuels to oxidizers, the oxidizer should, for a large energy release, be of high electronegativity and the fuel molecules should be highly electropositive.

1 Assumptions and Definitions

The chemical reaction of propellants is assumed to take place in an ideal rocket as explained in Section 1 of Chapter 3. The product gases are assumed to be in chemical equilibrium at the chamber pressure and no heat is transferred to the walls. There is no friction, and the gas mixture is assumed to be homogeneous in composition. The subsequent calculations apply equally well to liquid propellant and solid propellant rocket units. In an ideal rocket it is assumed that the method of mixing liquid propellants, the mechanism of the feed system, or the grain design of a solid propellant have no effect on the ideal chemical equilibrium of the combustion gases.

Before explaining the method of calculating the performance of rocket propellants, such required basic quantities as heat of formation and heat of reaction are defined.

The *heat of formation* is defined as the change in enthalpy which results when a compound is formed at standard conditions from its elements isothermally and at constant pressure. Heats of formation are given in Tables 4–1 and 5–3 and in the Reference Bibliography under Sections 3.3 and 4.1.

TABLE 4–1. HEATS OF FORMATION

(*References: NACA Report 1037* (1951) and *National Bureau of Standards Circular 500*).

Compound	Temperature, °F	Q_F, Btu/lb-mole
C (gas)	77	+309,060
CO (gas)	77	−47,550
CO_2 (gas)	77	−169,300
H (gas)	32	+92,910
H_2O (gas)	77	−104,000
N (gas)	32	+153,200
NH_3 (gas)	77	−19,870
N_2H_4 (liquid)	77	+21,690
NO (gas)	32	+38,660
NO_2 (gas)	77	+14,560
O (gas)	32	+105,400
OH (gas)	32	+18,000
N_2, H_2, O_2, Cl_2, He (gas at unit fugacity)	77	0
HNO_3 (liquid, 100% concentration)	77	−74,530
C_2H_5OH (gas, 100% concentration)	77	−101,232
C_8H_{18} (gas)	77	−96,430
H_2O_2 (liquid, 90% concentration)	77	−81,020

The *heat of reaction* is defined as the change in enthalpy which occurs when products are formed from reactants at standard conditions, namely at a constant reference temperature and pressure. This enthalpy change may be either positive or negative, depending upon whether the reaction is exothermic or endothermic. Combustion reactions are exothermic, i.e., heat is released during the process.

The heat of reaction can be computed from the difference between the sum of the heats of formation of the products minus the sum of the heats of formation of the reactant compounds. A chemical reaction can be written as follows:

$$a(A) + b(B) \leftrightarrows c(C) + d(D) + \text{energy}$$

The large letters, A, B, C, and D, refer to various chemical compounds; the small letters indicate the number of moles of each.

The heat of reaction for this chemical reaction is defined in terms of the heats of formation.

$$Q_R = c(Q_F)_C + d(Q_F)_D - a(Q_F)_A - b(Q_F)_B$$

where Q_R is the heat of reaction in Btu per mole, Q_F is the heat of formation in Btu per mole, and a, b, c, d are the number of moles of compounds A, B, C, and D.

In more general terms the heat of reaction is:

$$Q_R = \sum [n(Q_F)_{products}] - \sum [n(Q_F)_{reactants}] \qquad (4\text{-}3)$$

where n is the number of moles of the respective compounds or elements. For any given propellant combination Q_R is a function of the product gas composition, which in turn depends on the combustion temperature, as will be shown in Section 5.

2 Mixture of Gases

In rocket combustion devices the working substance consists of a mixture of several gases; this mixture of gases can be analytically treated as a perfect gas. The specific heat, the molecular weight, and the specific heat ratio of a mixture can be determined from the gas analysis and the properties of the individual gases. A propellant product gas mixture is usually defined by its chemical analysis, which is generally a volumetric analysis or a molar analysis. The volumetric analysis is often simplest to measure; it expresses the amount of a particular gas as a percentage of the

total volume which the gas mixture occupies. The molar analysis
gives the fraction of moles of each gas for one mole of gas mixture.
The molar analysis percentages are identical in number with the
volumetric analysis percentages.

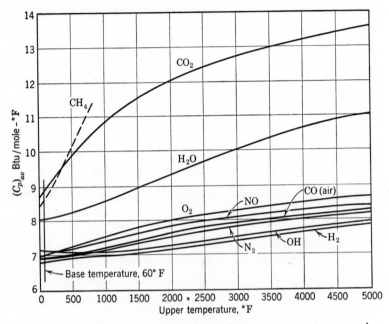

FIGURE 4–1. Average molar specific heats of gases at constant pressure between 60° F and abscissa temperature.

The molecular weight for a gas mixture is

$$\mathfrak{M} = \Sigma(X\mathfrak{M}_x) \tag{4–4}$$

The gas constant is

$$R = R'/\mathfrak{M} \tag{4–5}$$

The specific heat * can be determined from the molar analysis
and the molar specific heats as

$$C = \Sigma(XC_x) \tag{4–6}$$

* In this chapter the specific heats per mole C_p and C_v are used to simplify
the calculation. In other chapters the specific heats c_p and c_v refer to a unit
of weight.

The specific heat ratio is

$$k = \frac{C_p}{C_v}$$

$$= \frac{C_p}{C_p - 1.99} \tag{4–7}$$

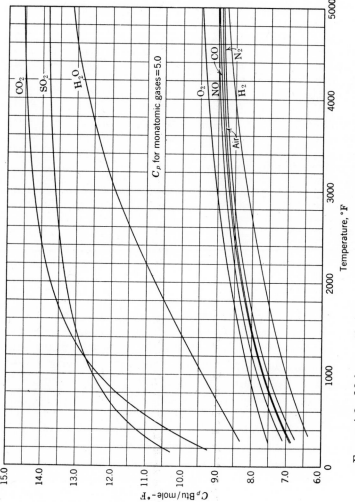

FIGURE 4-2. Molar specific heats of gases at constant pressure versus temperature.

The average and instantaneous molar specific heats for various gases commonly found in rocket combustion gases are shown in Figures 4–1 and 4–2.

Example 4–1. The following volumetric exhaust gas analysis is measured on a rocket nozzle: 16.6 per cent CO_2; 26.2 per cent CO; 30.5 per cent H_2O; 6.8 per cent H_2; 19.9 per cent N_2. Determine the molecular weight, the gas constant, and the average specific heat C_p up to 3000° F, the specific heat C_p at 3000° F, and the specific heat ratio k at 3000° F.

	X	$\mathfrak{M}_x$	$X\mathfrak{M}_x$	$(C_p)_{av}$	$(C_p)_{av}X$	C_p	C_pX
CO_2	0.166	44	7.31	12.77	2.12	14.25	2.36
CO	0.262	28	7.34	7.92	2.08	8.77	2.30
H_2O	0.305	18	5.48	10.01	3.06	11.9	3.63
H_2	0.068	2	0.136	7.41	0.504	8.15	0.554
N_2	0.199	28	5.57	7.83	1.56	8.53	1.70
	1.00		26.24		9.32		10.54

According to equation 4–4, the molecular weight equals $\Sigma(X\mathfrak{M}_x) = 26.24$ lb/mole. In equation 4–5, the gas constant R equals $1544/26.24 = 58.9$ ft-lb/lb °F. The specific heats were taken as the average molar specific heats between 60° F and 3000° F and were found from Fig. 4–1.

The average specific heat $(C_p)_{av}$ up to 3000° F equals $\Sigma[(C_p)_{av}X] = 9.32$ Btu/mole °F or $9.32/26.24 = 0.355$ Btu/lb °F. The instantaneous specific heats at 3000° F were obtained from Figure 4–2 for each gas. The instantaneous specific heat of the mixture C_p at 3000° F equals $\Sigma(C_pX) = 10.54$ Btu/mole °F or 0.402 Btu/lb °F. The specific heat ratio is found from equation 4–7 to be

$$k = \frac{C_p}{C_p - 1.99} = \frac{10.54}{10.54 - 1.99} = 1.23$$

3 Chemical Equilibrium

A chemical reaction is said to be in equilibrium when the reactants are being transformed into products at the same rate that the products are being reverted into the reactants. Many substances, when mixed in definite proportions, combine almost completely to form products which cannot be transformed into reactants by the application of pressure, heat, or changes of concentration. This type of reaction is called an irreversible reaction. A reversible reaction is one which will go in either direction. It is this type of reaction with which equilibrium conditions of hot gases are concerned. For example, the water gas equation is

$$CO + H_2O \rightleftarrows CO_2 + H_2$$

For perfect gases the equilibrium constant K_p for this relation is expressed as a function of the respective partial pressures

$$K_p = \frac{p_{CO_2} p_{H_2}}{p_{CO} p_{H_2O}}$$

The numerical value of K_p for any given reaction depends only on the temperature and is independent of other physical conditions. At any given temperature, the composition of the products and the reactants is fixed by the attainment of equilibrium. The partial pressures may be expressed in terms of pressure units (millimeters of mercury, atmospheres, or pounds per square inch), or they may be expressed as functions of the pressure of the mixture and the respective molar or volumetric concentrations, for the partial pressures are proportional to the volumetric composition of a gas mixture. Here K_p is independent of the pressure units used.

A more general form of the equilibrium constant is

$$K_p = \frac{p_A{}^a \cdot p_B{}^b \cdot p_C{}^c \cdots}{p_Z{}^z \cdot p_Y{}^y \cdots} \qquad (4\text{--}8)$$

$$K_n = \frac{X_A{}^a \cdot X_B{}^b \cdots}{X_Z{}^z \cdot X_Y{}^y \cdots} \qquad (4\text{--}9)$$

where K_n is the equilibrium constant, when the concentrations are expressed in volume percentages or molar percentages; K_p is the equilibrium constant, when concentrations are expressed in terms of pressure units, usually atmospheres; a, b, c, etc., are the number of moles of the reactant substances A, B, C, etc.; p_A, $p_B \cdots$ are the partial pressures of the substances A, B, C, etc.; X_A, X_B, X_C, etc., are the respective mole fractions or molar percentages. The number of moles of the reaction products x, y, z, etc., refer to the mole fractions of the reaction products designated by the subscripts X, Y, Z, etc. The equilibrium constant K_p is more commonly used than K_n. For any general reaction, the conversion between these values is:

$$K_p = K_n p^{n'} \qquad (4\text{--}10)$$

where n' is the number of moles of products diminished by the number of moles of reactants ($n' = a + b + c \cdots -x - y - z$), and p is the pressure of the mixture.

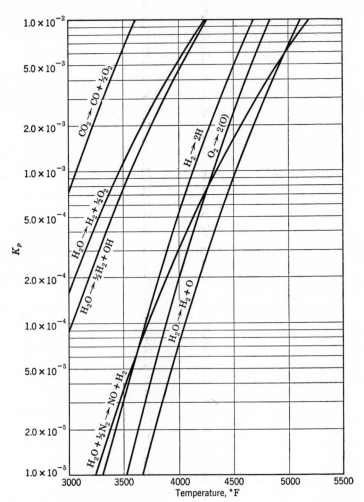

FIGURE 4–3. Equilibrium constant K_p versus temperature. (Based on OSRD

When the number of moles of products equals the number of moles of reactants, the numerical value of the equilibrium constants when expressed as a function of the number of moles and when expressed as a function of the partial pressures will be equal ($K_n = K_p$).

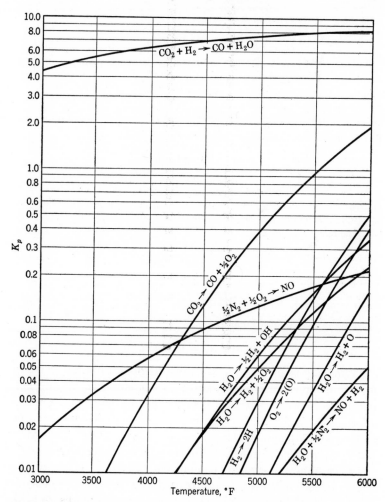

Thermodynamic Properties of Propellant Gases, by Hirschfelder *et al.,* Report 1087.)

Values of the equilibrium constants for several important reactions are given in Figure 4–3 and in references 3.303 and 3.304 with the pressure units expressed in atmospheres.

Example 4–2. Write the equilibrium equation for the reaction between hydrogen and monatomic hydrogen at 4000° F and 20 atm.

Solution.   From equation 4–8,

$$K_p = \frac{p^2_H}{p_{H_2}} \quad \text{for the reaction} \quad H_2 \rightleftarrows 2H$$

From Figure 4–3 the value of $K_p = 5.30 \times 10^{-4}$. If no other gases are present to react with H_2 and H, then the pressure balance is

$$20 = p_{H_2} + p_H$$

To solve these two equations for the partial pressures,

$$p_{H_2} = 19.8974 \text{ atm}$$

$$p_H = 0.1026 \text{ atm}$$

Since at any given pressure the volume occupied by one mole of a perfect gas is equal to the volume occupied by one mole of another perfect gas (Avogadro's law), the mole fractions are

$$H_2 = \frac{19.8974}{19.8974 + \frac{1}{2} \times 0.1026} = 0.9973$$

$$H = \frac{\frac{1}{2} \times 0.1026}{19.8974 + \frac{1}{2} \times 0.1026} = 0.0026$$

Therefore at the specified conditions

$$0.9973 \, H_2 \rightleftarrows 0.0026 \, H$$

Although it is not possible to write a single equilibrium equation for the complex reaction within a rocket chamber, equilibrium relations of several of the product gas components can be determined. The water gas equilibrium equation, for instance, can be used to relate the proportions of carbon dioxide, carbon monoxide, water vapor, and hydrogen within the rocket exhaust gases.

The equilibrium of rocket combustion gases is very sensitive to temperature. When the overall temperature is raised, the chemical reaction will tend to shift in such a manner as to absorb heat. The rocket combustion equilibrium products at the high flame temperature are, therefore, very different in proportion from the equivalent equilibrium products at lower temperature. If the temperature is very suddenly decreased, the reaction may be frozen, that is, the reaction velocities at room temperatures are so low that very little change in concentration and composition occurs. When gas samples are taken for analysis from a rocket, the equilibrium is effectively frozen by cooling the sampling probe.

The effect of pressure on the equilibrium will depend on the molar proportions as can be seen from equation 4–10. Consider these three reactions:

Reaction	Relative Volume of Reactants	Relative Volume of Products	Volume Ratio
1. $2H_2 + O_2 \rightleftarrows 2H_2O$	3	2	1.5
2. C(Solid) * $+ O_2 \rightleftarrows CO_2$	1	1	1
3. $H_2 \rightleftarrows 2H$	1	2	0.5

* Solid carbon is assumed to have no volume.

When a reaction system is subjected to increased pressure, it tends to react in such a manner as to reduce its volume. An increase in pressure for systems of type 1 (reactant volume larger than product volume and $n' < 0$) will tend to drive the reaction to completion, while for a system of type 3 (reactant volume smaller than product volume and $n' > 0$) the reaction will tend to go toward the left. For systems in which the volume is the same before and after reaction ($n' = 0$), pressure will have no effect. The pressure effects on the equilibrium of rocket propellant products is usually slight. In most rocket reactions the combustion temperature increases slightly with increased chamber pressure.

4 Dissociation

The high combustion temperature in rockets assists the dissociation of some of the reaction products by permitting them to break up into simpler molecules and into monatomic constituents, such as

$$H_2O \rightleftarrows HO + \tfrac{1}{2}H_2 - heat$$

$$O_2 \rightleftarrows 2O - heat$$

$$H_2 \rightleftarrows 2H - heat$$

These dissociation reactions take place only if the combustion temperature exceeds approximately 4800° F. At lower temperatures, the chemical equilibrium condition is such that only negligibly small fractions of the products dissociate. The value of the equilibrium constant as shown in Figure 4–3 indicates the amount of dissociation. For most rocket combustion reactions the equilibrium temperature is above 4800° F, and dissociation reactions must be considered in calculating accurate chemical equilibrium conditions for performance evaluations.

The error in the exhaust velocity introduced by neglecting dissociation for a propellant system consisting of the elements carbon, hydrogen, oxygen, and nitrogen is usually less than 3 per cent for a combustion temperature of 5000° F, and less than 13 per cent for a combustion temperature of 5500° F.

The *effects* of dissociation for rocket propulsion units are:

1. Dissociation consumes energy and therefore decreases the amount of energy available for conversion into the kinetic energy of the jet, thereby limiting the maximum attainable exhaust velocity and flame temperature.

2. Dissociation usually produces an increase in the average specific volume of the combustion gases and a lowering of the average molecular weight of the products. This raises the exhaust velocity slightly.

3. The reassociation of dissociated reaction products occurs when the gas stream temperature is lowered. In a nozzle with isentropic gas expansion the temperature drops steadily as the gases flow toward the nozzle exit; here the equilibrium composition will change and additional heat will be liberated in the exhaust portion of the nozzle. This phenomena is discussed further in Section 6.

4. The boundary layer near the wall is usually cooler than the main body of the rocket gases, because of the conduction of heat through the wall. Some scientists believe that the cooling of the gases in the boundary layer causes additional heat release by reassociation in the boundary layer immediately adjacent to the wall. The presence of dissociated reaction products thus can cause an increase in heat transfer to the wall.

In most cases the first effect is the predominant one on the performance of a rocket. In general, dissociation tends to limit the specific impulse. It is for this reason that it is desirable to select propellants which yield stable reaction products, such as N_2 or CO.

It can be seen that the number of moles and therefore the volume of the products of the three equations above is usually larger than the volume of the reactants. Increasing the chamber pressure will, therefore, decrease the amount of dissociation and increase the combustion temperature slightly.

5   Determination of Combustion Temperature and Composition of Reaction Products

The exact rate and mechanism of the chemical reaction of rocket propellants are not fully understood, although reaction rates and ignition time delays are known to vary for different propellant combinations. Their influence on the combustion equilibrium appears to be negligible. Rocket performance calculations may be solved satisfactorily by the principle of conservation of energy, provided chemical equilibrium is established at constant pressure within the combustion chamber and the assumptions for ideal rockets are valid.

Calculations of the combustion temperature and the product gas composition are based on equating the heat of reaction of the propellant combination and the rise in enthalpy of the product gases.

$$[Q_R]_{T_0} = \sum \left(n_p \int_{T_0}^{T} C_p \, dT \right) = \Delta h \qquad (4\text{--}11)$$

where $[Q_R]_{T_0}$ is the heat of reaction of propellant combination at reference temperature T_0. $\int C_p \, dT$ is the enthalpy change necessary to heat one mole of each product gas from the reference temperature T_0 to the flame temperature T; n_p is the number of moles of each product gas; C_p is the average molar specific heat at constant pressure between the combustion temperature and the reference temperature for a particular product gas in Btu per mole per degree Rankine (see Figure 4–1); T_0 is the datum or reference temperature; T is the absolute reaction temperature, and Δh is the total enthalpy gain of the reaction products.

The equation above, solved for T, will give the combustion temperature. The heat of reaction at reference temperature T_0 is a function of composition and temperature and is determined from the heats of formation by use of equation 4–3. This value is corrected for the heat necessary to bring the reactants up to the reference temperature.

Data listing various heats of formation and the quantities necessary to correct the heat of reaction are shown in Tables 4–1 and 4–2. The correction consists of the enthalpy change neces-

TABLE 4–2.   THERMODYNAMIC PROPERTIES OF SEVERAL PROPELLANTS

Compound	Boiling Point, °F	Heat of Evaporation, Btu/Mole	Mean Molar Specific Heat at Constant Pressure of Gases from Boiling Point to 80° F
H_2	−424	388	6
O_2	−298	2,930	7
H_2O	+212	17,480	9
CH_4	−258	3,970	8
H_2O_2 (98%)	+302	19,950	—
NH_3	−28	10,000	9
HNO_3	+147	13,000	—
N_2	−321	2,409	6
O_3	−169.5	6,530	9
C_2H_6	−127	6,860	11
C_3H_8	−43.7	8,070	16.5
N_2O_4	70	15,470	18
C_2H_4O	51	11,010	11
C_8H_{18}	258	14,520	

sary to bring the reactants to the standard reference temperature. For liquefied gases it includes the heat necessary to raise the liquid to the boiling point, the heat of vaporization, and the heat necessary to raise the gasified reactants from the boiling point to the reference temperature. For solid propellants it includes also the heat of fusion and the heat necessary to raise the solid to the melting point.

To evaluate the equilibrium temperature T, the number of moles of each product gas, that is, the composition, must be evaluated, using the equilibrium relations described above and the principle of conservation of matter. The amount of each element in combined and free form must be the same before and after the reaction. If a large number of possible products are formed, the calculation becomes quite tedious because of the large number of unknowns which must be determined before the combustion temperature can be computed.

Propellant combinations containing only carbon, oxygen, and hydrogen have at least eight possible combustion products. Typical combinations are liquid oxygen and gasoline, liquid oxygen and alcohol, and hydrogen peroxide and alcohol. The eight possible products are carbon dioxide, carbon monoxide, hydrogen, water vapor, oxygen, and the dissociation products monatomic hydrogen, monatomic oxygen, and hydroxyl. In solving for the equilibrium composition and temperature it is necessary to determine the relative proportion of each of these constituents. This calculation involves eight equations with eight unknowns. Three of these equations are material balance equations which equate the amount of each element (carbon, oxygen, and hydrogen) in the reactants to that in the products. The five other equations are equilibrium equations. Since the final combustion temperature must be known before the equilibrium constants for the equilibrium equations can be determined, a tedious, but relatively straightforward, trial and error solution is indicated. Recently many propellant performance calculations of this type have been performed by means of automatic computing machinery.

Reaction gases which contain only hydrogen, carbon, oxygen, and nitrogen are obtained from the following common propellant combinations: nitric acid and aniline, nitric acid and furfural alcohol, and hydrogen peroxide and German "C" Stoff (mixture of hydrazine hydrate, water, and alcohol). At least eleven products may be formed: carbon monoxide, carbon dioxide, water vapor, hydrogen gas, oxygen gas, nitrogen gas, monatomic hydrogen, monatomic oxygen, monatomic nitrogen, hydroxyl, and nitrous oxide. Other possible reaction products such as solid carbon, ozone, nitric oxide, and various hydrocarbons are discounted because the magnitude of the equilibrium constants and experience have shown that very little of these products is formed.

In a simplified method, such as that devised by Satterfield, Hottel, and Williams (Ref. 3.305), charts and curves are constructed for a fixed chamber pressure which permit the ready determination of the equilibrium composition and the chamber temperature for any given propellant combination containing the four elements above.

The *combustion efficiency* can now be defined as the ratio of the actual change in enthalpy per unit propellant mixture to the calculated change in enthalpy necessary to transform the propellants from the initial conditions to the products at the calculated chamber temperature. The actual enthalpy change can be evaluated if initial propellant condition and the composition and the temperature of the combustion gases are measured. Experimental measurements of combustion temperature and gas composition are difficult to perform accurately, and the combustion efficiency is therefore actually evaluated only in rare instances. The combustion efficiency in rocket thrust chambers depends on the method of injection and mixing and increases with increased combustion temperature. In solid propellants the combustion efficiency is a function of the grain design and the degree of mixing between the several solid constituents. Measurements performed by methods outlined in Chapter 13 indicate efficiency values of 94 to 99 per cent.

6   Chemical Reaction in Nozzle

In the discussion of ideal nozzles, it was assumed that the nozzle expansion process is isentropic and that gases do not change in chemical composition. The ideal nozzle exit temperatures, as evaluated in the problems of the previous chapter, were of the order of 1500° to 3500° F.

Since the temperature and pressure drop continuously in an expansion process, the equilibrium will also shift continuously as the gases flow through a real rocket nozzle. For most propellants, burning and recombination in the nozzle will permit further release of chemical energy into heat, causing a higher exit temperature than anticipated. The average molecular weight of most propellant products will increase slightly and be a maximum at the nozzle exit. This increase tends to decrease the exhaust velocity. The properties of the exhaust gases (C_p, R, k, etc.) will change in the exhaust nozzle. As explained in Section 4, the added heat release usually outweighs the effect caused by an increase in the molecular weight, so that the exhaust velocity and rocket performance increase slightly.

If the enthalpy drop in the nozzle is assumed or known, the equilibrium condition at the nozzle exit section or of any other nozzle section can be determined. The actual enthalpy drop in a nozzle can be approximated by the ideal enthalpy drop as determined from nozzle theory.

Specific impulse values calculated to account for the reaction occurring in the nozzle are usually referred to as *shifting equilibrium* values, because the equilibrium composition shifts as the gases pass from the high pressure and high temperature to the low pressure and low temperature regions. Since the gases move very fast, the time allowed for equilibrium to change is indeed very short (perhaps 1 to 3 milliseconds). Thus the shift to a steady state, uniform temperature equilibrium may not be complete.

It has been argued that the chemical reaction is frozen at the nozzle entrance section because individual gas particles travel at supersonic velocities through the nozzle in such a short time that it may not be possible to maintain instantaneous chemical equilibrium with the adjoining particles as the pressure decreases. Specific impulse values calculated on this basis are referred to as *specific impulse at frozen equilibrium.* The actual nozzle exit gas condition usually lies in between these two calculated conditions of changing equilibrium and frozen reaction.

7   Results of Thermochemical Computations

Thermochemical calculations may be used to obtain the performance of parameters of rockets. Results for different liquid propellant combinations are given in Figures 4–4 to 4–9, in Tables 4–3 to 4–5, and in several of the references. Results of calculations and tests on solid propellant rockets are given in Chapters 9 and 10. It can be seen that the peak sea level exhaust velocities, with but few exceptions, have values between 6800 and 8000 feet per second for nominal values of chamber pressure.

A high exhaust ·velocity can be obtained by lowering the molecular weight of the combustion products or by increasing the chemical energy per unit of propellant weight, which in turn increases the combustion temperature. A combustion temperature above approximately 6500° F does not appear feasible because of dissociation effects and the relatively low chemical energy content of existing propellants. The dissociation of combustion gases into monatomic constituents and radicals lowers the

TABLE 4-3. CALCULATED PERFORMANCE OF VARIOUS LIQUID PROPELLANT COMBINATIONS

(Specific impulse and exhaust velocities were calculated for an expansion to one atmosphere)

(Reproduced in part from G. P. Sutton, "Thermochemistry of Rocket Propellants," *Journal of the American Rocket Society*, Vol. 72, December 1947 and in part from *Pocket Data for Rocket Engines*, published by Bell Aircraft Corporation, Buffalo, 1953.)

Propellant Combination (Oxidizer and Fuel)	Chamber Pressure, psi	Mixture Ratio (Oxidizer to Fuel)	Exhaust Velocity, ft/sec	Specific Impulse, sec	Characteristic Velocity, ft/sec	Chamber Temperature, °F	Mean Molecular Weight, lb/mole	Specific Heat Ratio	Average Specific Gravity of Mixture
Liquid oxygen and ammonia	300	1.4	8,220	255	5,840	4,950	19.7	1.23	0.98
Liquid oxygen and ammonia	500	1.3	8,550	265	5,720	4,940	19	1.23	0.88
Liquid oxygen and 100% ethyl alcohol	300	1.5	7,810	243	5,560	5,250	22.9	1.22	0.966
Liquid oxygen and 75% ethyl alcohol, 25% water	300	1.3	7,700	239	5,480	5,080	22	1.22	0.994
Liquid oxygen and gasoline	300	2.5	7,780	242	5,540	5,470	22.7	1.22	0.965
Liquid oxygen and hydrazine	300	0.5	8,350	259	6,050	4,500	15.9	1.23	1.05
Liquid oxygen and liquid hydrogen	340	5.33	10,800	335	7,720	5,430	11.7	1.25	0.33
Liquid oxygen and liquid hydrogen	500	8.0	10,120	317	6,860	5,870	16	1.22	0.43

Liquid oxygen and liquid hydrogen	3.5	11,700	364	7,930	4,500	9	1.26	0.26
Liquid oxygen and kerosene	2.2	7,970	248	5,700	5,570	21.6	1.24	1.01
Liquid oxygen and liquid methane	3.0	8,220	255	....	5,040	....	....	0.747
Liquid oxygen and 100% methyl alcohol	1.25	7,660	238	5,430	5,180	22.8	1.20	0.895
Liquid oxygen and methyl amine	2.06	8,185	252	5,760	5,600	21.2	1.21	0.94
Chlorine trifluoride and ammonia	3.0	7,635	225	5,230	4,980	22	1.32	1.26
Fluorine and hydrazine	1.9	9,610	299	6,910	7,530	18	1.33	1.31
Hydrogen peroxide (90%) and hydrazine	1.5	8,045	252	5,470	4,170	18	1.25	1.2
Hydrogen peroxide (87%), water (13%)	∞	4,060	126	2,900	1,310	22	1.25	1.42
Hydrogen peroxide (87%) and C-Stoff (57% alcohol, 13% water, 30% hydrazine hydrate)	2.5	6,920	215	4,940	3,800	....	1.23	1.24
Red fuming nitric acid and aniline	3.0	7,090	221	5,030	5,020	25	1.22	1.37
Red fuming nitric acid (6.5% NO$_2$) and n-octane	4.5	7,610	235	5,100	5,100	24	1.24	1.26
Nitrogen tetroxide and hydrazine	1.0	7,955	249	5,695	4,905	18.8	1.27	1.19
Nitromethane	∞	7,010	218	5,010	3,950	20	1.25	1.139
Gaseous oxygen and nitromethane	0.05	7,300	227	5,300	4,500	21	1.23	....
White fuming nitric acid and furfural alcohol	1.9	6,890	214	4,890	5,020	....	1.2	1.37

combustion temperature because energy is consumed which otherwise would be available for raising the temperature of the gases; and as yet there are no known propellants which have a chemical energy content twice as high as that of the common existing rocket fuels and oxidizer combinations.

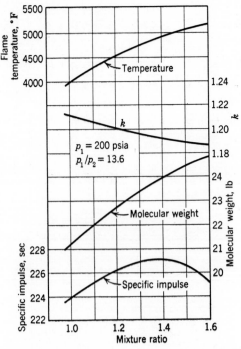

FIGURE 4–4. Calculated performance of liquid oxygen–ethyl alcohol (with 25 per cent water) propellant system.

In Table 4–3 only the combination of liquid hydrogen with liquid oxygen shows a high exhaust velocity (10,800 feet per second). A few propellant combinations rich in hydrogen, such as liquid hydrogen reacting with liquid fluorine (exhaust velocity of over 10,900 feet per second), may be added in the high performance range.

In general, thermochemical calculations will show that one definite mixture ratio gives an optimum rocket performance and that an excess of fuel or an excess of oxidizer will reduce this performance. This optimum mixture ratio shifts slightly with chamber pressure.

This *optimum mixture ratio* occurs usually at a value which is richer in fuel than the stoichiometric mixture ratio, at which all

TABLE 4–4. REACTION OF NITROMETHANE AND OXYGEN

(Reference: M. Weissbluth, *A Study of the Nitromethane-Oxygen Combination as a Rocket Propellant,* Jet Propulsion Laboratory, California Institute of Technology, Pasadena, Progress Report 1–22, 1944.)

	Calculated	*Measured* *
Chamber pressure, psia	270	270
Composition of chamber gases, % by volume:		
CO_2	7.20	5.5
CO	25.91	19.4
H_2O	31.57	26.8
H_2	17.42	12.4
H	0.68	
HO	0.63	
N_2	16.56	7.9
NO		20.1
Hydrocarbon		7.9
Mixture ratio (oxygen to nitromethane)	0.05	0.047
Calculated reaction temperature, °F	4500	2470
Calculated average molecular weight	21.22	22.77
Calculated specific heat at constant pressure, Btu/°F lb	0.498	0.492
Calculated specific heat ratio	1.232	1.216
Exhaust velocity based on isentropic expansion without reaction, ft/sec	7307	5386
Measured and calculated data:		
Propellant flow, lb/sec		1.23
Duration of run, sec		61
Nozzle throat area, in.^{2}		0.462
Average trust, lb		169
Exhaust velocity		4420
Nozzle coefficient		1.35

* This test showed partially incomplete combustion.

the fuel is theoretically completely oxidized and the flame temperature is a maximum. The molecular weight usually tends to become lower as the fuel concentration is increased slightly over that of the stoichiometric value. With many propellants the exact value of the optimum mixture ratio shifts slightly with changes in chamber pressure. In many applications the mixture ratio of the rocket is so selected as to be very close to this optimum value. In liquid propellant rockets this optimum mixture ratio determines the proportions of the propellant tank volumes and in solid propellant rockets it determines the proportions of

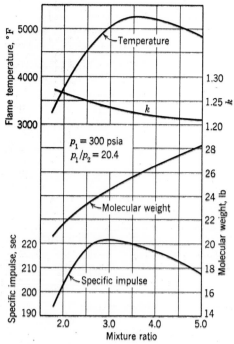

FIGURE 4–5. Calculated performance of the red fuming nitric acid (with 15 per cent NO_2)–aniline propellant system.

oxidizer and fuel to be used during propellant preparation. A slight excess of fuels containing low molecular weight compounds such as chemicals with large amounts of combined hydrogen are particularly desirable. In Figure 4–7 is can be seen that a mixture ratio (weight of oxidizer flow to fuel flow) of about 2.5 gives an optimum performance for the liquid oxygen–gasoline propellant combination, while the stoichiometric mixture ratio is close to 3.5.

Propellant mixtures with low combustion temperatures but relatively high exhaust velocities are particularly desirable, since the design of rocket units is thereby simplified. For example, hydrazine, reacting with liquid oxygen, and the monopropellant nitromethane fall into this classification.

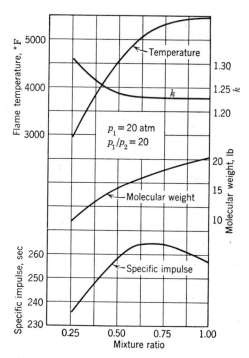

FIGURE 4–6. Calculated performance of the liquid oxygen–hydrazine propellant system.

The calculated variation of performance with chamber pressure approaches a finite maximum at infinite chamber pressure (see Figure 4–10). The effect of higher chamber pressure is to change the term $\sqrt{1 - (p_2/p_1)^{(k-1)/k}}$ in the exhaust velocity and to change T, k, and $\mathfrak{M}$ by a shift in equilibrium and dissociation. Propellant product gases which do not dissociate experience no change in combustion temperature or gas properties with increased pressure; when, for example, liquid oxygen reacts with an excess of liquid hydrogen, the reaction temperature at certain mixture ratios is too low to permit appreciable dissociation. Here increase

TABLE 4–5. REACTION OF GASOLINE AND LIQUID OXYGEN AT 300 PSI

(*Reference:* R. N. Wimpress and B. H. Sage, *Composition of Products of Reaction of Gasoline and Liquid Oxygen*, Jet Propulsion Laboratory, California Institute of Technology, Pasadena, Progress Report 19, 1944.)

Mixture ratio (oxidizer to fuel)	1.5	2.0	2.25	2.5	2.75	3.0	3.5
Volume percentages:							
CO	0.455	0.411	0.37	0.322	0.280	0.243	0.198
CO_2	0.023	0.079	0.109	0.137	0.160	0.180	0.202
H_2	0.382	0.215	0.152	0.105	0.074	0.057	0.028
H_2O	0.125	0.278	0.326	0.330	0.330	0.325	0.305
H	0.000	0.012	0.026	0.028	0.027	0.025	0.021
OH	0.000	0.009	0.028	0.061	0.085	0.104	0.124
O_2	0.000	0.000	0.003	0.008	0.019	0.028	0.085
O	0.000	0.000	0.002	0.006	0.010	0.016	0.026
Flame temperature, °F	2700	4700	5160	5470	5590	5630	5680
Theoretical specific impulse, sec	200	236	240	242	241	238	234
Mean molecular weight	17.2	20.4	21.6	22.7	23.6	24.3	25.3
Specific heat ratio	1.285	1.235	1.225	1.219	1.215	1.212	1.211
Exit velocity, assuming no chemical reaction in nozzle, ft/sec	6440	7580	7740	7780	7740	7650	7520
Average specific heat of chamber gases, Btu/°F lb	0.521	0.510	0.499	0.488	0.478	0.468	0.452

TABLE 4–6. EFFECT OF CHAMBER PRESSURE ON ROCKET PERFORMANCE

Chamber Pressure	10 atm		20 atm		50 atm	
Combustion equilibrium temperature, °R, and specific impulse, sec	T_1	I_s	T_1	I_s	T_1	I_s
61.1% Liquid oxygen 38.9% {75% Ethyl alcohol, 25% Water} (Stoichiometric mixture)	5400	205	5630	228	6000	253
56% Liquid oxygen 44% {75% Ethyl alcohol, 25% Water}	5130	210	5150	233	5200	256
88.8% Liquid oxygen 11.2% Liquid hydrogen (Stoichiometric mixture)	6100	271	6280	297	6575	341
76.2% Liquid oxygen 23.8% Liquid hydrogen	4800	323	4800	354	4810	388

in chamber pressure does not produce a noticeable increase in combustion temperature (see Table 4–6). For many liquid propellants any appreciable increase in chamber pressure above 300 pounds per square inch results in only a small increase in performance. Since the selection of the design chamber pressure for any particular

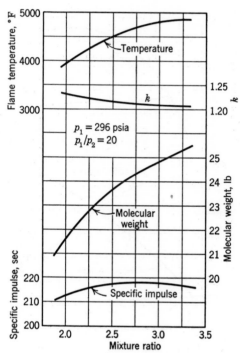

FIGURE 4–7. Calculated performance of red fuming nitric acid (with 13 per cent NO_2)–ethyl alcohol propellant system.

application depends on feed system complications, installation weight, and other considerations besides performance, it is not possible to make a general conclusion regarding its optimum value. For solid propellant rockets other considerations generally require higher chamber pressures, usually between 700 and 2000 pounds per square inch.

If the changes in reaction temperature and the gas properties (for example, specific heat ratio) are neglected, then the specific impulse and the exhaust velocity can be corrected for changes in chamber pressure by a proportionality to the optimum thrust coefficient. The thrust coefficients can be found in equations 3–30, and in Figures 3–11, 3–12, and 3–13. More generally these changes in specific impulse are proportional to the square root of the ideal cycle efficiency defined by equation 3–16 and shown

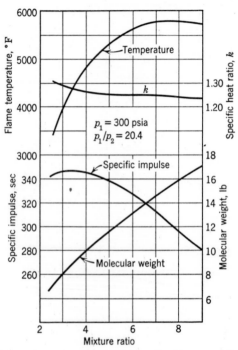

FIGURE 4–8. Calculated performance of the liquid oxygen–liquid hydrogen propellant system.

in Figure 3–4. This simplified correction applies to both liquid and solid propellants.

Propellant combinations with sea level exhaust velocities above 9000 feet per second have, to the best of the author's knowledge, not yet outgrown the research stage and are as yet not suitable for extensive flight applications. Existing and proved propellant combinations are low in performance and therefore do not permit the design of efficient long range or interplanetary rocket vehicles.

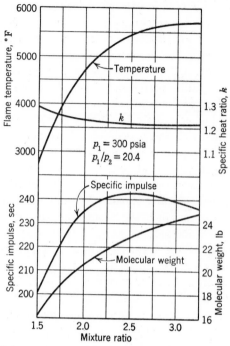

FIGURE 4-9.   Calculated performance of the liquid oxygen–gasoline propellant system.

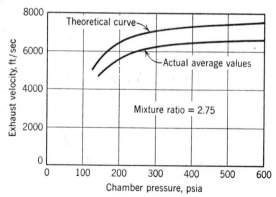

FIGURE 4-10.   Performance variation with chamber pressure for the red fuming nitric acid–aniline propellant system.

The possible increase in exhaust velocity is estimated at 30 to 60 per cent above the present average values. A radical and large increase in rocket exhaust velocity by improved chemical propellants is, however, not to be expected. The choice of rocket propellants, therefore, will be decided largely by practical utilization factors rather than by performance considerations.

Theoretical studies indicate that the use of *nuclear energy* permits a much higher kinetic jet energy per pound of propellant than is possible by chemical reaction. This method of propulsion relies on a suitable propellant, which is to be heated by a nuclear reactor and then ejected at high velocity through a nozzle. If hydrogen is the working fluid and if it is heated in a pile to 7000° F and isentropically expanded from a chamber pressure of 300 pounds per square inch, the theoretical exhaust velocity will be approximately 23,500 feet per second. If higher temperatures can be withstood by the reactor materials, a corresponding increase in exhaust velocity is to be expected. If H_2 could be dissociated into monatomic hydrogen, an exhaust velocity of 32,200 feet per second might be possible because of a lower molecular weight of product gases. The problem of applying nuclear energy to rocket propulsion, however, is difficult. It will require considerable development and research effort.

Example 4–3. A complete sample calculation has not been included here, because a trial-and-error computation would have to be unnecessarily repetitive and long to be explicit and because it is of interest only to the propellant specialist. However, the steps to be taken in computing the combustion temperature, the equilibrium gas composition of the reaction products, and the theoretical performance of rockets are outlined here in a simplified example in order to give a general understanding of the method.

The quantities usually given are the propellant combination and composition, the chamber pressure, the initial temperature of the propellants entering the chamber, the mixture ratio, and the nozzle exit pressure.

In this example the thermochemical calculations for liquid oxygen at −298° F and liquid hydrogen at −424° F are outlined. Let the mixture ratio be 4.0, the chamber pressure 335 psia, expanding to atmospheric pressures. All probable product constituents are selected, and a general chemical equation is written:

$$n_A H_2 + n_B O_2 \rightarrow n_{H_2O} H_2O + n_{H_2} H_2 + n_{O_2} O_2 + n_O O + n_H H + n_{OH} OH$$

Other possible products such as hydrogen peroxide or ozone are discounted because they are not likely to occur at the given thrust chamber condition.

The equation above contains six unknowns, namely, the number of moles of the product constituents.

From the given data the molar proportions for the reactants (n_A, n_B) can be determined by selecting an arbitrary basis of the weight involved in the reaction, for example, 100 lb of propellant. At a mixture ratio of 4.0 there will be 80 lb of oxygen and 20 lb of hydrogen.

$$n_A = \frac{80}{32} = 2.5$$

$$n_B = \frac{20}{2.01} = 9.96$$

A flame temperature or combustion temperature is estimated. This assumed temperature may be higher or lower than the eventual calculated temperature of the chamber gases. In this example, let $T = 5290°$ R. Material balance relations are then determined; the amount of each element present is the same before and after the reaction. The relationships are determined most conveniently on the basis of pound-atoms of each element.

Oxygen:
$$n_B = 2(2.5) = n_{H_2O} + 2n_{O_2} + n_O + n_{OH}$$

Hydrogen:
$$n_A = 2(9.96) = 2n_{H_2O} + 2n_{H_2} + n_H + n_{OH}$$

For any hydrogen-oxygen system there are only two weight balance relations, one for each of the basic atomic constituents. In order to solve for six unknowns, four more equations have to be established.

Equilibrium equations for selected equilibrium reactions are determined. The equilibrium constants for these relations are determined for the assumed temperatures from charts or tables such as Figure 4–3. For the reaction above, the following equilibrium equations may be selected:

Reactions	*Equilibrium Equations*
$H_2O \rightleftarrows H_2 + \frac{1}{2}O_2$	$(K_p)_1 = \dfrac{n_{H_2}\sqrt{n_O}}{n_{H_2O}}\sqrt{\dfrac{p}{\Sigma n}}$
$H_2 \rightleftarrows 2H$	$(K_p)_2 = \dfrac{n_H^2}{n_{H_2}}\dfrac{p}{\Sigma n}$
$H_2O \rightleftarrows \frac{1}{2}H_2 + OH$	$(K_p)_3 = \dfrac{\sqrt{n_{H_2}}n_{OH}}{n_{H_2O}}\sqrt{\dfrac{p}{\Sigma n}}$
$H_2O \rightleftarrows H_2 + O$	$(K_p)_4 = \dfrac{n_{H_2}n_O}{n_{H_2O}}\dfrac{p}{\Sigma n}$

where Σn is the sum of all moles of reaction product gases involved in each reaction; this quantity has to be introduced to convert mole fractions into **moles.**

A sufficient number of equations has now been determined so that a solution for the unknown quantities can be attempted. Because the general solution of six simultaneous equations by strictly algebraic and arithmetic means is a long, tedious, and often an impossible task without automatic computing machinery, simplified solutions are used. One such simplified method assumes as a first approximation that the product gases do not dissociate and consist only of H_2O and H_2. By means of two simplified material balance equations an approximation of the molar composition of these two gases can be found. The values thus obtained can be used to determine the approximate values of the other product constituents from equilibrium equations. By trial and error the values of the molar proportions can then be adjusted to satisfy all equations. The results for hydrogen and oxygen are:

$$n_{H_2O} = 4.93$$

$$n_{H_2} = 4.88$$

$$n_{O_2} = 0$$

$$n_O = 0$$

$$n_H = 0.201$$

$$n_{OH} = 0.05$$

The heat of reaction of the propellant combination (oxidizer and fuel) is determined by means of equation 4–3. It is corrected for the heat necessary to bring 80 lb of oxygen and 20 lb of hydrogen from their boiling points to the reference temperature (enthalpy increase).

Gas	n	Q_F	nQ_F
H_2O	4.93	104,042	514,000
H_2	4.88	0	0
O_2	0	0	0
O	0	0	0
H	0.201	−93,400	−18,700
OH	0.05	−10,620	− 530
			494,770

Correction	n	Enthalpy Change	
H_2 (liquid)	9.96	−3,400	−34,000
O_2 (liquid)	2.5	−6,570	−16,400

Heat of reaction	444,370 Btu per 100 lb of reactants

The enthalpy of the product gases is determined from the sum of the enthalpies of each gas according to equation 4–11.

Gas	n	$\int_{T_0}^{5290} C_p \, dT$	Enthalpy
H_2O	4.93	53,050	261,000
H_2	4.88	36,900	180,000
O_2	0	......	....
O	0	......	....
H	0.201	36,700	7,550
OH	0.05	23,700	1,180

Δh = Enthalpy gain of gases = 449,730 Btu per 100 lb
of propellant

If the enthalpy of the products Δh equals the heat of the reaction of the reactants Q_R, the assumption of the reaction temperature is correct. If $\Delta h < Q_R$, the assumed temperature was too low. If $\Delta h \neq Q_R$, a new temperature is assumed and the calculation has to be repeated. In this example the temperature was assumed slightly too high. Since Δh differs from Q_R by only 1.1 per cent, the error is small and will be neglected.

The *specific heat* of the products may now be determined from equation 4-6. It is $C_p = 0.954$ Btu/lb °F.

The *mean molecular* weight and the gas constant of the product gases may now be determined from equations 4-4 and 4-5 as 9.95 lb/mole and 155.5 ft/°R. The *specific heat ratio* k may be found from equation 4-7 as 1.267. The specific impulse, the exhaust velocity, and the exit temperature can be calculated assuming that the values of the mean molecular weight of the product gases and their specific heat ratio do not vary with temperature. The result from equations 4-1 and 4-2 is $I_s = 343$ sec. In refined calculations k and $\mathfrak{M}$ are recomputed for the nozzle exit conditions and average values for the nozzle and chamber are selected for computing the specific impulse.

Problems

1. Determine the heat of formation of the following, using the heats of reaction with oxygen as given: (*a*) ethane C_2H_6 ($Q_R = 663,000$ Btu/mole); (*b*) octane C_8H_{18} ($Q_R = 2,350,000$ Btu/mole).

2. A rigid, closed container is filled with equal volumes of hydrogen and carbon dioxide at 60° F and 1 atm. What will be the composition when the gases are heated to 5000° F, assuming only CO, CO_2, H_2O, and H_2 to be present?

3. Water dissociates into hydrogen and oxygen gas at high temperatures. Assuming that no other products are formed, what is the percentage of water which dissociates at 5000° F and 10 atm pressure? What is this percentage at 25 atm?

4. How much heat is required to bring 1 lb of saturated liquid oxygen at 1 atm up to 60° F?

5. Using the data given in Figure 4–9, compute the following for gasoline and liquid oxygen at a mixture ratio of 2.5: (a) Molar specific heat. (b) Exit temperature assuming no further chemical reaction in nozzle and an isentropic expansion process. (c) Compute the heat of reaction for 1 lb of propellants, for 1 lb of fuel, and for 1 gallon of fuel. Assume C_p = constant.

6. Compute the equilibrium composition and the equilibrium temperature for the propellant combination of liquid oxygen with liquid hydrogen, assuming a mixture weight ratio of oxygen to hydrogen of two to one. Neglect the dissociation into monatomic constituents. Assume that each liquid is at its saturation temperature for 1 atm pressure when entering the combustion chamber. The chamber pressure equals 160 psia.

7. Compute the following theoretical quantities for problem 6: (a) Mean specific molar heat of reaction gases. (b) Mean molecular weight of chamber gases. (c) Assuming an expansion to 14.0 psia, compute the specific impulse, the nozzle exit temperature, and the exit velocity. (Let the expansion process be isentropic.)

Symbols

(Symbols referring to chemical elements and compounds are not included in this list.)

C_p molar specific heat at constant pressure of gas mixture, Btu/mole °F

C_v molar specific heat at constant volume of gas mixture, Btu/mole °F

d total derivative

I_s specific impulse, lb/lb sec

g acceleration of gravity, 32.2 ft/sec²

Δh enthalpy change, Btu

K_n equilibrium constant, when expressed in terms of mole fractions

K_p equilibrium constant, when expressed in terms of partial pressures

k specific heat ratio of gas mixture $(k = C_p/C_v)$

$\mathfrak{M}$ molecular weight of gas mixture, lb/mole

n number of moles, mole

n' number of moles in products minus number of moles in reactants, mole

p pressure of gas mixture, lb/ft²

p_1 combustion chamber pressure, lb/ft²

p_2 nozzle exhaust pressure, lb/ft²

Q_F heat of formation, Btu/mole

Q_R heat of reaction, Btu

R gas constant, ft-lb/lb °F

R' universal gas constant, 1544 ft-lb/mole °F

T absolute temperature, °R

T_1 combustion temperature, °R

T_0 reference temperature, °R

v gas velocity, ft/sec

X volume percentage or mole fraction of gas X

Σ summation sign

Subscripts

av average

p products

x any gas X

Chapter 5

Heat Transfer

In almost all designs and operations of rockets, considerable heat is transferred, and the phenomena of heat transmission often control the proper functioning of the units. This chapter gives a general and brief discussion of some of the more significant applications of heat transfer theory in the field of rocketry. For the sake of orientation they are classified in the following five categories:

1. *Heat transfer from the hot reaction gases to the walls of the combustion device.* In the general sense these devices include all types such as solid propellant combustion chambers and nozzles, liquid propellant gas generators and their piping, and injectors, nozzles, and chambers of liquid propellant thrust chambers. In this chapter these combustion devices will be divided into two categories: those that are *cooled by liquid propellants* and those that act as a heat sponge and are essentially *uncooled*. In cooled combustion devices the heat transfer usually reaches a thermal equilibrium condition. In an uncooled unit the operating time is usually short and the heat transfer is a transient phenomenon.

There are at least three accepted ways of cooling the walls of a thrust chamber with liquid propellant: *regenerative cooling* denotes the type in which the rocket chamber is cooled by circulating some or all of the liquid propellant (fuel or oxidizer) through a jacket (or coils) around the combustion device. The heat absorbed by the coolant is therefore not wasted but actually augments the heat content of the propellant prior to combustion. *Film cooling* implies that either the fuel or the oxidizer liquid is injected into the combustion devices in such a manner as to form a protective film of liquid, vapor, or cool gas adjacent to the walls. *Transpiration* or *sweat cooling* permits uniform, continuous injection of liquid over the entire surface of the wall to be cooled, by using a porous wall material, through which the propellant is fed. Further discussion on different methods of cooling is given in Chapter 8.

Uncooled chambers are used in almost all solid propellant rockets and in some short duration liquid propellant rockets. Here the reduction of heat transfer to the wall by means of insulation and clever design usually permits a lowering of the chamber weights. Ceramic materials, special paints, and slow-burning organic materials bonded to the wall have been used here with success.

The major portion of this chapter is devoted to this first category, namely to the discussion of the transfer of heat from hot gases to enclosing walls.

2. *Selection of propellants with favorable heat transfer characteristics.* The desirable physical and chemical heat transfer properties of propellants are discussed in Chapters 6 and 11. The mechanism of heat transfer to liquid propellants is described briefly in another section of this chapter; here the phenomenon of film boiling permits unusually high heat transfer rates. The mechanism of heat transmission to solid propellant grains is not well understood at this time and is not described further in this book.

3. *Heat exchangers.* Many of the more complex liquid propellant rocket engines incorporate one or more heat exchangers. For example, the German V-2 rocket had a coiled heat exchanger in its tank-pressurizing system; it permitted the heating and vaporization of tank-pressurizing fluids by extracting energy from the turbine exhaust gases. This type of heat transfer problem is encountered in many applications other than rockets, and ample references can be found in the literature; it is, therefore, not discussed any further here.

4. *Jet flame heating.* The heat transfer from jet flames, or from hot exhaust streams to the surrounding equipment, often presents design problems. This includes radiation and convection effects of the jet on aircraft and missile parts (e.g., blast and

radiation effect of ATO units on aircraft fuselage and tail sections) and on equipment of rocket test stands.

5. *Heat transfer to flying vehicles at high speed.* Aerodynamic heating of vehicles can result in a substantial rise in the skin temperature. Although a detailed technical discussion of skin heating is beyond the scope of this text, this phenomenon causes two important effects on a rocket engine. First, it requires the rocket hardware to operate at elevated temperature conditions, in some applications perhaps several hundred degrees above ambient conditions, and, secondly, it often causes the heating of propellants, particularly in flying vehicles which use integral skin wall designs of liquid propellant tanks or solid propellant chambers. This increase in propellant temperature during flight usually causes undesirable rocket operating characteristics.

The balance of this chapter is intended to discuss in a general manner several of these heat transfer problems as they are encountered in rockets. For a more specific and basic treatment of heat transfer theory the reader is referred to the literature on this subject, such as the references listed under Section 5.0 of the Reference Bibliography at the end of this book.

1   General Steady State Heat Transfer Relations

For heat transfer conduction the general relation applies:

$$Q/A = -\kappa \frac{dT}{dL} = -\kappa \frac{\Delta T}{L} \qquad (5\text{--}1)$$

where Q is the heat transferred per unit time across a surface A, dT/dL is the temperature gradient with respect to thickness at the surface A, and κ is the thermal conductivity expressed as the amount of heat transferred in Btu per unit time through 1 square foot of surface for $1°$ F temperature difference over a wall thickness of 1 foot. The negative sign indicates that temperature decreases as thickness increases.

The convective heat transfer through the chamber wall of a rocket can be treated as a series type, steady state heat transfer problem with a large temperature gradient across the gaseous film on the inside of the chamber wall, and a third temperature drop across the film of the moving cooling fluid. The problem is basically one of heat and mass transport associated with conduction through a wall. It is shown schematically in Figure 5-1.

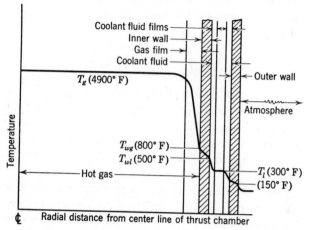

FIGURE 5-1. Temperature gradients in cooled rocket thrust chamber. Given temperature values are typical.

The general steady state heat transfer equations can be expressed as follows:

$$q = h(T_g - T_l) = Q/A \qquad (5-2)$$

$$= \frac{1}{1/h_g + t_w/\kappa + 1/h_l} \qquad (5-3)$$

$$= h_g(T_g - T_{wg}) \qquad (5-4)$$

$$= (\kappa/t_w)(T_{wg} - T_{wl}) \qquad (5-5)$$

$$= h_l(T_{wl} - T_l) \qquad (5-6)$$

where q is heat transferred per unit area per unit time, T_g is the absolute chamber gas temperature, T_l is the absolute coolant liquid temperature, T_{wl} is the absolute wall temperature on the liquid side of the wall, T_{wg} is the absolute wall temperature on the gas side of the wall, h is the overall film coefficient, h_g is the gas film coefficient, h_l is the coolant liquid film coefficient, t_w is the thickness of the chamber wall, and κ is the conductivity of the wall material (see Table 7-2). Any consistent set of units can be used in these equations.

Since the film coefficients, the gas and liquid coolant temperatures, the wall thickness, and the surface areas usually vary with the axial distance within a combustion chamber (assuming axial heat transfer symmetry), the total heat transfer per unit time Q can be found from

$$Q = \int q \, dA = \pi \int Dq \, dL \qquad (5\text{--}7)$$

Since both q and D are complicated functions of L, the equation usually has to be solved by numerical methods. The arbitrary division of the rocket chamber into finite lengths and the assumption that q is given by equations 5–2 to 5–6 and remains constant over the length of each element will give an approximate solution.

The important quantities for controlling the heat transfer across a rocket chamber wall are the fluid film boundaries established by the combustion products on one side of the wall and the coolant flow on the other. The gas film coefficient largely determines the numerical value of the heat transfer rate. Known equations are based on experimental data and cannot be accurately applied to calculate this gas film coefficient, because rocket conditions differ from conditions existing in ordinary heat transfer problems. They differ in these nine ways:

1. The *energy release per unit volume* is very large. Good conventional heat transfer equipment, for example, a steam boiler furnace, has energy releases above 60,000 Btu/ft³ hr atm. Good gas turbine combustion chambers have a heat release of 3 million to 4 million Btu/hr ft³ atm, while rocket combustion chambers range from 13 million to 20 million Btu/hr ft³ atm.

2. The best *heat transfer rates* per unit area obtained in conventional boilers and superheaters are of the order of 15,000 Btu/ft² hr. In rocket combustion the rates are 20 to 200 times as large.

3. The *combustion temperature* in rockets (4000 to 6000° F) is usually higher than the combustion temperature in standard furnaces, since no or very little inert material, such as atmospheric nitrogen, has to be heated and carried along.

4. The *surface velocities* of the gases along the chamber wall are very high, increasing the heat transferred by convection. In

the nozzle the gases reach supersonic speeds. Accurate and applicable heat transfer data at these high velocities, pressure, unusual velocity gradients, and temperatures inside tubes or nozzles have to be obtained experimentally.

5. Some of the *properties of hot propellant gases* are not very well known; for example, few good data are available on the conductivity and viscosity of gases at high temperatures and pressure. When dissociation is present (see Chapter 4), the properties of the gas mixture will change appreciably.

6. *The boundary layer effects* are difficult to evaluate analytically. The boundary layer is in a continuous transition caused by the changing velocity gradient, the combustion turbulence, the pressure and the temperature gradients in the rocket. The boundary layer temperature is believed to be an important heat transfer parameter, since it is the temperature immediately adjacent to the wall. While the conventional heat transfer theory assumes a uniform gas temperature, the boundary layer temperature will differ from the free wall temperature, causing a shift in chemical equilibrium. In certain parts of a combustion device the boundary layer temperature approaches the stagnation temperature of the gas, which can be considerably above the free stream temperature. Propellant products which dissociate freely will tend to reassociate near the wall and release additional heat in the boundary layer.

7. The equations developed for gas film coefficients assume an *equilibrium velocity profile,* which implies also a length of several diameters of chamber ahead of the section to which the heat transfer computations are applied. Unfortunately, such an equilibrium condition cannot normally be established in a rocket combustion device, where the length-to-diameter ratio is small and where turbulence tends to diminish the insulating effect of the boundary layer. Therefore, the heat transfer resistance is often lower than can be determined from conventional boundary layer theory. Some experimental evidence indicates that this effect alone can change the coefficient by a factor of two.

8. *The injector design in liquid propellant rockets* and the *grain design in solid propellant rockets* have a profound influence on the gas film. It is readily possible to change the heat flux and the wall temperatures by large factors simply by changing these de-

signs. In liquid propellant design the heat transfer to the chamber wall is affected by many injector parameters, such as the mixture ratio, impingement angles, injector pressure drop, injector orifice pattern, or hole distribution and size. In solid propellant rockets the heat transfer to the wall is affected by such quantities as the chamber liner design, the grain configuration, or the pressure-time history.

9. *Diffusion effects*, which become significant above 4500° F, are usually neglected in rocket heat transfer calculations.

No simple theory exists now which covers all the important variables in the heat transfer of hot rocket gases to the wall. Until research provides accurate and adequate values of the gas film coefficient in rockets, the following limited method is recommended (see Ref. 5.101):

$$\frac{h_g D}{\kappa} = 0.023 \left(\frac{Dv\rho}{\mu g}\right)^{0.8} \left(\frac{gc_p}{\kappa}\right)^{0.33} \tag{5-8}$$

where h_g is the film coefficient in Btu/sec °R ft², D is the diameter of the chamber in feet, v is the calculated average local gas velocity in feet per second, κ is the conductivity of the gas in Btu/sec ft² °R/ft, μ is the absolute gas viscosity in lb sec/ft², c_p is the specific heat of the gas in Btu per degree per pound, and ρ is the gas density in pounds per cubic foot.

Example 5–1. The effects of varying the film coefficients on the heat transfer and the wall temperatures are to be explored. The following data are given:

Wall thickness	0.175 in.
Wall material	Low carbon steel
Average conductivity	300 Btu/hr ft² °F/in.
Average gas temperature	5000° F
Average liquid bulk temperature	100° F
Gas film coefficient	0.00005 Btu/sec °F in.²
Liquid film coefficient	0.070 Btu/sec °F in.²

Vary h_g (at constant h_l) and then vary h_l (at constant h_g) and determine the heat transfer rate and the wall temperatures on the liquid and the gas side of the wall.

Solution. Use equations 5–3, 5–4, 5–5, and 5–6 and solve for q, T_{wg}, and T_{wl}. The answers shown in Table 5–1 indicate that variations in the gas film coefficient have a profound influence on the heat transfer rate but relatively little effect on the wall temperature. The exact opposite is true for variations in the liquid film coefficient; here changes in h_l produce little change in q but a fairly substantial change in the wall temperature.

TABLE 5-1

*Per Cent Change in
Film Coefficient*

Gas film	Liquid film	q Btu/sec in.^{2}	T_{wg} °F	T_{wl} °F
50	100	1.22	124	118
100	100	2.43	147	135
200	100	4.81	193	169
400	100	9.45	288	235
100	50	2.41	181	169
100	25	2.37	248	236
100	12.5	2.32	368	256
100	6.25	2.20	614	603

2 Rocket Thrust Chamber Heat Transfer

Heat is transmitted to all parts exposed to hot gases, such as injector faces, nozzles, and chamber walls.

The *heat transfer rate* or *heat transfer intensity*, that is, heat transfer per unit area, varies within the rocket and is usually highest at, and immediately upstream of, the nozzle throat with local wall temperatures having the highest values in this region. Rocket thrust chambers with local heat transfer rates of 0.1 to

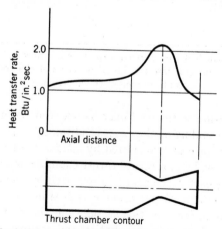

FIGURE 5-2. Typical heat transfer rate distribution along thrust chamber wall

10.0 Btu/sec in.[2] have been successful. A typical heat transfer rate distribution is shown in Figure 5–2. Only ½ to 5 per cent of the total energy generated in the gas is transferred as heat to the chamber walls. For a typical rocket of 10,000-pound thrust

FIGURE 5–3. Scorched and eroded experimental rocket thrust chamber which had leaky injector inserts. Metal on parts of chamber and injector has been melted or vaporized.

the heat rejection to the wall may be between 700 and 3000 Btu per second, depending on the exact conditions.

The amount of heat transferred by *conduction* from the chamber gas to the walls in a rocket thrust chamber is negligible. By far the largest part of the heat is transferred by means of *convection*. A part (5 to 25 per cent) of the transferred heat is attributed to *radiation*. In this section and the next few sections of this chapter discussion of radiation and conduction effects will be omitted. It should, however, be pointed out that radiation

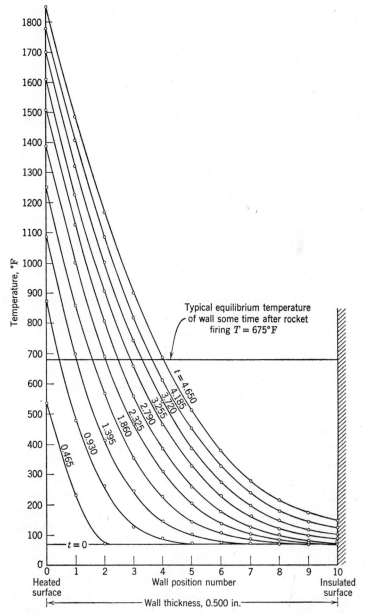

FIGURE 5–4. Typical temperature distribution through the wall of an uncooled combustion chamber as a function of heating time.

effects are more pronounced in large rocket thrust chambers than in small ones, because the mass of radiating substance is bigger in a large chamber; the radiation effects are treated in another section of this chapter.

The amount of heat transfer increases as the exposed wall surfaces of the combustion chamber increases. For constant chamber pressure, the surface area of a combustion chamber generally increases with thrust. Usually the chamber wall surface increases less rapidly than the volume as the thrust level is raised. The cooling of combustion chambers by liquid propellants is thus generally easier in large thrust sizes, and the capacity of the coolant to absorb all the heat rejected by the hot gas is generally more critical in smaller sizes, because of the volume-surface relationship. *The nozzle surface area* of a combustion device is not subject to a simple surface-to-volume relationship and must be considered separately. As the nozzle exit areas become larger, the exposed nozzle wall surface subject to heat transfer increases.

Variations in chamber pressure seriously affect the heat transfer. In many cases the heat transfer rate per unit surface area has been found to be almost proportional to the chamber pressure; theoretically the gas film coefficient is proportional to the 0.8 power of the gas density. The increase of heat transfer with chamber pressure often imposes design limits on the maximum practical chamber pressure for both liquid and solid propellant rockets.

3   Heat Transfer Failures

There appear to be at least two basic types of heat transfer failures in combustion chambers. In one type the wall temperature on the gas side T_{wg} exceeds the value at which the material is readily melted or oxidized. The local loss of material and the local heating weakens the wall so that the remaining material is inadequate to take the imposed load. This failure is characterized by melting, erosion, or severe oxidation on the gas side surface of the wall. This type of failure occurs primarily in uncooled chambers and uncooled nozzles, but also in cooled chambers or nozzles with relatively thick walls. Figure 5–3 illustrates a failure of this type.

The other type of failure is essentially caused by the local inability of the liquid film of the cooling jacket to transfer the heat from the wall to the liquid coolant. This type occurs only in liquid propellant cooled chambers and is characterized by a sudden increase in the local heat flux and wall temperatures, usually resulting in melting of the metal. This breakdown of the liquid film occurs if the wall temperature on the coolant side exceeds the boiling point of the coolant liquid by a considerable margin. A discussion of some of the factors governing the behavior of liquid film in forced convection cooling jackets is given in another section of this chapter.

4 Uncooled Combustion Devices

Uncooled walls act essentially as heat sponges and absorb heat from the hot gases. With the aid of experimental data to determine some typical coefficients, it is possible in some cases to predict the transient heating of uncooled walls.

Heat is transferred from the hot gases to the wall, and during operation a changing temperature gradient exists across the wall. The heat transferred from the hot wall to the surrounding atmosphere and by conduction of metal parts to the structure is negligibly small. During the combustion process the gas side of the wall is always hotter than the outside wall surface. Each local point within the wall has its temperature raised as the burning process is extended in time. At the completion of the rocket's operation, the wall temperatures tend to equalize. A typical temperature-time-location history is given in Figure 5–4. Here the line at $T = 70°$ F denotes the initial equilibrium condition of the wall before the rocket operates; the various curves show the temperature profile across the wall at successive time intervals after initiation of combustion. The line at $T = 675°$ F shows an equilibrium temperature of the wall a finite time after cut-off.

In all flying articles weight is at a premium and only sufficient metal is built into the walls to absorb the rejected heat without risking a failure from a weakening of the metal with increasing wall temperature. Thus the rocket designer has to satisfy himself on having the ability to carry all the applied load in the wall at the elevated temperature condition and thus to minimize the weight of the rocket. This condition implies that the heat transferred across the hot surface of the wall (and distributed within the wall by conduction) must be less than the heat-absorbing capacity of the wall material below the critical temperature. If heat transfer to the outside atmosphere is neglected, then this can be expressed in a very simplified form:

$$Q \, \Delta t = -\kappa A \, (dT/dL) \, \Delta t = W\bar{c} \, \Delta T \qquad (5\text{--}9)$$

Q is the heat in Btu per second transferred across area A expressed in square inches. The heat conductivity κ depends on the material and the temperature and is expressed in Btu per square inch, second, degree Fahrenheit per linear inch; ΔT denotes the average wall temperature increment in degrees Fahrenheit, dT/dL the temperature gradient of the heat flow near the hot wall surface in degrees per inch, W the weight of the wall in pounds, $\bar{c}$ the average specific heat of the wall material in Btu per pound per degree; and Δt denotes the time increment in seconds. Detailed analysis of this problem requires iterative mathematical treatment as shown below. The simple relation of equation 5–9 indicates the following trends:

1. A short operating duration (Δt) should favor uncooled chamber design, because it minimizes the amount of heat to be absorbed by the wall.
2. A low value of the conductivity at the hot surface of the wall is desirable. This can be achieved effectively by an insulating layer on the hot gas side. Ceramic linings, special paints, and fuels which deposit a protective coating (carbon) on the wall are satisfactory for this purpose. Typical values are given in Table 5–2. Ceramic nozzle inserts have been used successfully in solid propellant rocket practice.
3. A high value of the specific heat of the wall material promotes a high heat-absorbing capacity.
4. A high value of the conductivity of the wall material (other than at the gas surface) will tend to minimize temperature gradients within the wall and thus not only reduce thermal stresses (which are superimposed on the stresses induced in the wall by pressure loads) but also tend to increase the heat-absorbing capacity of the wall material.
5. A high value of the maximum permissible stress at the highest possible elevated temperatures will permit a large in-

TABLE 5–2. PHYSICAL PROPERTIES OF TYPICAL REFRACTORY MATERIALS FOR ROCKET APPLICATIONS

Material	Typical Composition	Melting Point, °F	True Specific Gravity	Apparent Specific Gravity	Linear Coefficient of Thermal Expansion, $(°F)^{-1}$	Thermal Conductivity, Btu/hr ft² °F/in.	Specific Heat, Btu/lb °F	Resistance to Thermal Shock
Alumina	99.2% Al_2O_3 0.6% SiO_2	3720	3.95	2.9–3.2	0.0000040 at 60° to 1850° F	17 at 2000° F	0.28–0.30 at ambient to 3100° F	Good
Magnesia	97% MgO 1.2% SiO_2	4900	3.58	3.0	0.0000085 at 60° to 2700° F	18 at 2000° F	0.29 at 60° to 3270° F	Good
Zirconia	94.5% ZrO_2	4600–4700	5.6	4.4	0.0000045 at 30° to 2000° F	6.0 at 2000° F	0.175 at 60° to 2550° F	Excellent
Silicon nitride	Si_3N_4	Decomposes in inert atmosphere at 3450	3.44	2.0–2.4	0.00000145 at 1650° F	—	—	Excellent
Carbon	Essentially C	Sublimates 6402	1.8–2.1	1.03–1.77	0.0000016 to 0.0000029 at 60° to 220° F	12 to 104 at 2000° F	0.29 at 60° to 1850° F	Excellent
Graphite	Essentially C	3681	2.25	1.03–1.91	0.0000010 to 0.0000024 at 60° to 220° F	240 to 1132 at 2000° F	0.29 at 60° to 1850° F	Excellent
Silicon carbide	SiC with complex nitride bond	SiC decomposes at 4010	—	2.77	0.0000037 at 60° to 2750° F	113	—	Excellent

crease in wall temperature without undue weakening of the wall. Unfortunately all metals lose strength as their temperature is increased as shown in Figure 5–5 and Table 5–3.

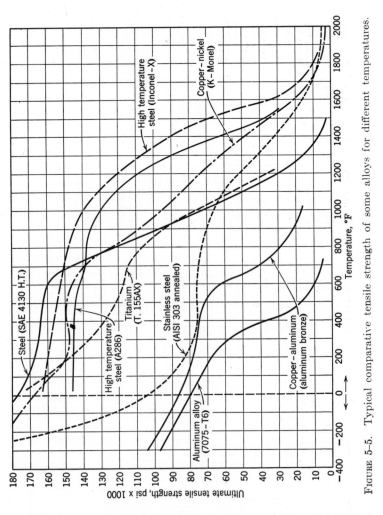

FIGURE 5–5. Typical comparative tensile strength of some alloys for different temperatures.

A graphical or tabular method for solving complex mathematical transient heat transfer problems is credited to E. Schmidt (Ref. 5.101); here a differential equation is replaced by a finite increment. This method is based on dividing the wall thickness

TABLE 5-3. ELEVATED TEMPERATURE PROPERTIES OF VARIOUS MATERIALS

	Copper, Com. Pure	Aluminum Alloy, 24S-T	Low Carbon Steel, SAE 1020	Alloy Steel, SAE X4130	Stainless Steel, AISI Type 302	Nickel Alloy, Inconel
Ultimate tensile strength, psi	75°F 33,000	75°F 68,000 212 62,000 300 58,000 400 53,000 500 26,000 600 15,000 700 7,500	85°F 62,400 900 45,500 1000 36,500 1200 20,000 1300 13,500 1400 9,025	75°F 98,300 400 94,200 600 97,000 800 84,000 900 72,800 1000 65,000	75°F 93,000 200 83,000 400 75,400 600 76,200 800 73,000 1000 65,600 1200 52,000 1400 31,800 1600 15,700 2000 4,700 2200 2,500 2300 2,300	75°F 85,000 200 81,000 400 78,000 600 79,000 800 83,000 1000 79,000 1200 71,000 1400 47,000 1600 23,000 1800 15,000 2000 11,000
	(1) Annealed	(2) Short time test	(3)	(4) Normalized	(5) Annealed	(6) Short time test
Yield strength, psi	75°F 10,000	75°F 45,000 212 41,500 300 39,000 400 35,000 500 23,000 600 13,000 700 6,500	85°F 42,000 900 23,700 1000 20,100 1200 10,200 1300 7,375 1400 3,750	75°F 74,000 400 73,600 600 70,300 800 66,000 900 59,300 1000 53,400	75°F 37,000 200 29,700 400 23,400 600 22,000 800 19,800 1000 17,100 1200 15,500 1400 14,900	75°F 36,000 200 32,000 400 28,000 600 27,000 800 28,000 1000 22,000 1200 22,000 1400 19,000
	(1) Annealed	(2) 0.02% offset Short time test	(3)	(4) Normalized	(5) Annealed	(6) 0.2% offset Short time test
Modulus of elasticity, psi $\times 10^6$	75°F 16.0	75°F 10.3 212 10.0 300 9.78 400 9.27 500 8.24	70°F 29.5 400 24.5 600 21.5 800 18.5 1000 15.5 1200 12.5	70°F 29.5 400 24.5 600 21.5 800 18.5 1000 15.5 1200 12.5	85°F 27.5 900 23.4 1000 22.2 1100 21.6 1200 20.7 1300 19.5 1400 18.3 1500 13.3	75°F 31.0 500 28.7 1000 25.0 1200 23.0 1350 21.0 1500 18.5
	(7)	(8)	(3)	(3)	(3)	(6) Inconel X

TABLE 5–3.　ELEVATED TEMPERATURE PROPERTIES OF VARIOUS MATERIALS (Continued)

	Copper, Com. Pure		Aluminum Alloy, 24S-T		Low Carbon Steel, SAE 1020		Alloy Steel, SAE X4130		Stainless Steel, AISI Type 302		Nickel Alloy, Inconel	
Thermal conductivity, Btu/hr ft² °F/in.	32°F	2,648.6	64°F	1,567.0	32°F	360.5	32°F	298.1	32°F	110	86°F	124.8
	68	2,641.7			392	339.7	212	298.1	212	113	392	131.7
	212	2,614.0			752	298.1	392	291.2	392	119	1472	194.1
	392	2,579.3			932	270.4	572	284.3	572	125	2192	249.6
	572	2,551.6			1472	179.6	752	270.4	752	136		
	752	2,516.9			1652	182.3	932	249.6	932	148		
	932	2,482.2			1832	187.2	1112	235.7	1112	159		
	1112	2,392.1			2012	194.1	1292	214.9	1292	168		
					2192	208.0	1472	180.3	1472	180		
							1652	187.2	1652	186		
							1832	194.1	1832	194		
							2012	201.1	2012	200		
							2192	208.0	2192	206		
	(7)		(9)		(10)		(10)		(10)		(11)	
Coefficient of thermal expansion, in./in. °F × 10⁻⁶	32°F	8.83	68–212°F	12.9	68– 212°F	6.5	32– 212°F	7.04	32°F	8.23	50°F	5.6
	68	8.93	68–392	13.3	68– 392	6.7	32– 392	7.28	32– 212°F	9.15	100	6.0
	77	8.95	68–572	13.7	68– 572	7.1	32– 572	7.48	32– 392	9.50	200	6.8
	122	9.09			68– 752	7.4	32– 752	7.68	32– 572	9.78	300	7.5
	212	9.39			68– 932	7.7	32– 932	7.88	32– 752	10.02	400	8.0
	392	10.09			68–1112	8.0	32– 112	8.08	32– 932	10.24	500	8.4
	572	10.91			68–1292	8.2	32–1292	8.24	32–1112	10.43	600	8.7
	752	11.86					32–1472	6.62	32–1292	10.57	700	9.0
	932	12.94					32–1652	7.23	32–1472	10.67	800	9.3
	1112	14.15					32–1832	7.70	32–1652	10.75	900	9.8
									32–1832			
	(7)		(9)		(10)		(10)		(10)		(11)	

	(7)	(10)	(6)
	1292 15.49	32-2012 8.04	1000 10.1
	1472 16.97		1100 10.2
			1200 10.2
			1300 10.2
			1400 10.2

Specific heat, Btu/°F lb	(7)	(9)	(12)	(10)	(10)	(6)
	75°F 0.0918	64-212°F 0.212	68°F 0.115	212°F 0.114	212°F 0.122	78-212°F 0.109
	392 0.096		212 0.120	392 0.123	392 0.127	
	752 0.100		392 0.125	572 0.130	572 0.131	
	1112 0.104		572 0.133	752 0.142	752 0.136	
	1472 0.109		752 0.140	932 0.157	932 0.142	
	1832 0.114		932 0.150	1112 0.176	1112 0.155	
			1112 0.151	1292 0.197	1292 0.149	
			1292 0.152	1382 0.386	1472 0.153	
			1472 0.153	1472 0.211	1652 0.156	
			1652 0.154	1652 0.141	1832 0.156	
			1832 0.155	1832 0.145	2012 0.158	
			2012 0.156	2012 0.148	2192 0.161	
			2192 0.160	2192 0.152	2282 0.162	
			2372 0.166	2282 0.154		
	(7)	(9)	(10)	(10)	(10)	(6)
Melting point	1981.4°F	Approx. 1200°F	Approx. 2780°F	Approx. 2700°F	2550°F	2540°F

References: (1) *Copper and Copper Alloys,* Anaconda Copper Co., Waterbury, Connecticut. (2) L. L. Wyman, *High Temperature Properties of Light Alloys,* (NA-137), Part I, Aluminum; OSRD Report 3607, April 15, 1944. (3) S. L. Hoyt, *Metals and Alloys Data Book,* Reinhold Publishing Corp., New York, 1943, pp. 100, 101, 191. (4) C. M. Campbell, *Short Time Tensile Properties of Low Alloy Steels at Elevated Temperatures,* North American Aviation, Inc., Report NA-47-825, October 15, 1947. (5) *Elevated Temperature Properties of Stainless Steel,* Allegheny Ludlum Steel Corp., Backenridge, Pennsylvania. (6) *Nickel and Nickel Alloys,* International Nickel Co., New York, 1946. (7) C. S. Smith, "Physical Constants of Copper," *Metals Handbook,* 1939 edition. American Society for Metals, pp. 1380–1388. (8) R. L. Templin, *Some Mechanical Properties of Selected Currently Available Aluminum and Magnesium Alloy Products at Various Temperatures,* Bulletin of Aluminum Corporation of America, New Kensington, Pennsylvania, October 7, 1947. (9) "Aluminum and Aluminum Alloys," *Alcoa Handbook,* 1947, Aluminum Corporation of America, Pittsburgh, Pennsylvania. (10) *The Physical Properties of a Series of Steels,* The Iron and Steel Institute, London, September 1946. (11) *Mechanical Properties of Metals and Alloys,* National Bureau of Standards, Washington, D.C., Circular C447, p. 372. (12) P. Hidnert, "Coefficients of Linear Expansion of SAE Steels," *Metals Handbook,* 1939 edition, American Society for Metals, Cleveland, Ohio, pp. 486, 487.

t_w into n finite slabs of thickness ΔL, so that $\Delta L = t_w/n$. Figure 5–4 illustrates this situation. At any given time the rate of heat conduction into a given slab exceeds the rate of heat conduction into the next slab by the amount of heat absorbed in raising the temperature of the particular slab, namely

$$\frac{\kappa A(T_{n-1} - T_n)}{\Delta L} - \frac{\kappa A(T_n - T_{n+1})}{\Delta L} = \frac{A\,\Delta L\,\rho\bar{c}(T_n' - T_n)}{\Delta t} \qquad (5\text{–}10)$$

where T_n refers to the specific slab under consideration, T_{n-1} to the slab ahead and T_{n+1} to the slab at the lower temperature. T' refers to the temperature a finite time Δt thereafter. If we designate the diffusivity $\kappa/(\rho\bar{c})$ as α, then the equation above can be rewritten as

$$\frac{T_{n-1} + T_{n+1}}{2} - T_n = \frac{(\Delta L)^2(T_n' - T_n)}{2\alpha\,\Delta t} \qquad (5\text{–}11)$$

By proper choice of ΔL or Δt the quantity $\Delta t\,2\alpha/(\Delta L)^2$ can be made equal to one and the equation reduces to

$$T_n' = \frac{T_{n-1} + T_{n+1}}{2}$$

Thus the new temperature at section n is the arithmetic mean of the temperatures previously prevailing at the sections ahead and behind at a time Δt prior to this event. This method is repeated for each slab, and an approximate solution is then found. It should be noted that this method in its simple form assumes uniform wall properties κ, ρ and $\bar{c}$, which do not vary with temperature. Equations 5–10 and 5–11 apply to flat plates; for cylinders and cones such as thrust chambers and nozzles, the use of flat plate relations is usually satisfactory, provided the ratio of radius to wall thickness is larger than four.

Example 5–2. Determine the transient temperature distribution of the wall of an uncooled stainless steel rocket combustion chamber with the following data:

Propellants	Nitric acid and aniline
Mixture ratio	2.75
Chamber pressure	300 psia
Atmospheric pressure	14.7 psia
Thrust	1000 lb

Chamber convective heat transfer coefficient	500 Btu/hr ft^2 °F (assumed constant in chamber)
Chamber wall material	Stainless steel
Wall thickness	0.500 in.
Inside chamber diameter	5.0 in.
Wall specific heat	0.15 Btu/lb °F (assumed average value)
Wall density	0.30 lb/in.^{3}
Wall thermal conductivity	15.6 Btu/hr ft^2 °F/ft (assumed average value)
Initial wall temperature	70°F

Neglect heat loss to atmosphere. Determine the time of rocket operation required for wall temperature to reach 1500° F.

Solution. From the first four items of data the gas temperature can be computed by the methods explained in the previous chapter. The results would be $T_{gas} = 4930°$ F. If 10 segments are chosen with $\Delta L = 0.050$ in. Δt must be determined from the condition which has to satisfy the Schmidt method, namely

$$\frac{(\Delta L)^2}{2\alpha \, \Delta t} = 1$$

$$\Delta t = \frac{(\Delta L)^2 \rho \bar{c}}{2\kappa} = \frac{(0.050)^2 \times 0.30 \times 0.15 \times 12 \times 3600}{2 \times 15.6} = 0.155 \text{ sec}$$

then time increments of 0.155 sec will be used in this calculation. In order to consider the convective heat transfer from the hot gas to the wall in this iterative method, the concept of a ficticious layer of wall of thickness ΔL is used; an extra thickness ΔL is added on the gas side of the wall, so that

$$h_g A(T_g - T_0) = -\kappa A \left(\frac{dT}{dL}\right)_0 = -\kappa A \left(\frac{T^* - T_0}{\Delta L}\right)$$

where T^* is the temperature at the outside of the fictitious layer and T_0 is the temperature of the wall surface. Here T^* is given by

$$T^* = T_0 + (h_g/\kappa) \, \Delta L \, (T_g - T_0)$$

$$= T_0 + \frac{500 \times 0.050}{15.6 \times 12} (4930 - T_0)$$

$$= 657 + 0.867 T_0$$

Equation 5–11 (the Schmidt method) will be used to obtain a step-by-step solution here. If an insulating layer is assumed on the outside of the thrust chamber wall, then there is no heat loss to the surroundings and all the heat is absorbed by the wall material; this eliminates the necessity of assuming another fictitious layer on the outside wall surface. Since the results show that the temperature of the outside wall surface remains low, this insulation assumption is justified and the heat transferred to the outer layer will be used solely to raise the temperature of the outer layer, namely

$$Q_{10} = \frac{\kappa A}{\Delta L}(T_9 - T_{10}) = A \, \Delta L \, \rho \bar{c}(T_{10}' - T_{10})$$

which reduces to

$$T_{10}' = \tfrac{1}{2}(T_9 - T_{10})$$

At time t_0 the initial temperature of the wall is $70°$ F. At $t = 0.155$ sec

$$T^* = 657 + 0.867 \times 70 = 719° \text{ F}$$

$$T_0 = T_1 = T_2 = T_n = 70° \text{ F}$$

At $t = 2 \times 0.155 = 0.310$ sec

$$T_0 = \tfrac{1}{2}(T^* + T_1) = \tfrac{1}{2}(719 + 70) = 394° \, F$$

$$T_1' = T_2 = T_n = 70° \text{ F}$$

$$T^* = 657 + 0.867 \times 394 = 999° \text{ F}$$

At $t = 3 \times 0.155 = 0.465$ sec

$$T_0' = \tfrac{1}{2}(T^* + T_1) = \tfrac{1}{2}(999 + 70) = 534° \text{ F}$$

$$T_1' = \tfrac{1}{2}(T_0 + T_1) = \tfrac{1}{2}(394 + 70) = 232° \text{ F}$$

$$T_2 = T_3 = T_n = 70° \text{ F}$$

$$T^* = 1119° \text{ F}$$

Further detailed calculations are not shown here, but results are plotted as faired curves in Figure 5–4. It can be seen that the poor conductivity of stainless steel induces a large temperature gradient within the wall. In 2.75 sec the wall surface will exceed a temperature of $1500°$ F; at this temperature the steel becomes very weak. The wall will probably fail (oxidize, melt, or erode) when the inside surface exceeds some 2000 to $2200°$ F, and it is therefore doubtful that the wall will survive for more than perhaps 6 sec without local melting in the chamber.

5 Steady State Transfer to Liquids in Cooling Jacket

The term *regenerative cooling* is used for rockets where one of the propellants is circulated through cooling passages around the combustion device prior to the injection and burning of this propellant in the chamber. This is really forced convection heat transfer. The term "regenerative" is perhaps not altogether appropriate here, and it bears little relation to the meaning given to it in steam turbine practice. It is intended to convey the fact that the heat absorbed by the coolant propellant is not wasted but augments initial temperature and raises the energy level of the propellant before it passes through the injector. This increase in the internal energy of the liquid propellant can be calculated as a correction to the heat of reaction (Chapter 4); however, the over-all effect on the rocket performance is usually very slight. With some propellants the specific impulse can be 1 per cent larger if the propellants are preheated through a temperature differential of 200 to 300° F. In small combustion chambers, where the wall

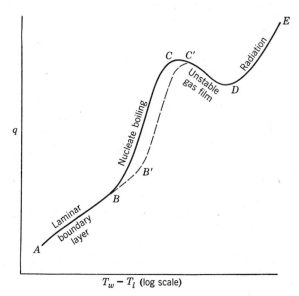

FIGURE 5-6. Regimes in transferring heat from a hot wall to a flowing liquid.

surface to chamber volume ratio is relatively large, the temperature rise in the regenerative coolant will be high and the resulting increase in specific impulse can sometimes be more than 1 per cent.

The behavior of the *liquid film* is the critical phenomenon controlling the wall temperatures in forced convection cooling of rocket combustion devices at high heat fluxes. At least four different types of film appear to exist, as can be interpreted from Figure 5-6.

Here the heat transfer rate per unit of wall surface is shown as a function of the difference between the wall temperature on the liquid side T_{wl} and the bulk temperature of the liquid T_l.

1. The normal *forced convection* region at low heat flux appears to have a typical liquid laminar boundary layer. It is indicated by region *A–B* in Figure 5–6. Here the wall temperature is usually below the boiling point of the liquid at the cooling jacket pressure. Since the present heat transfer analysis is generally valid for flow in pipes, conduits, and furnaces, it is adequate for determining the liquid film coefficient in this regime by the usual equation (see Ref. 5.101).

$$h_l = 0.023\bar{c}(\dot{w}/A) \left(\frac{Dv\rho}{\mu g}\right)^{-0.2} \left(\frac{\mu g\bar{c}}{\kappa}\right)^{-\frac{2}{3}} \tag{5–12}$$

where $\dot{w}$ is the fluid mass flow rate in pounds per second, $\bar{c}$ is the average specific heat of the fluid in Btu per degree Rankine per pound, A is the cross-sectional flow area in square inches, D is the equivalent diameter of the coolant passage cross section in feet, v is the fluid velocity in feet per second, ρ is the density in pounds per cubic foot, μ is the absolute viscosity in pound-seconds per square foot, and κ is the conductivity in Btu/sec ft^2 °R/ in. Many liquid-cooled rocket devices operate in this regime of heat transfer.

The helical or annular passages in liquid propellant rocket chambers are often of complex cross section. The equivalent diameter, needed for fluid film heat transfer calculations, is usually defined as four times the hydraulic radius of the coolant passage, where the hydraulic radius is the quotient of the cross sectional area of the coolant passage, divided by the wetted perimeter.

2. When the wall temperature T_{wl} exceeds the boiling point of the liquid by perhaps 10 or 40° F, then small vapor bubbles will form at the wall surface. These small nuclei-like bubbles will cause local turbulence, break away from the wall, and collapse in the cooler liquid. This phenomenon is known as *nucleate film boiling*. The turbulence induced by the bubbles changes the character of the liquid film and, augmented by the vaporization of some of the propellant, the heat transfer rate is increased without a proportional increase in the temperature drop across the film, as can be seen by the steep slope of the curve in Figure 5–6. The nucleate boiling region is shown as *B–C* in this figure. If the

pressure of the fluid is raised, then the boiling point is also raised and the nucleate boiling region shifts to the right to $B'-C'$. This film boiling permits a substantial increase in the heat transfer and often occurs locally in the nozzle throat area, where the heat flux is high. See Reference Bibliography, Section 5.3.

3. As the heat transfer is increased further, the rate of bubble formation and perhaps also the bubble size become so great that the bubbles are unable to escape from the wall rapidly enough. This region (shown as $C-D$ on Figure 5–6) is characterized by an unstable *gas film* and is difficult to obtain reproduceably in tests. When a film consisting largely or completely of gas forms along the hot wall surface, then this film acts as an insulation layer, causing a decrease in heat flux and usually a rapid increase in wall temperature, often resulting in a burnout or melting of the wall material. This limiting burnout heat transfer condition is a critical parameter in the design of a rocket; its location on the curve of Figure 5–6 appears to be a function of the cooling fluid properties, the presence of dissolved gases, the pressure, and the flow velocity. Several semi-empirical methods have been proposed for predicting the critical burnout conditions. It is essentially caused by a breakdown of the liquid film.

4. As the temperature difference across the film is further increased, the wall temperatures reach values in which heat transfer by *radiation* becomes important. Region $D-E$ is characterized by a very hot wall, an essentially continuous gas or vapor film, and the heat transferred almost completely by radiation. This region is of little interest to the rocket engineer.

The general phenomenon of changing film behavior is not fully understood; however, its general pattern is fairly well defined.

In addition to the liquid film phenomenon described above, chemical changes in the liquid can seriously influence the heat transfer from hot walls to liquids. Cracking of the fuel, with an attendant formation of gas or the formation of solid material which is deposited on the hot wall surface, tends to reduce the maximum heat flux and thus promote failure more readily.

The *heat-absorbing capacity of the coolant* has to be such that boiling is permitted locally but the bulk of the coolant does not reach this boiling condition. The heat rejected by the surface A

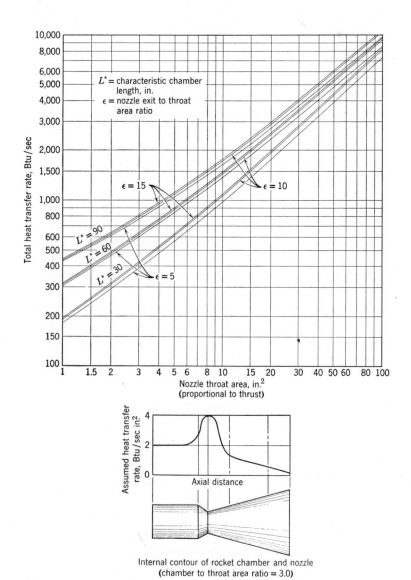

FIGURE 5–7. Typical rocket thrust chamber cooling load as a function of characteristic length, throat area, and nozzle area ratio.

of the hot walls, as given by equations 5–2 to 5–6, has to be less than that permitted by the temperature rise in the coolant

$$qA = Q = \dot{w}\bar{c}(T_1 - T_2) \qquad (5\text{–}13)$$

where $\dot{w}$ is the coolant flow rate, $\bar{c}$ the specific heat of the liquid, T_1 is the initial temperature of the coolant as it enters the cooling jacket, and T_2 is the final temperature of the coolant in the jacket. Q is the rate of heat absorption per unit time; q is this same rate per unit heat transfer area A. T_2 must be below the boiling point prevailing at the cooling jacket pressure. Typical values of the heat absorption by a coolant are shown in Figure 5–7.

6 Heat Transfer to Flying Vehicles

At high flight speeds the boundary layer around the vehicle is heated aerodynamically to relatively high temperatures. This boundary layer behavior governs the heating of the vehicle's skin, the aerodynamic drag, structural requirement, environmental conditions for men and equipment inside the vehicle, and the heating and possible boil-off of propellants. This whole subject is under intensive theoretical and experimental investigation.

The missile skin temperature is a function of the Mach number, altitude, aerodynamic configuration, and several dimensionless parameters such as Reynold's number. The type of boundary layer formed is very significant since a laminar boundary layer transfers less heat than a turbulent one. An analysis of these effects is beyond the scope of this chapter; however, the subject is briefly mentioned here to give the student an appreciation of the problem.

The stagnation temperature is the maximum temperature that can be obtained in the boundary layer. It is a function of Mach number, the specific heat ratio, and the initial air temperature as defined in equation 3–11; typical values are given in Figure 5–8. Most of the vehicle surfaces do not reach the full value of the stagnation temperature. Only on leading edges of aerodynamic surfaces or on the nose will the vehicle skin temperature approach the stagnation temperature.

The heating of propellants contained in thin-walled air-borne integral skin tanks is also a function of the time-altitude history of the flight with the most serious heating occurring at high flight speeds and in dense air at low altitudes. For liquefied gas type propellants, such as liquid oxygen, even a small rise in tempera-

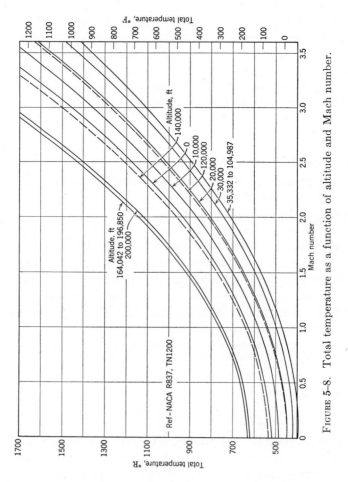

FIGURE 5-8. Total temperature as a function of altitude and Mach number.

ture causes a substantial change in vapor pressure and density and also therefore in pumping and rocket system characteristics. Rockets carried externally by high speed aircraft can be subject to intense skin heating. In some of these applications solid propellant rockets are subjected to excessive temperatures on the integral skin wall, so that their physical properties deteriorate (the propellant becomes too soft) or the danger of involuntary ignition exists.

Even if the rocket unit of a high speed vehicle is not directly exposed to the hot skin but is sheltered inside the vehicle, it may require special cooling provisions, the use of special materials, particularly plastics, seals, and electrical insulation, and the application of special design techniques.

7 Radiation

The heat transmitted by the mechanism of radiation depends primarily on the temperature of the radiating body. The second law of thermodynamics can be used to prove that the radiant energy E is a function of the fourth power of the absolute temperature T

$$E = \epsilon \sigma A T^4 \tag{5–14}$$

The energy E radiated by a body is defined as a function of the emissivity ϵ, which is a dimensionless factor for surface condition, material properties, or geometry relations, the Stefan-Boltzmann constant σ (0.1713 Btu/ft^2 hr °R^4), the surface area A, and the absolute temperature T. At low temperatures (below 1000° F), radiation accounts for only a negligible portion of the total heat transfer in a rocket device and can usually be neglected. In rocket combustion devices, gas temperatures are between 3500 and 7000° R, and radiation is believed to contribute between 5 to 25 per cent of the heat transfer to the chamber walls.

The absorption of radiation follows essentially the same laws as those of emission. A highly reflective surface on the inside wall of a combustor will tend to reduce absorption and to minimize the temperature increase of the walls.

The radiation in combustion devices comes usually from the hot reaction products. These gases are not as effective a radiator as solid matter; however, at the high combustion temperatures the contribution of gas-emitted radiation to the overall heat transfer is significant.

Gases with symmetrical molecules, such as hydrogen, oxygen, nitrogen, etc., have been found not to show emission bands in those wavelength regions of importance in radiant heat transfer. Also they do not absorb radiation and do not contribute energy.

Heteropolar gases such as water vapor, carbon monoxide, carbon dioxide, hydrogen chloride, hydrocarbons, ammonia, oxides of nitrogen, and the alcohols have strong emission bands of known wavelengths. The radiation of energy of these molecules is associated with their quantum changes in their energy levels of rotation and interatomic vibration. In general the radiation intensity of all gases increases with their volume, partial pressure, and the fourth power of their absolute temperature. For small thrust chambers and low chamber pressures, radiation contributes only a small amount of energy to the overall heat transfer.

When the combustion products contain clouds of finely divided solid matter, then their radiation power is generally increased by a large factor (two to ten times). There are two types of luminosity, depending on the size of particles of solid matter suspended in the gases: those flames containing relatively large particles are essentially opaque, and the gases with soot particles that are very small have flames that are essentially semi-transparent. The radiation behavior of these two types is different. In solid propellant rockets it is possible to obtain gases with entrained solid particles of fair size (above 0.1 micron). The incomplete burning of many hydrocarbons, such as aromatic hydrocarbon components, produces radiant soot in the flame with particles of very small size.

Relatively little is known about the radiation of propellant products under rocket operating conditions. It has been the subject of considerable research; the Reference Bibliography lists several works detailing this research.

8   Jet Flames

The jet from a rocket will heat its surroundings by means of (1) conduction and convection to objects directly in the jet, and (2) radiation to surrounding environment. In the first category are jet vanes, test stand flame deflectors, and other equipment; vehicle fuselage and aerodynamic surfaces, as well as test stand equipment, fall into the second category.

The flame shape or the region of the hot gases is a function of the nozzle geometry, the degree of underexpansion, the atmospheric pressure, the chemical composition, the vehicle velocity, and the aerodynamic vehicle configuration near the nozzle. The exact prediction of the flame shape and size is difficult; however, some general observations can be made.

An empirical and approximate formula for the length of the visible flame with ordinary propellants and near optimum sea level nozzle designs is as follows:

$$l = \sqrt{\frac{F}{f}} \qquad (5\text{--}15)$$

where l is the length of the visible flame in feet, F is the thrust in pounds, and f is an empirical factor with a value of 10 for the given dimensions. The shape of the flame depends largely on the

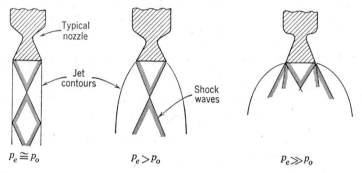

$p_e \cong p_o$ $p_e > p_o$ $p_e \gg p_o$

FIGURE 5-9. Typical jet contours for different ratios of the nozzle exit gas pressure p_e and the free stream atmospheric pressure p_o for moving vehicles.

gas pressure at the nozzle exit and the ambient atmospheric pressure; if the two are nearly equal, then the jet can have a nearly cylindrical boundary approximately parallel to the nozzle axis. At altitude, or when the nozzle exit pressure is larger than the atmospheric pressure, the jet has a tendency to spread out as illustrated in Figure 5-9. It can be seen that a rocket jet flame will tend to sweep out a larger cross section at altitude than at sea level. At very high altitudes it is theoretically possible to have the jet gases actually flow forward. The air flowing around the vehicle tends to act as an interface to jet gases and influences the jet's shape.

In conical nozzles shock waves are often visible in the exhaust jet. Certain propellants (for example ethyl alcohol when burned with liquid oxygen) have relatively non-luminous flames and therefore show a clean shock wave pattern. With other propellants, such as certain solid propellants, the exhaust jet is incandescently luminous or cloudy, and this phenomenon obscures the shock wave pattern.

The shock waves are a series of expansion and compression waves forming a diamond pattern. The first shock wave usually commences at the exit of the nozzle.

Problems

1. Compute the total or stagnation temperature which would occur ideally at the nose of a vehicle flying at an altitude of 80,000 ft and a Mach number of 6.0. Assume isentropic conditions, an ambient air temperature of $-66°$ F, $\kappa = 1.4$, and a molecular weight of 29 lb/mole.

Answer: 2770° F.

2. How much total heat per second can be absorbed in a thrust chamber with an inside wall surface area of 300 sq in., if the coolant is aniline, and the coolant should not exceed 275° F in the jacket? Assume the average specific heat of aniline to equal 0.55 Btu/°F lb, an inlet temperature of 70° F, and a coolant flow of 4 lb/sec. What is the average heat transfer rate per sec per sq in.?

3. During a static test a certain thrust chamber is cooled by water. The following data are given:

Average water temperature	100° F
Thermal conductivity of water	1.07×10^{-4} Btu/sec ft^2 °F/ft
Gas temperature	4500° F
Viscosity of water	2.5×10^{-5} lb-sec/ft^2
Specific heat of water	1.0 Btu/lb °F
Cooling passage dimensions	$\frac{1}{4} \times \frac{1}{2}$ in.
Water flow through passage	0.585 lb/sec
Thickness of inner wall	$\frac{1}{8}$ in.
Heat absorbed	1.3 Btu/in.^{2} sec
Thermal conductivity of wall material	26 Btu/hr ft^2 °F/ft

Determine the following: (*a*) film coefficient of coolant, (*b*) wall temperature on coolant side, (*c*) wall temperature on gas side.

4. In the example above determine the water flow required to decrease the wall temperature on the gas side by 100° F. What is the percentage increase in coolant velocity? Assume that the various properties of the water and the average water temperature do not change.

5. Express the total temperature drop in problem 3 in terms of the percentage temperature drops through the coolant film, the wall and gas film.

Symbols

A	area, ft^2
$\bar{c}$	average specific heat of fluid, Btu/°F lb
c_p	specific heat of gas at constant pressure, Btu/°F lb
D	diameter, ft
d	total derivative
E	radiation heat transfer rate, Btu/hr
F	thrust, lb
f	empirical flame length factor
g	acceleration of gravity, 32.2 ft^2/sec
h	film coefficient, Btu/in.^{2} sec °F
L, l	length, ft
Q	heat transfer rate, Btu/sec
q	heat transfer rate per unit area, Btu/sec ft^2
T	temperature, °R or °F
T^*	temperature of fictitious wall segment, °F
t	time, sec
t_w	wall thickness, in.
v	velocity, ft/sec
W	weight, lb
$\dot{w}$	weight flow rate, lb/sec

Greek Letters

α	thermal diffusity $= \kappa/(\rho\bar{c})$
Δ	finite difference
ϵ	emissivity
κ	conductivity, Btu/in.^{2} sec °F/in.
μ	absolute viscosity, lb sec/ft^2
ρ	density, lb/ft^3
σ	Stefan-Boltzmann constant (0.1713 Btu/ft^2 hr °R^4)

Subscripts

g	gas
l	liquid
n	number of wall segments
w	wall
wg	wall surface on gas side
wl	wall surface on liquid side

Chapter **6**

Liquid Propellants

1 Classification

The propellants, which are the working substance of rockets, constitute the fluid which undergoes chemical and thermodynamic changes. The term "liquid propellant" embraces all the various liquids used and may be any one of the following:

1. Oxidizer (liquid oxygen, nitric acid, etc.).
2. Fuel (gasoline, alcohol, etc.).
3. Catalyst (sodium permanganate, etc.).
4. Inert additive (water). Although it does not directly contribute to the chemical reaction, it sometimes permits a higher thrust by increasing the propellant mass flow.
5. Chemical compound or mixture of two or more of the above.

There is a large variety of liquid propellant combinations which have been analytically and experimentally investigated. Unfortunately, it has not been possible to discover an ideal liquid propellant combination which will have only desirable characteristics. Almost every liquid propellant, especially every liquid oxidizing agent, has at least one or more undesirable properties, and no standard liquid propellant has as yet been developed.

A **monopropellant** contains an oxidizing agent and combustible matter in a single substance. It may be a mixture of several compounds such as hydrogen peroxide mixed with alcohol, or it may be a homogenous chemical agent, such as nitromethane. Monopropellants are stable at ordinary atmospheric conditions but decompose and yield hot combustion gases when heated and pressurized. The feed system of monopropellant units is usually simple, because only one liquid needs to be supplied.

160

A **bipropellant** rocket unit has two separate propellants which are not mixed outside the combustion chamber. The majority of successful liquid propellant units has used bipropellants.

Occasionally, rockets with three or more liquid propellants have been used, but never very extensively.

The following discussion lists in detail some of the general properties, specifications, and characteristics of liquid rocket propellants.

2   Propellant Properties and Specifications

It is important to distinguish between the characteristics and properties of the *liquid propellants,* that is, the fuel and oxidizer liquids in their unreacted condition and the properties of the *hot gas mixture* which results from the reaction in the combustion chamber. The chemical nature of the liquid propellants determines the properties and characteristics of both of these types; some of the more significant data are given in this section.

Economic Factors

Availability in large quantity and a *low cost* are very important considerations in the selection of a propellant.

In military applications consideration has to be given to *logistics* of production, supply, and other possible military uses. The production process should be simple, requiring only simple chemical equipment and available raw materials.

Transportation problems can be simplified when the liquid is stored in simple, cheap containers requiring a minimum of surveillance, complex handling equipment, and safety precautions.

Performance of Propellants

The performance can be compared on the basis of the *specific impulse,* the *effective exhaust velocity,* the *characteristic exhaust velocity,* the *specific propellant consumption,* the *ideal exhaust velocity,* or other parameters. They have been explained and discussed in Chapters 3 and 4. The specific impulse and the exhaust velocity are plotted as functions of pressure ratio, specific heat ratio, combustion temperature, and molecular weight in Figure 3–5. Values of performance parameters for various propellant combinations are listed in Table 4–3.

Very often the performance is expressed in terms of *flight performance parameters* for a given rocket application, as explained in Chapter 12. Here the density as well as the specific impulse usually enter into a complex flight relation equation. For simplified evaluations between several propellant combinations, the product of the specific impulse and the average specific gravity is used. This product is also known as the *density specific impulse*, even though the actual density is not used directly in its calculation.

A good performance of a propellant combination is determined by the following propellant properties, already mentioned in Chapter 4.

A *high content of chemical energy* per unit of propellant mixture is desirable because it permits a high chamber temperature. Because of friction and dissociation, the full value of the propellant energy is, however, never realized. This heat content differs from that used in conventional combustion engines, because it refers to a unit weight of mixture and not a unit weight of fuel. It has values in the order of 1500 to 2400 Btu per pound of mixture.

A *low molecular weight* of the product gases of the propellant combination is desirable. It can be accomplished by using fuels rich in combined hydrogen or other lightweight atoms which in turn are liberated during the reaction. A low molecular weight is obtained if an excess of hydrocarbon fuel is used, so that a large portion of the produced hydrogen gas will not combine with oxygen. In general, the best mixture ratio for many bipropellants is therefore not necessarily the stoichiometric one (which yields the highest flame temperature), but usually a rich mixture which contains a large portion of low molecular weight reaction products.

The effect of the *specific heat ratio* k of the propellant products on the exhaust velocity is small compared to the other two effects. However, there is a slight increase with a reduction in k as shown in Table 6–1.

TABLE 6–1. VARIATION OF SPECIFIC IMPULSE WITH k FOR A PRESSURE
RATIO OF 20

$k = 1.1$	1.2	1.3	1.4
$I_s = 114\%$	107%	104%	100%

Common Physical Hazards

Corrosion. Various propellants, such as nitric acid and hydrogen peroxide, have to be handled in containers and pipelines of special materials. If the propellant were permitted to become contaminated with corrosion products, the physical and chemical properties of the propellant would change sufficiently to make it unsuitable for rocket operation. Contact with skin causes very serious burns. The corrosion of the gaseous reaction products is important in applications, where the reaction products are likely to damage structure and parts of the vehicle.

Explosion Hazard. Some propellants such as hydrogen peroxide and nitromethane are unstable and tend to detonate under certain conditions of impurities, temperature, and shock.

Fire Hazard. Many oxidizers will start chemical reactions with a large variety of organic compounds. Nitric acid and hydrogen peroxide will react spontaneously with many organic substances. Most of the fuels are readily ignitable when exposed to air and heat.

Toxicity. Many propellants are toxic or poisonous, and special precautions have to be taken to protect personnel. Aniline, for example, is poisonous if it contacts the skin (see Ref. 4.201).

The corrosion, explosion, and fire hazards of many propellants put severe limitations on the materials, the handling, and the design of rocket-propelled vehicles. Not only is the rocket system itself exposed to the hazardous propellant, but adjacent structural parts and electrical and other vehicle equipment have to be properly protected against the effects of possible leaks, fumes, and of possible propellant accumulations within the rocket engine compartment.

Desirable Physical Properties

Low Freezing Point. This permits operation of rockets in cold weather. The addition of small amounts of special chemicals has been found to aid in depressing the freezing point of liquid propellants, which solidify readily at relatively high temperature.

High Specific Gravity. In order to accommodate a large weight of propellants in a given missile space, a dense propellant is required. It permits a small missile construction and, consequently, a relatively low structural missile weight and low aerodynamic drag. Specific gravity, therefore, has an important effect on the maximum flight velocity and range of any rocket-powered vehicle or missile, as explained in Chapter 12. Specific gravities for various propellants are plotted in Figure 6–1. For any given mixture ratio r, the average specific gravity of a propellant combination δ_{av} can be determined from the specific gravities of the fuel δ_f and of the oxidizer δ_o. The average specific gravity is defined as the weight of the fuel and oxidizer, divided by the sum of their volumes. Here the mixture ratio is defined as the oxidizer weight flow rate divided by the fuel weight flow rate.

$$\delta_{av} = \frac{\delta_o \delta_f (1 + r)}{r \delta_f + \delta_o}$$

Values of δ_{av} for various propellant combinations are listed in Table 4–3.

No *deterioration* with storage and no *reaction with the atmosphere*.

No appreciable *absorption of moisture* and no adverse effects of small amounts of *impurities*.

High specific heat, high thermal conductivity, and a *high boiling or decomposition temperature* are desirable for propellants which are used for thrust chamber cooling.

No *chemical reaction* with piping, tank walls, valve seat, and gasket materials, even at relatively high ambient temperatures.

A low *vapor pressure* will permit not only easier handling of the propellants but also a more effective pump design in applications where the propellant is pumped. If the *viscosity* of the propellant is too high, then pumping and engine system calibration become difficult. Propellants with high vapor pressure such as liquid oxygen, liquid methane, or other liquefied gases require special design provisions, unusual handling techniques, and often special low temperature materials.

The *temperature variation* of the physical properties of the liquid propellant should be small. For example, a wide temperature variation in vapor pressure and density (*thermal coefficient of expansion*) or an unduly high change in viscosity with temperature will make it very difficult to accurately calibrate a rocket engine flow system or predict its performance over any reasonable range of operating temperatures.

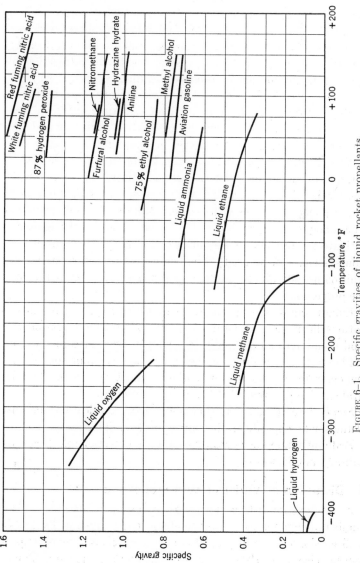

FIGURE 6-1. Specific gravities of liquid rocket propellants.

Combustion

If the propellant combination is *spontaneously ignitable,* it will not require an ignition system. This means that burning will be initiated as the oxidizer and the fuel come in contact with each other. Spontaneously ignitable propellants are often termed *hypergolic.* Although an ignition system is not a very objectionable feature, its elimination is usually desirable, because it will simplify the propulsion system. All rocket propellants should be readily ignitable and have a small ignition time delay, in order to reduce the explosion hazard during starting. Starting and ignition problems are discussed further in Chapter 8.

Non-spontaneously ignitable propellants have to be heated by external means before ignition can be initiated. Igniters are devices which accomplish an initial heating of the propellant mixture to the point where steady flow combustion can be self-sustained. The amount of energy which has to be added by the igniter to activate the propellants should be small so that low power ignition systems can be used. The energy required for satisfactory ignition usually diminishes for increasing ambient temperature of the propellant.

Experimental evidence indicates that certain propellant combinations burn very smoothly without combustion vibration and lend themselves more readily to a simple, reproduceable, and reliable starting technique. Other propellant combinations do not demonstrate this *combustion stability* and therefore are less desirable. See Reference Bibliography, Section 3.7.

Smoke formation is objectionable in many applications, because of the smoke deposits on the surrounding equipment and parts.

Brilliantly luminous *exhaust flames* are objectionable in certain military applications.

3   Discussion of Various Liquid Propellants

A comparative listing of various performance quantities for a number of common propellant combinations is given in Table 4–3. A discussion of several propellants is given below. Some important physical properties of various propellants are given in Tables 6–2A and 6–2B. Specific gravities and vapor pressures are shown in Figures 6–1 and 6–2.

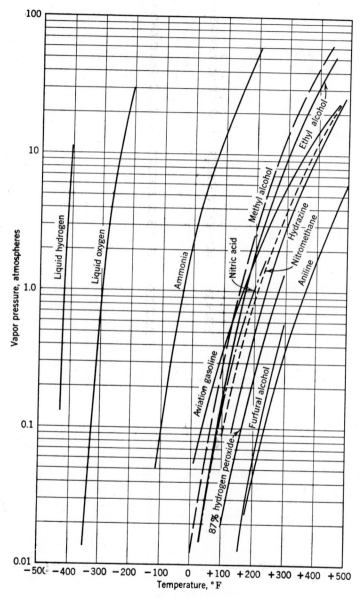

FIGURE 6–2. Vapor pressures of propellants.

TABLE 6–2A. SOME PHYSICAL PROPERTIES

Propellant	Ammonia	Aniline	Ethyl Alcohol 95%	Furfural Alcohol	Aviation Gasoline	Hydrazine	Hydrazine Hydrate
Chemical formula	NH_3	$C_6H_5NH_2$	C_6H_5OH	$C_4H_3OCH_2OH$	$C_{8.5}H_{18}$ average	N_2H_4	$N_2H_4 \cdot H_2O$
Molecular weight, lb/mole	17.03	93.06	46.06	98.10	120 average	32.05	50.06
Melting point, °F	−108	20	−179	−25	Under −76	34.5	−40
Boiling point, °F	−28	364	173	340	150 to 300	236	245
Heat of vaporization at 1 atm, Btu/lb	587	187	367	....	100 to 130	....	
Heat of formation, Btu/lb-mole	+28,900 (65°F)	−13,200 (77°F)	+121,000 (65°F)				
Specific heat, Btu/lb °F	1.05 (−76°F)	0.48 (50°F)	0.62 (68°F)	0.58 (70°F)	0.49 (50°F)	0.75 (80°F)	....
	1.13 (68°F)	0.542 (200°F)	0.65 (100°F)		0.56 (200°F)		
	1.48 (212°F)	0.65 (300°F)					
Viscosity, centipoises	0.27 (−76°F)	6.6 (50°F)	1.4 (68°F)	8.1 (50°F)	0.8 (0°F)	1.0 (80°F)	....
	0.14 (68°F)	0.88 (200°F)	0.93 (100°F)	3.1 (100°F)	0.26 (200°F)		
Color	Colorless	Colorless to dark yellow	Colorless	Yellow to dark amber	Colorless	Colorless	Colorless
Effect on metals	Corrodes copper and brass	None	None	None	None	Slightly corrosive	Slightly corrosive
Effect on most organic material (grease, oil, skin, etc.)	Solidifies many liquids and gases	Good solvent	Solvent	Solvent	Fair solvent		
Fire hazard	Slight	Slight	High	High	High	Dangerous	Dangerous
Toxicity	Toxic	Skin poisoning	Mild	Mild	Mild	Mild	Toxic vapors

* For specific gravity and vapor pressure see Figures 6–1 and 6–2.

OF LIQUID ROCKET PROPELLANTS *

Liquid Hydrogen	Hydrogen Peroxide 87%	Methyl Alcohol	Nitric Acid, White Fuming	Nitric Acid, Red Fuming	Nitro-methane	Octane	Liquid Oxygen	Water
H_2	H_2O_2	CH_3OH	HNO_3	2% H_2O 6-15% NO_2 Rest HNO_3	CH_3NO_2	C_8H_{18}	O_2	H_2O
2.016	34.02	30.5	63.02	60 average	61.04	114.23	32.00	18.02
−434.5	14	−144	−60	−57	−20	−69	−363	32
−423	288	148	191	NO_2 vapor given off first	214	257	−297	212
196	623	474	207			242	128	91.6	969
Zero (65°F)		+103,000 (65°F)	+75,000 (65°F)			121,000 (68°F)	Zero (65°F)	123,070 liquid (65°F)
1.75 (−434°F)		0.59 (50°F)	Approx. same as red fuming acid	0.418 (50°F)	0.41 (63°F)	0.50 (77°F)	0.4 (−343°F)	1.008 (32°F)
2.33 (−423°F)	0.61 (60°F)	0.62 (125°F)		0.424 (100°F)		0.58 (160°F)		1.002 (212°F)
			0.47 (200°F)					1.018 (400°F)
0.024 (−434°F)	1.87 (32°F)	0.66 (50°F)	0.418 (50°F)		....	0.54 (68°F)	0.87 (−363°F)	1.00 (68.4°F)
0.013 (−423°F)	1.29 (65°F)	0.39 (125°F)	0.424 (100°F)			0.26 (100°F)	0.19 (−297°F)	0.284 (212°F)
Colorless	Colorless	Colorless	Colorless to yellow	Orange to dark red	Colorless	Colorless	Very pale blue	Colorless
Severe embrittlement	Very corrosive	None	Very corrosive	Very corrosive	Corrosive	None	Embrittlement	None if pure
Solidifies liquids and gases	Reaction, often spontaneous	Fair solvent	Reaction	Reaction	Good solvent	Fair solvent	Will accelerate combustion	None
High when gaseous	Dangerous explosive when impure	High	Dangerous	Dangerous	Explosive when hot	High	High	None
Not known	Poison, causes burns	Toxic	Very toxic	Very toxic fumes	Mild	Mild	None	None

TABLE 6-2B. SOME PHYSICAL PROPERTIES OF LIQUID ROCKET PROPELLANTS

Propellant	Aluminum Borohydride	Chlorine Trifluoride	Diethylene Triamine	Ethyl Nitrate	Ethylene Oxide	Fluorine	Hydrazine Hydrate	Isopropyl Alcohol
Chemical formula	$Al(BH_4)_3$	ClF_3	$NH_2CH_2CH_2—NHCH_2CH_2NH_2$	$C_2H_5NO_3$	C_2H_4O	F_2	$N_2H_4 \cdot H_2O$	$CH_3CHOHCH_3$
Molecular weight, lb/mole	71.526	92.457	103.1	91.07	44.05	38.0	50.06	60.094
Melting point, °F	−84.1	−117.4	<−38	−151.6	−170.5	−361	−40	−129
Boiling point, °F	113	52.34	404	191.66	51.1	−306.3	245.3 (739 mm Hg)	180.2
Heat of vaporization at 1 atm, Btu/lb	181.2				250 (77°F)	73.89 (−306.3°F)		286.2 (180.2°F)
Heat of formation, Btu/lb-mole		−76,032 (liquid, 77°F)		−82,440 (77°F)	−32,920 (liquid, 77°F)	0	−104,310 (77°F)	−135,980 (77°F)
Specific heat, Btu/lb °F				0.447 (77°F)	0.471 (50°F)	0.36 (−320°F)		0.596 (68°F)
Density, lb/ft³	36 (32°F)	112 (32°F)	59.18 (77°F)	69.86 (59°F) 63.99 (68°F)	56.0 (32°F) 55.1 (50°F)	97 (−320°F)	65.5 (32°F) 64.4 (68°F)	50.01 (32°F) 49.01 (68°F)
Viscosity centipoises			6.6 (70°F) 0.2 (165°F)		0.58 (−58°F) 0.32 (32°F)		3.5 (32°F) 2.0 (68°F)	3.8 (32°F) 2.3 (68°F) 1.765 (86°F)
Shock sensitivity	Insensitive		Insensitive	Explosively sensitive	Liquid stable	Insensitive	Insensitive	Insensitive
Color	Colorless	Pale green	Slightly brown	Colorless	Colorless	Yellow-green	Colorless	Colorless
Effect on metals	Inert to glass, stainless steel, and iron	Very corrosive; inert to mild steel, if clean	Keep away from copper and alloys	Slightly corrosive	Non-corrosive	Must passivate most metals; nickel and monel are good	Slightly corrosive	Non-corrosive
Effect on most organic material (grease, oil, skin, etc.)	Burns skin, will react with organic material containing moisture in traces	Burns eyes and skin; reacts violently with most materials	Solvent action on many	Solvent	Solvent action on some, many unaffected	Violently reactive		Solvent
Fire hazard	Ignites spontaneously in air containing moisture	Reacts violently with water and many other compounds	Low	Flammable, dangerous	High	Very high	Dangerous	High
Toxicity	Inhalation causes chills and fever	Very high	Low		Medium	Very high	Toxic vapors	Mild
Stability, thermal	Decomposes slowly at room temperature	Begins to decompose at 570°F	Stable	Explosively sensitive	Sensitive; good below 86°F	Stable if clean	Explosive at 62°F	Stable to 1112°F

Propellant	Methane	Methyl Amine	Nitrogen	Nitrogen Tetroxide	Nitroglycerine	Ozone	Propane	n-Propyl Nitrate	Turpentine
Chemical formula	CH_4	CH_3NH_2	N_2	N_2O_4	$C_3H_5(NO_3)_3$	O_3	C_3H_8	$C_3H_7NO_3$	$\sim C_{10}H_{16}$
Molecular weight, lb/mole	16.04	31.058	28	92.02	227.094	48	44.094	105.094	$\sim$132
Melting point, °F	−299.2	−136.2	−346	12	55.76	−315.4	−305.8	<−150	−148
Boiling point, °F	−259	20.6	−321	70 (139.78 mm Hg)	500 (extrapolated)	−169.5	−43.7	220 (initial)	318
Heat of vaporization at 1 atm, Btu/lb	248.4 (−251.2° F)	370.9	86.04 (−320° F)	169.1 (61.4° F)		126.08 (−169.5° F)	183	164 (68° F)	123.5 (312.8° F)
Heat of formation, Btu/lb-mole	−32,200 (gas, 77° F)	−13,140	0	−12,240 (liquid, 77° F)	−159,840 (68° F)	−61,920 (gas, 77° F)	−51,555 (liquid, 77° F)	−88,280	
Specific heat, Btu/lb °F	.....					.....	0.576 (32° F)	0.419 (77° F)	~0.42 (68° F)
Density, lb/ft³	22.16 (−184° F) 17.92 (−139° F)	43.7 (0° F)	50.44 (−321° F)	90.52 (63° F)	99.51 (68° F)		36.54 (−48° F)	66.17 (−68° F)	55.56 (32° F) 54.56 (68° F)
Viscosity centipoises	0.185 (−292° F) 0.140 (−274° F) 0.115 (−256° F)	0.236 (32° F)	.....	0.44 (59.65° F)	36.0 (68° F) 21.0 (86° F)	~1.55 (−297.4° F) 4.2 (319° F)	8.78 (−301° F) 0.216 (−49° F)	0.69 (68° F)	~1.78 (50° F) ~1.49 (68° F)
Shock sensitivity	Insensitive	Insensitive	Insensitive	Insensitive	Very sensitive to percussion	.....	Insensitive	Low sensitivity	Insensitive
Color	Colorless	.....	Colorless	Yellow to red	.....	Colorless to blue	Colorless	Colorless to light straw	Colorless when pure
Effect on metals	Non-corrosive	Use stainless steel; avoid copper	Non-corrosive	Corrodes steel when wet	.....	.....	Non-corrosive	Relatively non-corrosive, avoid copper and nickel	Non-corrosive
Effect on most organic material (grease, oil, skin, etc.)	Solvent	Reactive	None	Reacts with many	.....	Explosive with many	Solvent	Solvent	Solvent
Fire hazard	High	High	None	Low	High	Very high	High	Low	Fairly high
Toxicity	Asphyxiant	Mild	Non-toxic	Very toxic	High	Very Toxic	Mild anaesthetic	Low	Non-toxic
Stability, thermal	Stable	Stable	Stable	Stable at room temp.	Stable	Explosively unstable	Stable	Stable	Stable

The number of different liquid propellants which have been used or proposed for rocket engines is large. The propellants discussed in this section have been selected to give the student a representative picture of the properties and limitations of the liquid chemicals used in rockets. Other additional propellants have been omitted from this book, not because they are less common or significant but because the main problems involved in their handling, storing, burning, etc., will not be materially different from those discussed on the next few pages. General data on propellants can be found in the Reference Bibliography, Section 4.

Nitromethane (CH₃NO₂)

Nitromethane is a somewhat oily liquid, colorless when pure. It is used commercially as a chemical solvent and also as a constituent of lacquers and coatings. It boils at 214° F and melts at −19.5° F. It is produced by a nitration of hydrocarbon vapors (see Refs. 4.317–4.320).

Nitromethane is a monopropellant at chamber pressure above approximately 500 pounds per square inch. Compared to other propellants, it has a relatively low flame temperature of 3950° F. At low chamber pressures a small addition of an oxidizer is required for stable combustion.

It is not corrosive or toxic and therefore can be easily handled. However, it can be an explosive chemical and, what is worse, a liquid explosive. Under certain conditions of pressure and temperature and in the presence of various impurities, nitromethane is capable of propagating detonations. Since the speed of a detonation is much faster than the flame speed, a detonation is capable of traveling upstream through an injector, since the injection velocity is usually designed to be slightly above the flame speed. The detonation wave then can travel rapidly in fuse-like fashion through pipelines and storage tanks and can cause severe explosions. Elaborate tests have shown that it is possible to stop the propagation of detonations within nitromethane lines, but no method devised to date is considered fully reliable. The application of nitromethane to rocket propulsion has therefore been limited.

Nitromethane requires a special ignition system. Combustion of nitromethane is usually started by the addition of a small initial amount of gaseous oxygen and the action of a spark plug. It burns with a very pale, almost invisible, flame.

Hydrogen Peroxide (H_2O_2)

In rocket application, hydrogen peroxide is used in a highly concentrated form of 70 to 90 per cent; the remainder is water. Commercial peroxide is never more concentrated than approximately 30 per cent.

In the combustion chamber, the propellant decomposes according to the following chemical reaction, forming superheated steam and gaseous oxygen:

$$H_2O_2 \rightarrow H_2O + \tfrac{1}{2}O_2 + \text{heat}$$

This decomposition is brought about by the action of catalysts such as calcium permanganate, sodium permanganate, manganese dioxide, potassium permanganate, platinum, and iron oxide. In fact, most impurities act as a catalyst.

Hydrogen peroxide has a relatively low performance as a monopropellant. If the gaseous oxygen generated by the decomposition of peroxide is used to oxidize a fuel, the combustion temperature will be appreciably higher and the performance accordingly better. Some 42 per cent of the total weight of the decomposition products of 90 per cent peroxide is gaseous oxygen. Therefore, hydrogen peroxide has been used as an oxidizer in combination with alcohol, hydrazine hydrate, and other organic fuels in order to take advantage of the liberated free oxygen. The German Messerschmitt Me 163 rocket fighter used 80 per cent hydrogen peroxide with a fuel mixture consisting of 57 per cent methyl alcohol, 30 per cent hydrazine hydrate, and 13 per cent water. Hydrazine and hydrazine hydrate, pure or in solution with water and/or alcohols, are spontaneously ignitable in contact with hydrogen peroxide.

The storage and handling of hydrogen peroxide are difficult because the propellant reacts to some extent with almost every substance. Materials which seem to be suitable for storage containers are glass, pure aluminum, pure tin, and certain types of stainless steels. It is necessary to clean and chemically treat the tanks thoroughly prior to exposure to the propellant. If the filled storage tanks are inspected regularly for decomposition activity, such as heating or bubbling, then it will be possible to dispose of contaminated liquid before it reaches a danger point in temperature, beyond which an explosion may occur. With suitable precautions this propellant can be handled safely.

Concentrated peroxide causes severe burns when in contact with human skin and may ignite and cause fires when in contact with wood, oils, and many other organic materials. Storage and operating areas have to be kept clean and free of organic matter and must be provided with ample safety features.

When concentrated hydrogen peroxide becomes contaminated by reaction with container materials or impurities it will decompose. This decomposition proceeds at first at a slow rate, but later, because of the energy release, a gradual heating and often a violent bubbling of the peroxide will occur. When the temperature exceeds some 350° F, the decomposition may become spontaneous, and a violent explosion may occur.

In spite of its fire and explosion hazard, hydrogen peroxide has become a desirable oxidizer, primarily because of its high specific weight. Various properties of hydrogen peroxide are given in Table 6–3. Further data on hydrogen peroxide can be found in references 4.301–4.311.

TABLE 6–3. PHYSICAL PROPERTIES OF HYDROGEN PEROXIDE

Concentration, %	100	90	80	70
Specific heat, Btu/lb °F at 64.4° F	0.57	0.61	0.65	0.70
Freezing point, °F	30.4	12.6	−10.8	−38.2
Boiling point, °F	312	288	269	254
Specific gravity at 64.4° F	1.4502	1.3943	1.3411	1.2907
Viscosity at 64.4° F, centipoise	1.307	1.301	1.297	1.287
Heat of vaporization, Btu/lb	540	588	634	682
Vapor pressure at 100° F, psia	0.007	0.012	0.016	0.023

Liquid Oxygen (O_2)

Liquid oxygen boils at −298° F at atmospheric pressure; it has a specific gravity of 1.14 and a heat of vaporization of 91.6 Btu per pound. It is widely used as an oxidizer and burns with a bright white-yellow flame with most hydrocarbon fuels.

Liquid oxygen has been used in combination with alcohols and gasolines. As shown in Table 4–3, the attainable specific impulse with either combination is relatively high. The chamber temperature is above 5200° F. The German V-2 uses 75 per cent ethyl alcohol as a fuel in conjunction with liquid oxygen. Many early experimenters in this country and abroad have used the liquid oxygen–gasoline combination. See Figures 4–4, 4–6, 4–8, and 4–9.

Although it usually will not burn spontaneously with organic materials at ambient pressures, combustion or explosions occur when confined mixtures of oxygen and organic matter are suddenly pressurized. Impact tests show that mixtures of liquid oxygen with many commercial oils or organic materials will detonate violently when suddenly pressurized.

Liquid oxygen will support and accelerate the combustion of other materials. Handling and storage are safe when contact materials are clean. Liquid oxygen is a non-corrosive and non-toxic liquid and will not appreciably deteriorate the container walls. When in prolonged contact with human skin, the propellant will cause severe burns.

Because liquid oxygen evaporates rapidly, it cannot be stored readily for any great length of time. If liquid oxygen is used in large quantities, it is often produced very close to its geographical point of application.

It is necessary to insulate all lines, tanks, valves, etc., which contain liquid oxygen in order to reduce the evaporation loss. Rocket propulsion systems, which will remain filled with liquid oxygen for several hours, and liquid oxygen storage systems have to be particularly well insulated. External drainage provisions have to be made on all liquid oxygen tanks and lines to eliminate the water which condenses on the walls.

Liquid oxygen can be obtained in several ways, such as by boiling liquid nitrogen out of purified liquid air. Further information on oxygen can be found in references 4.441 and 4.442.

Nitric Acid (HNO_3)

There are several types of nitric acid mixtures which are used as oxidizers.

White fuming nitric acid is concentrated nitric acid containing approximately 2 per cent of water and impurities. It gives off pale, almost invisible, vapors which cause a biting sensation in the nose.

Mixed acid consists of concentrated nitric (HNO_3) acid with a small percentage of concentrated sulphuric acid (H_2SO_4). It is less corrosive in contact with several steels than the other two acids.

Red fuming nitric acid consists of concentrated nitric acid (HNO_3) which contains some dissolved nitrogen dioxide (NO_2). It usually contains between 5 and 20 per cent (NO_2). The color of the acid varies from orange to dark red. It is a more powerful oxidizer than the other two. Because of the brownish red color of the nitrogen dioxide fumes, this acid is called "red fuming nitric acid." The fumes are exceedingly annoying and poisonous.

Nitric acid is produced commercially in relatively large quantities, for it has a wide market as a raw material for explosives, fertilizers, dyes, and medical products. It is usually produced by oxidizing ammonia (NH_3) to nitrogen dioxide (NO_2), which in turn is dissolved in water to form dilute nitric acid. Concentrated acid is produced from dilute nitric acid by absorbing the water with sulphuric acid and by distilling off the nitric acid. A small percentage of sulphuric acid is therefore commonly found in nitric acid propellants. Red fuming nitric acid is produced from concentrated nitric acid by dissolving nitrogen dioxide (NO_2).

All types of nitric acid are highly corrosive. Only certain types of stainless steels, gold, and a few other materials are satisfactory as storage containers or pipeline materials. Material, bearing, and sealing studies have been performed, but no material has been found to be entirely satisfactory for long durations.

In case of accident or spilling, the acid should be diluted or chemically deactivated. Lime and alkali metal hydroxides and carbonates are common neutralizing agents. However, nitrates formed by the neutralization are also oxidizing agents and must be handled accordingly. Ammonium hydroxide must never be used as a neutralizing agent because of the formation of ammonium nitrate, which is highly explosive. Flushing with water will dilute the acid to a safe limit.

Nitric acid oxidizers have been used with a variety of fuels such as aniline (see Figures 4–5 and 4–10), gasoline, various amines, and alcohols. They ignite spontaneously with furfural alcohol, aniline, and other amines. The addition of 4 per cent by weight of iron trichloride to the acid will reduce the ignition delay below 0.001 second.

Pure nitric acid and aniline reach a specific thrust of 218 seconds at a mixture ratio of 2.75 at 300 pounds per square inch absolute and almost 5000° F chamber temperature. The specific gravity of nitric acids varies from 1.5 to 1.6, depending upon the percentages of nitric oxide, water, and impurities. This high density permits compact missile and airplane construction.

Red fuming nitric acid has a relatively high vapor pressure at ambient temperatures and presents some storage and transfer problems. Because of the red fumes, pipe leaks and spilled acid are easily detected.

Further information on nitric acid propellants can be found in references 4.401 and 4.419.

Liquid Fluorine

In combination with most fuels, liquid fluorine affords higher values of performance and energy than most other oxidizers. For example with hydrogen its specific impulse is calculated to be over 365 seconds at 300 pounds per square inch chamber pressure, optimum expansion sea level condition and a mixture ratio between 3.7 and 9.0. Its high specific gravity of approximately 1.5 is another advantage. Disadvantages include its extreme toxicity and reactivity, being spontaneously reactable with many common materials and metals. Special passivation techniques have to be used on containers, pipelines, and valves, to permit handling of liquid fluorine in common construction metals. Like oxygen it evaporates readily and cannot be stored for long periods. Its low boiling point of −260° F requires insulation of equipment containing fluorine.

The reaction products usually contain gaseous fluorine or hydrofluoric acid (HF); both are corrosive, toxic, and poisonous exhaust gases which must be handled by special techniques.

Although fluorine is naturally found in relatively large quantities, the process of obtaining it in concentrated form in the free state is relatively expensive and commercial consumption is low. Further information on fluorine can be found in references 4.431–4.434.

Aniline ($C_6H_5NH_2$)

Commercial aniline is an oily, yellowish, clear liquid with a specific gravity slightly higher than water. It is readily available and has a wide industrial market in dyes, solvents, paints, and pharmaceutical products. It is spontaneously ignitable with red fuming nitric acid. This propellant combination was invented in America and has been used on American assisted take-off units and on American missiles, such as the Wac Corporal. Some impurities in aniline or acid will cause ignition difficulties. Various ethyl and methyl aniline compounds and mixtures of aniline with various organic compounds have been used to improve the ignition characteristics and the combustion and heat transfer properties.

Because aniline has a relatively high freezing point ($-20°$ F) various chemicals which depress the freezing point are frequently added in small proportions. The addition of furfural alcohol up to 20 per cent has been successful in lowering the freezing point without performance loss.

Aniline is produced commercially from benzene (C_6H_6), which is transformed into nitrobenzene ($C_6H_5NO_2$) by nitration, which in turn is reduced by hydrogen in the presence of catalysts to form aniline. This aniline is purified, and in commercial form it usually has less than 0.2 per cent impurities.

Hydrazine Hydrate ($N_2H_4 \cdot H_2O$)

This propellant is a colorless liquid. It is inflammable, and its vapors may form explosive mixtures in air. It is readily mixed with water, alcohols, and other organic compounds. Spontaneously ignitable with hydrogen peroxide, it was used by the Germans as a major constituent of a fuel for the Me 163 fighter plane. Hydrazine hydrate is toxic, and exposure to its vapors may cause temporary blindness. See references 4.315, 4.316, and 4.446.

Hydrazine (N_2H_4)

This propellant is a toxic, colorless liquid with a high freezing point ($+34°$ F). It is readily soluble in water (it forms hydrazine hydrate), alcohol, and other polar organic compounds. It is spontaneously ignitable with nitric acid and concentrated hydrogen peroxide. Being very inflammable, its vapors may form explosive mixtures with air. Hydrazine is characterized by a positive heat of formation and therefore generally gives good performance when compared with many common fuels. It can also act as a monopropellant. With liquid oxygen hydrazine will give a theoretical specific impulse of 259 seconds at sea level optimum expansion conditions and a chamber pressure of 300 pounds per square inch. See references 4.312–4.316, 4.444, and 4.445.

Ethyl Alcohol (C_2H_5OH)

Ethyl alcohol or ethanol has wide commercial uses in the chemical and liquor industries and is produced commercially in large quantities. The German V-2 used a fuel mixture of 75 per cent ethanol and 25 per cent water which was burned with liquid oxygen (Refs. 3.306 and 4.422). The addition of water to the alcohol improves the regenerative cooling characteristics of the fuel and reduces the combustion temperature, but it also decreases the average molecular weight of the exhaust gases slightly. Because of the lower chamber gas temperature the cooling of a rocket thrust chamber is less critical; the water addition decreases the performance slightly. The performance of combinations of ethyl alcohol and liquid oxygen and of ethyl alcohol and red fuming nitric acid is shown in Figures 4–4 and 4–7.

Methyl Alcohol (CH_3OH)

Methyl alcohol, also known as methanol and wood alcohol, is a colorless liquid. Its properties resemble those of ethyl alcohol. It is inferior as a rocket chamber coolant (lower specific heat) and has a lower performance than ethyl alcohol with a given oxidizer. It is toxic and, when taken internally, leads to severe injury of vital organs. Methyl alcohol can be synthesized from carbon monoxide and hydrogen.

Liquid Ammonia (NH_3)

Although ammonia itself is toxic, the exhaust gases from the combustion of ammonia and oxygen are non-toxic because they do not contain oxides of carbon. The performance of liquid ammonia with liquid oxygen is high, with a specific thrust of 255 seconds at a chamber pressure of 300 pounds per square inch, absolute, and a chamber temperature of 4950° F. Ammonia has a high value of specific heat as shown in Table 6–2A.

Because of its high vapor pressure the propellant is difficult to store. Because of its many commercial applications in the chemical, agricultural, and refrigeration industries it is readily available.

Liquid Hydrogen (H₂)

Liquid hydrogen, when burned with liquid oxygen, will give a high performance as shown in Figure 4–8.

Of all known fuels, liquid hydrogen is the lightest and the coldest, having a specific gravity of 0.07 and a boiling point of $-424°$ F. The low fuel density requires very bulky fuel tanks, which necessitate very large missile volumes. The extremely low temperature makes the problem of choosing suitable tank and piping materials difficult, because many metals lose their strength at low temperatures. The impact strength of most metals is usually decreased to less than 30 per cent of that at room temperature.

Because of its low temperature, liquid hydrogen tanks and lines have to be well insulated in order to prevent the evaporation of hydrogen. A vacuum jacket often has been used in addition to insulating materials. All common liquids and gases solidify in liquid hydrogen. These solid particles in turn will plug orifices and valves. Care, therefore, has to be taken to scavenge all lines and tanks of air and moisture before introducing the propellant. Mixtures of liquid hydrogen and solid oxygen or solid air are believed to be explosive.

Hydrogen consists of several species, notably ortho-hydrogen and para-hydrogen. As hydrogen is liquefied the relative equilibrium composition of ortho- and para-hydrogen changes. The transformation from one species to another is accompanied by a transfer of energy. This phenomenon makes liquefaction more difficult.

Liquid hydrogen is manufactured from gaseous hydrogen by successive expansion process.

Hydrocarbon Fuels

Petroleum derivatives encompass a large variety of different hydrocarbon chemicals, most of which can be used as a rocket fuel (Refs. 3.307, 4.423, 4.424, and 4.425). Most common are those types, which are in use with other applications and engines, such as gasoline, kerosene, diesel oil, paint thinner, or turbojet fuel. They contain straight chain type hydrocarbon compounds, such as heptane or octane, also aromatics, olefins, and many other more complex hydrocarbons. Their physical properties and chemical composition vary widely with the type of crude oil from which they were refined with the chemical process used in their production and the accuracy of control exercised in their manufacture. Typical values are listed in Table 6–4.

TABLE 6–4. PROPERTIES OF SOME TYPICAL HYDROCARBON FUELS

	Jet Fuel	Jet Fuel	Kerosene	Aviation Gasoline 100/130	Diesel Fuel
Specific gravity at 60° F	0.78	0.76	0.81	0.73	0.85
Density at 60° F, lb/ft^3	48.7	47.5	50.6	45.6	53.0
Freezing point, °F	−76 (max)	−76 (max)	−45	−76	−10
Viscosity at 60° F, centipoise	1.4	1.3	1.6	0.5	2.0
Flash point, °F (TCC)	24	−17	137	−20	140
ASTM distillation, °F					
10% evaporated	165	163	—	147	440
50% evaporated	340	313	—	205	—
90% evaporated	460	435	—	245	650
Reid vapor pressure, psia	2 to 3	5 to 7	below 1	7	0.1
Specific heat, Btu/lb °F	0.50	0.51	0.49	0.53	0.47
Average molecular weight, lb/mole	130	125	175	90	—

In general these petroleum fuels form yellow-white, brilliantly radiating flames and give good performance. They are relatively easy to handle and in general there is an ample supply of these fuels available at low cost.

Other Propellants

Many other propellant combinations have been proposed and used. Some are described in Tables 6–2A and 6–2B and in the material listed in the Reference Bibliography at the back of this book.

Problems

1. Plot the variation of the average specific gravity of the red fuming nitric acid–aniline propellant combination against mixture ratio between the values of 2.0 and 4.0 at 60° F. The respective specific gravities can be found from Figure 6–1.

Answers: check point at $r = 3.0$; $\delta_{av} = 1.32$.

2. Using the results of problem 1 above, plot the variation of the "density specific impulse" (product of average specific gravity and specific impulse) and explain the meaning of the curve. Use the theoretical specific impulse values of Figure 4–5.

Answers: check point at $r = 3.0$; $I_s = 292$.

3. Prepare a table comparing the relative merits of liquid oxygen and nitric acid as rocket oxidizers.

4. Derive the equation for the average specific gravity.

Symbols

r mixture ratio (weight flow rate of oxidizer to weight flow rate of fuel)

δ_{av} average specific gravity of mixture

δ_f specific gravity of fuel

δ_o specific gravity of oxidizer

Chapter 7

Liquid Propellant

Rocket Thrust Chambers

A thrust chamber is essentially a special combustion device where liquid propellants are metered, injected, atomized, mixed, and burned at a high combustion pressure to form gaseous reaction products, which in turn are accelerated and ejected at high velocities. This chapter deals with the design and construction of these liquid propellant rocket thrust chamber assemblies. Because of the high rate of energy evolution the cooling, stability of

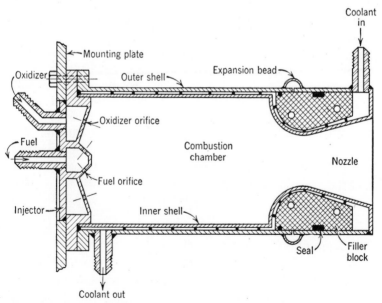

FIGURE 7–1. Proposal for cooled rocket thrust chamber assembly (1942).

183

combustion, ignition, and injection problems deserve special consideration. Since rocket thrust chambers are air-borne devices, the weight has to be a minimum. A desirable rocket thrust chamber, therefore, combines lightweight construction with high performance, simplicity, and reliability.

A typical rocket thrust chamber assembly (Figure 7–1) consists of the following principal parts, each of which will be discussed in detail below: nozzle, combustion chamber, injector, mounting provision, and an ignition system, if non-spontaneously ignitable propellants are used. In some cases the thrust chamber assembly also includes integrally mounted propellant valves and controls; these are described in Chapter 8.

In some publications the terms *rocket motor, thrust cylinder* or *rocket combustor* are used instead of *thrust chamber assembly.* In this text the term *thrust chamber* will be used, because it is preferred in official technical specifications. References to further study on thrust chambers can be found in several sections of the Reference Bibliography, particularly in Sections 6.1, 6.2, and 6.6.

1 Nozzle

The nozzle is that part of the rocket thrust chamber assembly in which the gases are accelerated to high velocities. For prolonged durations nozzles have to be cooled. Since the construction problems are essentially the same as those of combustion chambers, and since nozzles and chambers are usually made integrally, nozzle construction will not be discussed here separately. The heat transfer problems also are similar to those of rocket chambers; they have been discussed in general terms in Chapter 5.

The nozzle size and proportions determine the chamber pressure, thrust, propellant flow, and exhaust velocity of thrust chambers and the variations of these performance parameters. The basic design relations of these quantities have been developed and summarized in Chapter 3.

2 Combustion Process *

The general aspects of the combustion process which takes place in a rocket combustion device are fairly well known and apply to

---

* Contributed by E. M. Redding, formerly Assistant Technical Director, Aerophysics Laboratory, North American Aviation, Inc.

practically all liquid propellant combinations commonly used or considered (Refs. 3.304, 3.317, and others in Sections 3.3, 3.4, 3.5, and 3.7). Although it has not been possible to determine the exact mechanism of the combustion process, the development of successful injectors and combustion systems has not been prevented.

In general, the following steps take place as the propellants progress from the injector manifolds to the motor nozzle exit. Each liquid propellant is injected into the combustion chambers at some high velocity, through holes or injector nozzles, of which there are innumerable designs. The streams of propellant either impinge and form a fine spray of droplets or enter the hot gases of the combustion chamber in a jet or series of droplets. In every case, however, the *liquid* droplets must vaporize by the addition of heat. The gaseous propellants mix, and *gas phase reaction* between oxidizer and fuel takes place. In some cases part of the reaction takes place in the liquid phase.

The exact mechanism of the gas phase combustion reaction will generally be different for each particular propellant combination. In all cases, an intimate *mixing* of the propellants must take place before reaction can occur. After mixing, the propellants are heated principally by convective heat transfer from the reacting or reacted gases previously injected into the chamber and by radiation from the hot walls and gases. The turbulent movement of hot burning gas eddies between unreacted vapors contributes to the heat transfer and the propagation of the flame. The actual propagation of the flame front through the unburned gaseous propellant mixture is probably carried out by the high speed diffusion of certain active groups, molecules, or atoms, such as OH, N, H, or CH_2, which are formed in the combustion process. These active constituents act as chain carriers.

The flame front is not a simple plane surface across the combustion chamber. The injection process and combustion process introduce an intense turbulence in the gases of the combustion chamber, and the flame front progresses throughout the mass. It is fairly well established that the velocity of the flame front through the reacted mass is due in part to the turbulence or mass movement of the gas eddies and also to the actual velocity of the flame through the discrete volumes of unmixed gas within each eddy.

Certain conclusions as to the results of this combustion process have been reached which are generally adequate for empirically designing liquid rocket combustion chambers. Among these conclusions are:

1. Given sufficient combustion chamber space and burning time, the chemical reaction will reach equilibrium.
2. The combustion process takes place over a definite length of the combustion chamber and is not an instantaneous process.
3. The velocity distribution and distribution of propellants across the combustion chamber cross section are never perfectly uniform but can be made adequately uniform by proper injector design.
4. The mixing of the propellants in the liquid phase is not necessary, if the droplets of each propellant are well dispersed among the droplets of the other propellant.
5. Smooth combustion is generally a function of the degree of atomization and mixing of the propellant droplets and the ease of vaporizing a given propellant.
6. Once ignition has been initiated the flame is self-supporting.

3   Chamber Volume

The chamber is that part of the rocket thrust chamber assembly in which the combustion or burning of propellants takes place at a high pressure.

The *combustion chamber volume* in a liquid propellant rocket thrust chamber is ordinarily selected with attention to the following considerations.

1. The volume has to be adequate to permit adequate *mixing, evaporation,* and *complete combustion* of propellants. Chamber volumes vary for different propellants with the time delay necessary to vaporize and activate the propellants and with the speed of reaction of the propellant combination. When the chamber volume is too small, combustion will be incomplete. With higher chamber pressures or with highly reactive propellants and with injectors which give improved mixing, a smaller chamber volume is usually permissible.

2. For prolonged firing durations the wall surface area has to be cooled by one of the cooling methods mentioned in the next sec-

tion. In order to reduce the *cooling requirements* it is desirable to decrease the exposed wall surface area and the local heat transfer intensity. As the chamber volume is decreased, the exposed wall surface area is also decreased, but the average heat transfer intensity is increased, because a small chamber volume necessitates

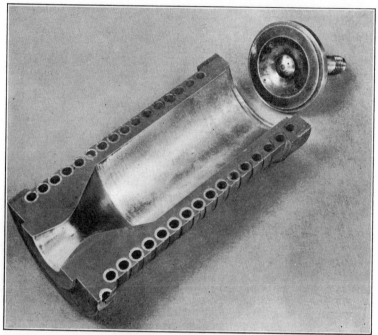

FIGURE 7-2. Cooled acid-aniline rocket thrust chamber with doublet multiple hole injector. (Developed by Jet Propulsion Laboratory, California Institute of Technology, 1942.)

high gas velocities. For any given rocket chamber size, geometry, and propellant, there will be a chamber volume for which the product of the average heat transfer intensity and the wall surface area is a minimum.

3. Since rockets power air-borne vehicles, their *weight* is at a premium. A small weight dictates a small chamber volume. The weight will be a function of the chamber pressure and the configuration. The minimum wall surface area, and therefore the least weight for a given volume, is that of a spherical shape.

4. Manufacturing and design considerations indicate a preference for a simple chamber geometry, such as a cylinder or a sphere. Cooling jackets for more complicated shapes are difficult to design and build. American rocket practice has generally

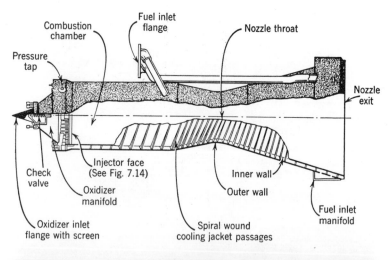

Figure 7–3. Artist's cut-away sketch and test stand installation of rocket thrust chamber. (Courtesy General Electric Company.)

favored the cylindrical shape. Various geometrical shapes of the combustion chamber have been used, such as those shown in Figures 7–2, 7–3, 7–4, 7–5, and 7–6.

5. The *maximum chamber diameter* often determines various

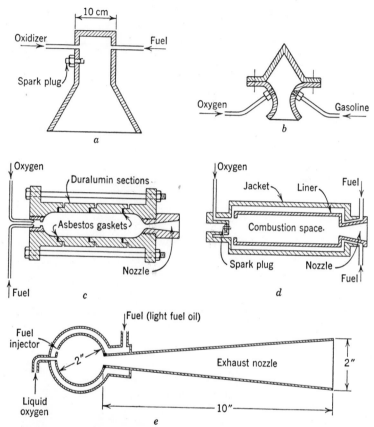

FIGURE 7–4. Typical and historical rocket thrust chambers. (*a*) Paulet's rocket, 1895. (Described by *El Commercio,* Lima, Peru, 1927.) (*b*) Oberth's cone motor. (H. Oberth, *Wege zur Raumschiffahrt,* R. Oldenburg, Munich, 1929.) (*c*) Heat sponge thrust chamber, American Rocket Society. (*Astronautics,* 1936.) (*d*) Wyld's regeneratively cooled thrust chamber, 1938. (J. H. Wyld, "The Liquid Propellant Rocket Motor—Past, Present and Future," *Mechanical Engineering,* p. 457, June 1947.) (*e*) Sänger's spherical thrust chamber, 1932. (From E. Sänger, "Recent Results in Rocket Flight Technique," *NACA Technical Memorandum* 1012, April 1942.)

vehicle dimensions. A small unit, therefore, often permits a lower aerodynamic drag and a smaller structure.

6. The *vibration* characteristics of rockets are not fully understood, but experience to date has shown that the combustion

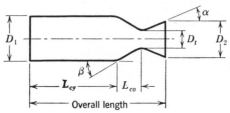

FIGURE 7–5. Nomenclature for rocket thrust chamber configuration ($\epsilon_c = A_1/A_t$, $\epsilon = A_2/A_t$).

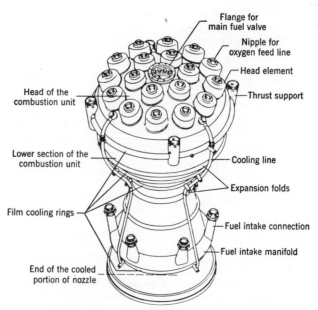

FIGURE 7–6. V-2 rocket thrust chamber

chamber volume and geometry determine certain acoustic vibration frequencies. Sometimes the chamber volume can be so selected as to avoid the excitation of natural frequencies, which may be critical to other components in the vehicle.

7. The *gas pressure drop* for accelerating the combustion products within the chamber should be a minimum; any reduction in the nozzle inlet pressure will reduce the exhaust velocity and the performance of the vehicle. When the chamber gas velocity is low—that is, when the chamber cross section is large—these losses are negligible. As shown in Chapter 3, Section 5, the losses become appreciable when the chamber area is less than two times the throat area.

8. The *coolant pressure loss* in the cooling jacket should be a minimum. Any excessive cooling jacket pressure drop due to hydraulic friction will necessitate a higher feed pressure in order to attain the same chamber pressure, which will require a more powerful and heavier feed system. Small chamber volumes usually permit short coolant passages with low pressure drops.

9. The type and method of *injection* determine the initial mixing of propellants in the chamber. Good injectors, that is, injectors which mix and atomize the oxidizer and fuel very thoroughly, require less combustion chamber space.

The chamber considerations above conflict with each other. It is, for instance, impossible to have a large chamber which gives complete combustion, but has also a low weight and a small cooling jacket loss. A compromise solution which will satisfy the majority of these considerations is, therefore, usually selected, depending on the application of the combustion chamber.

For a cylindrical rocket combustion chamber the *chamber volume* has arbitrarily been defined to include the convergent conical portion of the nozzle up to the throat. It can be approximated by the relation

$$V_c = A_t[L_{cy}\epsilon_c + (L_{co}/3)(\epsilon_c + \sqrt{\epsilon_c} + 1)]$$

$$= A_t[L_{cy}\epsilon_c + \tfrac{1}{3}\sqrt{A_t/\pi}\cot\beta(\epsilon_c^{3/2} - 1)] \qquad (7\text{--}1)$$

The symbols are defined in Figure 7–5. The surface area of the chamber and nozzle exposed to hot gases can be approximated from the following geometrical relation:

$$A = A_t\left[\epsilon_c + \frac{\epsilon_c - 1}{\sin\beta} + \frac{\epsilon - 1}{\sin\alpha}\right] + 2L_{cy}\sqrt{\frac{\epsilon_c A_t}{\pi}} \qquad (7\text{--}2)$$

Both equations neglect the effect of radii at the nozzle throat and entrance.

The chamber volume which will permit complete and stable combustion appears to be a function of many variables. The effects of chamber size and pressure are discussed in this section. The effect of the particular propellant combination, of its physical and chemical properties, of the chamber temperature, of the speed of reaction, and of the injection penetration and pattern is difficult to analyze and needs to be experimentally investigated.

The following simplified relations and parameters have been established for the minimum satisfactory chamber volume. Until better relations are established, which will consider more variables, these simplified parameters are recommended.

The *characteristic chamber length* is defined as the length a rocket of the same volume would have, if it were a straight tube and had the same volume and had no converging section.

$$L^* = V_c/A_t \qquad (7\text{--}3)$$

where L^* is the characteristic chamber length in feet, A_t is the nozzle throat area in square feet, and V_c is the chamber volume in cubic feet. Here the chamber is considered to include all the volume up to the throat area. Typical values for L^* are given in Table 7–1. Since this parameter does not consider any vari-

TABLE 7–1. CHARACTERISTIC CHAMBER LENGTH ($p_c = 300$ psia)

Propellant Combination	L^* (feet)
Nitric acid and aniline	3.75 to 6.5
Liquid oxygen and alcohol	3 to 10
Nitromethane	above 16

ables except the throat area, it is useful only for a particular propellant combination and a narrow range of mixture ratio and chamber pressure.

The *stay time t_s* of the propellant gases is the average value of the time spent by each gas molecule or atom within the chamber volume. It is defined by

$$t_s = \frac{V_c}{\dot{w} V_1} \qquad (7\text{--}4)$$

where $\dot{w}$ is the propellant flow in pounds per second, V_1 is the average specific volume of propellant gases in the chamber in cubic feet per pound, and V_c is the chamber volume. The minimum stay time at which a good performance is attained defines the chamber volume that gives complete combustion. The stay time varies for different propellants and has to be experimentally determined. It includes the time necessary for vaporization, activation, and complete burning of the propellant.

If V_1 is the specific volume of the product gases and the time for vaporization and activation is neglected, the average stay time in a rocket thrust chamber can be expressed as a function of the propellant properties and the chamber geometry by means of equations 3–3 and 3–24.

$$t_s = \frac{V_c}{A_t} \sqrt{\frac{\mathfrak{M}}{kgR'T_1}} \sqrt{\left(\frac{k+1}{2}\right)^{(k+1)/(k-1)}} \tag{7-5}$$

The relation above is useful in comparing different propellants. It can be seen that the average stay time depends on the molecular weight, the combustion temperature, the chamber volume, the throat area, and the specific heat ratio and is independent of chamber pressure. Stay times have values of 0.002 to 0.040 second for different types of thrust chambers and propellants.

Some experiments with nitric acid and vinyl butyl ethers have shown that the chamber volume required for complete combustion is proportional to the thrust, and inversely proportional to the chamber pressure raised to a power larger than two.

$$V_c = bF(1/p_1)^n \tag{7-6}$$

In this relation V_c is the chamber volume in cubic feet, F is the thrust in pounds, b is a constant which depends on the combustion temperature and the energy of activation, and n is a constant larger than two. High combustion pressures, therefore, permit small combustion chambers. This relation permits the evaluation of the chamber volume for any thrust with one given propellant combination, if the minimum satisfactory chamber volume has been determined for two or more values of thrust and chamber pressure. Experimental results indicated that, for a fivefold chamber pressure increase, the calculated volume differed from the actual optimum chamber volume by one-half per cent of the original volume.

4   Cooling of Thrust Chamber Assemblies

The fundamental principles for transferring heat from the hot combustion gases to the walls of the thrust chambers have been discussed in Chapter 5. Here the various methods of cooling are described in more detail.

Uncooled liquid propellant rocket thrust chambers can be fired for durations up to about 25 seconds, in some cases for even longer durations. They are used in some short duration liquid units and almost exclusively in solid propellant rocket units. Some solid propellant rockets have operated for over 50 seconds in uncooled chambers. The wall acts as a "heat sponge" and absorbs heat energy. When the wall temperature approaches the melting point of the wall material, then the danger of local melting, high internal stresses, and the reduced physical strength properties make a prolonged rocket operation hazardous. By thickening the walls in critical places, such as near the throat, an efficient use can be made of the chamber material.

If the combustion temperature for a given liquid propellant combination is low, it may be possible to use an uncooled rocket thrust chamber for continuous firing. Hydrogen peroxide when used as a monopropellant has a very low reaction temperature and has been used for this type of thrust chamber construction.

Cooled liquid propellant thrust chambers have provisions for cooling some or all metal parts coming into contact with hot gases, such as chamber walls, nozzle walls, and injector faces.

A cooling jacket or cooling coil permits the circulation of a *coolant*. Jackets consist of an inner and an outer wall. The inner wall confines the gases, and the space between the walls serves as the coolant passage. The *nozzle throat region* is usually the location which has the highest heat transfer intensity and is, therefore, the most difficult to cool. For this reason the cooling jacket is often designed so that the coolant velocity is highest at the critical regions by restricting the coolant passage cross section, and so that the fresh cold coolant enters the jacket at or near the nozzle. While the selection of the coolant velocity and its variation along the wall for any given thrust chamber design depends on heat transfer considerations, as discussed in Chapter 5, the selection of the coolant passage geometry depends on pressure loss and manufacturing considerations. An *axial flow cooling jacket* has a low hydraulic friction loss but is practical only for large coolant flows (above approximately 20 pounds per second). For small coolant flows and small motors, the design tolerances of the cooling jacket width between inner and outer

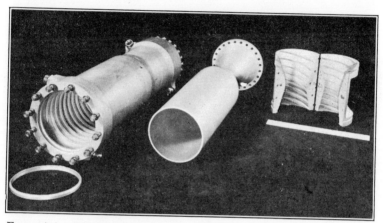

FIGURE 7-7. Disassembled German 109-709 rocket thrust chamber. Note inner and outer chamber shell, split filler block, and seal ring.

wall become prohibitive with axial flow. *Helical cooling passages* are used frequently in small thrust chambers, but they require more pressure drop than comparable axial flow jackets for large thrust chambers. A typical helical type regenerative cooling jacket of steel construction is shown in Figure 7-3.

In *regenerative cooling* the thrust chamber walls are cooled by a built-in jacket or cooling coil in which the oxidizer or the fuel are used as the coolant fluid. The heat absorbed by the coolant is therefore not wasted, but it augments the initial energy content of the propellant prior to injection, increasing the exhaust velocity slightly (0.1 to 1½ per cent). As explained in Chapter 5, this method is called regenerative cooling because of the similarity to steam regenerators. The majority of flying liquid propellant cooled rocket thrust chambers have used this cooling principle.

Often water (or another relatively inert fluid neither oxidizer nor fuel) is circulated in the cooling jacket. This cooling method, used extensively in static test stand firings, is referred to as *water cooling*.

The thrust chamber shown in Figure 7–2 is suitable for either water or regenerative cooling. Figure 7–7 shows an aluminum rocket thrust chamber in which the regenerative coolant is circulated in a helical path around the inner chamber. The helix guide

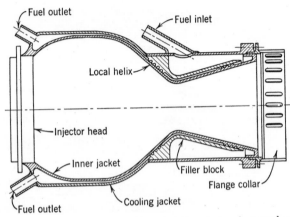

FIGURE 7–8. German Walter 109-509 rocket thrust chamber used on Me 163 airplane.

fins are made integral with the outer chamber wall and the nozzle filler blocks. The German Me 163 thrust chamber has a steel cooling jacket in which fuel cools the unit regeneratively, as shown in Figure 7–8; here the flow is essentially axial, except for a local helix in the converging nozzle section.

Film cooling is a method of cooling whereby a thin fluid film covers and protects exposed wall surfaces from excessive heat transfer. The film is introduced by injecting small quantities of fuel, oxidizer, or an inert fluid at very low velocities in a large number of places along the exposed surfaces in such a manner that a protective film will be formed. This method is quite effective because it forms a relatively cool boundary layer and because the coolant is able to absorb considerable heat by evaporation. A coolant with a high heat of vaporization and a high boiling point is particularly desirable. Film cooling is often used to augment regenerative cooling in regions of the chamber and nozzle wall where regenerative cooling alone is insufficient. It does decrease the performance of the rocket slightly because the fluid used in the coolant film is not completely burned and is, therefore, not used efficiently.

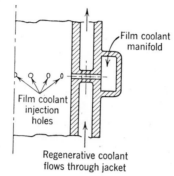

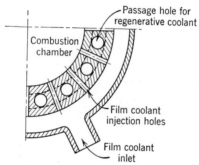

Figure 7-9. Film cooling injection method using a manifold external to the regenerative cooling jacket.

A special type of film cooling, called *sweat cooling* or *transpiration cooling,* uses a porous wall material which admits a coolant through pores uniformly over the surface. Considerable difficulty has been encountered in making the coolant distribution uniform along a porous surface because the pressure drop across the inner thrust chamber wall varies, particularly in the nozzle. The problem of manufacturing large chamber pieces of uniform porosity, variable thickness, and complex shape requires considerable ingenuity.

The *German V-2 combustion chamber* uses a combination of

film and regenerative cooling, as can be seen in Figure 7–6. The fuel is used as the regenerative colant; it flows axially upward through the jacket to the injectors. A small portion (approximately 12 per cent) of the coolant is injected into the chamber through many small holes which are arranged in four rows, similar to Figure 7–9. The holes are 0.06 to 0.09 inch in diameter and are spaced 1.1 to 0.62 inches apart. This additional injection gives a film cooling effect.

5 Materials

The wall materials have to withstand relatively high temperatures, high local gas velocities, the chemical action of corrosive and oxidizing propellant vapors, and a high stress. Since the rate of energy release is high, the walls have to withstand an initial heat shock and permit high heat transfer rates and thermal expansion. These severe conditions are somewhat alleviated by the short operational duration of rocket thrust chambers. A general discussion of materials can also be found in Chapter 5.

Since a *large temperature gradient* exists between the inner and outer surface of the wall, the variation of the properties of the wall material has to be considered and the average value of each property has to be evaluated. Various typical high temperature properties are listed for a number of materials in Table 5–3.

Considerable research effort has been spent on finding materials suitable for rocket combustion devices. A complete discussion of this subject is beyond the scope of this book, but a listing of the general requirements and the tendency of the present research will clarify the basic problems. The material requirements are critical only in those parts which come into direct contact with propellant reaction gases. Other thrust chamber components are constructed of conventional materials.

Properties which are to be sought in the inner walls of a cooled rocket thrust chamber are high strength at elevated temperatures, ease of fabrication, high thermal conductivity, resistance to chemical action of hot propellant vapors, high specific heat, resistance to corrosion and to mechanical and thermal shock, high melting point, low thermal expansion, and good vibration resistance.

The requirements of *high thermal conductivity* and *high strength* at elevated temperatures are two important properties which are not usually found in the same material. Materials which can withstand high stresses at high temperatures (stainless steels) usually have to be made into thinner walls for good heat transfer. These materials are not readily applicable to rocket chambers of large diameter in which heat transfer requires wall thicknesses too small to be useful in a large pressure vessel. On the other hand, high conductivity materials (copper or aluminum) have low strength properties at high temperatures and therefore require very heavy and thick chambers. Not only will the high weight decrease the vehicle performance, but the heat transfer will be increased so that more efficient cooling is required. Improved cooling, in turn, necessitates a more powerful and heavier feed system or additional film cooling, which decreases the effective exhaust velocity. Special alloys of high conductivity and high strength at high temperatures and composite materials consisting of an inner layer of high temperature material (ceramics or special alloys) and an outer layer of a high conductivity metal, bonded to each other, show promise for a good rocket thrust chamber wall material and need to be investigated.

Aluminum alloys, low carbon steel, alloy steels, and stainless steels have been used successfully in rocket thrust chamber assemblies. If sufficient film cooling or cooling jacket capacity is designed into a rocket, it can probably be made satisfactorily out of many common metals; but the additional cooling will require a heavier thrust chamber and propulsion system, with reduced vehicle performance. Estimates of cooling requirements and pressure loss can be made from the heat transfer theory given in Chapter 5, and the hydraulic jacket characteristics, as discussed in Section 6.

A production rocket thrust chamber wall material is selected after weighing the cooling requirements, performance losses, weight increases, and system complications, against availability and ease of fabrication.

The *operating temperatures* of inner walls of existing rocket thrust chambers usually do not exceed 600° to 1700° F, with an average near 1200° F on the gas side. Many metals have satisfactory strength at these temperatures. With materials which can withstand high wall temperatures, research may ultimately be able to dispense with the cooling of rocket walls and rely entirely on the radiation of heat from the outside wall surface. Uncooled walls of this type with durations exceeding one minute may become feasible by using special materials, such as ceramics or other materials of high melting point.

6   Hydraulic Losses in Cooling Passage

The cooling coil or cooling jacket should be designed so that not only will the fluid absorb all the heat transferred across the inner motor wall, but also the coolant pressure drop will be a minimum.   The high liquid coolant velocities necessary for good cooling unfortunately contribute to high pressure losses, which, in turn, necessitate a more powerful and heavier feed system.   For many liquid propellant rockets the coolant velocity in the chamber is approximately 10 to 15 feet per second and at the nozzle throat 20 to 45 feet per second.

A cooling passage can be considered to be a hydraulic pipe, and the friction loss can be calculated accordingly.   For a straight pipe,

$$\frac{\Delta p}{\rho} = f\frac{L}{D}\frac{v^2}{2g} \tag{7-7}$$

where Δp is the friction pressure loss, ρ the coolant density, L the length of coolant passage, D the equivalent diameter, v the velocity in the cooling coil, f the friction loss coefficient, and g the acceleration of gravity (32.2 feet per second).

The friction loss coefficient is a function of Reynolds number and can be found by means of Figure 7–10.

For a *curved or coiled cooling passage* the friction factor f has to be corrected by a multiplying factor.   This correction is a function of Reynolds number and curvature.   Empirical equations for the correction factor have been devised for different passage shapes such as the one mentioned on page 230.

A large portion of the pressure drop in a cooling jacket usually occurs in those locations where the flow direction or the flow passage cross section is changed.   Here the sudden expansion or contraction causes a loss, sometimes larger than the velocity head $v^2/(2g)$.   This hydraulic situation exists in inlet and outlet chamber manifolds, injector passages, and expansion joints.

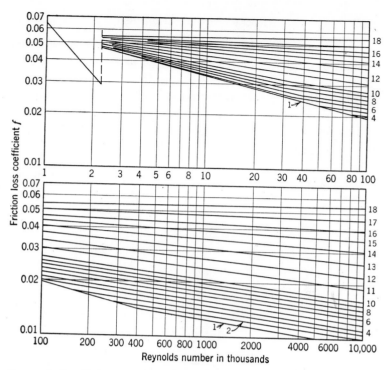

FIGURE 7–10. Hydraulic friction loss coefficient versus Reynolds number. (*Reference:* R. J. Pigott, "The Flow of Fluids on Closed Conduits," *Mechanical Engineering*, Vol. 55, No. 8, p. 497, 1933.)

TABLE FOR SELECTING CURVE IN FIGURE 7–10 FROM DIAMETER (INCHES) AND SURFACE CONDITION

Curve Number to Be Used	1	2	3	4	5	6	7	8	9
Tubing or very clean smooth machined surface	0.35 or more							0.20	
Clean machined surface or smooth cast-iron surface	72	66 to 48	42 to 14	12 to 6	5 to 4	3 to 2	1½	1¼ to 1	¾
Rough machined surface			30	17	7	4	2½	1¾	1¼
Dirty, rough machined surface with welds				34	14	7	3½	2¼	1½

Curve Number to Be Used	10	11	12	13	14	15	16	17	18
Tubing or very clean smooth machined surface					0.125		0.08		0.062 or less
Clean machined surface or smooth cast-iron surface	½	⅜	¼	⅛		⅟₁₆		⅟₃₂	
Rough machined surface	1	¾	½		⅜		¼		⅛
Dirty, rough machined surface with welds	1¼	1							

A *typical pressure loss* of a cooling jacket is between 25 to 100 pounds per square inch. The expansion of the inner and outer shells of a thrust chamber due to pressure and temperature effects causes the cooling coil cross section during operation to be different from the cross section during water tests. The pressure loss is therefore frequently slightly changed during operation.

7 Chamber Wall Loads and Stresses

Uncooled thrust chambers have only one wall, which is subjected to internal pressure. A typical pressure distribution is

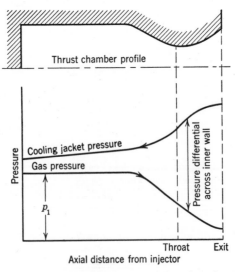

FIGURE 7–11. Pressure distribution in cooled rocket thrust chamber.

shown schematically in Figure 7–11. The chamber of cooled thrust chamber assemblies consists of two concentric walls or shells with the high pressure cooling fluid filling the space between the skins. The walls are subjected to *radial* and *axial pressure loads,* the *reaction* of the mounting device, *acceleration loads, vibration loads,* and *thermal expansion forces.* These loads are different for almost every design, and each unit has to be considered individually in determining the wall strengths. The pressure intensity across the inner wall in a cooled thrust chamber is highest in the nozzle exit region, as can be seen from Figure 7–11, requiring heavier construction in this location. This construction is almost exactly the reverse condition of that in an uncooled thrust chamber, where the differential pressure across the wall is highest in the chamber region.

The temperature differential introduces a compressive stress on the inside and a tensile stress on the outside of the inner wall, which can be calculated as

$$\sigma = \frac{2\lambda E \, \Delta T}{1 - \nu} \tag{7-8}$$

Here σ is the stress, λ is the coefficient of thermal expansion of the wall material, E is the modulus of elasticity of the wall material, ΔT is the temperature drop across the wall, and ν is the Poisson ratio of the wall material. Since temperature stresses frequently exceed the yield point and the materials experience a change in the modulus of elasticity, the equation above is applicable only to elastic deformations. This yielding of rocket thrust chamber wall materials can be observed by the small and gradual contraction of the inside chamber and throat diameters after successive runs. The 2-inch nozzle throat diameter of an experimental rocket was found to shrink approximately 0.001 inch in each of its first few runs.

In selecting a working stress for the wall material of a thrust chamber, the variation of strength with temperature and the temperature stresses over the wall thickness have to be considered. The temperature drop across the wall is usually between 200° and 1000° F, and an average temperature is often used for estimating the material properties, such as those listed in Table 5–3.

The outer shell of a cooled thrust chamber is usually subjected to a tension stress due to the internal pressure of the cooling fluid. The inner shell must ordinarily withstand the external pressure in the cooling jacket, the internal pressure of the chamber gases, an axial compression or tension load, and exposure to heat. Since the coolant pressure in regeneratively cooled thrust chambers exceeds the chamber pressure, the inner shell is in radial compression and has a tendency to buckle. For this reason stiffening rings are often attached to the inner shell.

There are essentially three possible *loading conditions*. At the *start* of the rocket the chamber pressure is zero, the jacket pressure is at full value, and the inner wall is cold. During *operation* the chamber pressure is at full value, the jacket pressure is also at full value, and the inner wall is hot. At the *shut-off* condition the

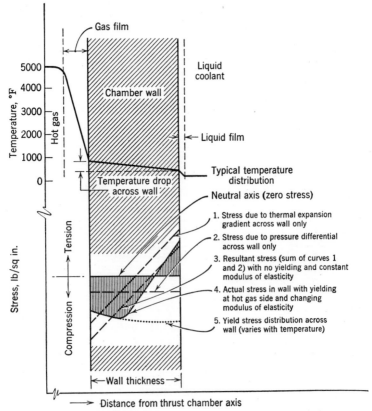

FIGURE 7–12. Typical stresses in thrust chamber inner wall.

cooling jacket pressure may be high or low, depending on the particular valve arrangement, the chamber pressure approaches the atmospheric pressure, and the inner walls are hot.

The last loading condition may be the most severe, because in some units the cooling jacket flow and pressure are maintained at full value, even though the chamber pressure diminishes. This additional flow of coolant after shut-off is necessary only with certain propellants to prevent the overheating of trapped, regenerative, coolant fluid.

A more accurate picture of a typical stress distribution caused by pressure loads and thermal gradients is shown in Figure 7–12. Here the inner wall is subjected to a compressive pressure differential caused by high liquid pressure in the cooling jacket and a relatively large temperature gradient. In a large rocket chamber, such as the V-2, the wall thickness of the nozzle may be in excess of one-fourth inch and the temperature differential across it may readily exceed several hundred degrees. This temperature gradient causes the hot inner wall surface to expand more than the wall surface on the coolant side and imposes a high compressive thermal stress on the inside surface and a high tensile thermal stress on the coolant side. In these thick walls the stress induced by the pressure load is usually small compared to the thermal stress. The resultant stress distribution in thick inner walls (shown shaded in the sample stress diagram of Figure 7–12) indicates that the stress in the third of the wall adjacent to the hot gases has exceeded the yield point. Because the modulus of elasticity and the yield point diminish with temperature, the stress distribution is not uniform over the yielded portion of the wall. In effect this inner portion acts as a heat shield for the other portion which carries the load.

Because of the differential expansion between the hot inner shell and the relatively cold outer shell, it is necessary to provide for *expansion joints* to prevent severe temperature stresses. This is particularly critical in larger thrust chambers. The German V-2 thrust chamber expands more than $3/16$ inch in an axial and $5/32$ inch in a radial direction. The expansion joints may be welded beads, as shown in Figure 7–1 and Figure 7–6 or sliding seals as in Figure 7–7.

8 Vibration

All rocket thrust chambers vibrate, but certain designs have been proved to shake worse than others. The physical mechanism of these vibrations is not clearly established.

Three types of vibrations have been observed in various rocket thrust chamber assemblies. The first type is believed to be a chamber pressure oscillation with relatively low frequencies of 15 to 0.1 cycles per second. These pressure oscillations may perpetuate themselves by alternately increasing and decreasing the injection pressure drop, thereby varying the propellant flow, which in turn varies the chamber pressure. The second type of vibration is that caused by the excitation of the natural frequency of metal parts such as chamber, pipelines, and structural parts. The frequency is usually below 100 cycles per second. The third type of vibration is a high pitch, high energy vibration, and is associated with the combustion. These oscillations may become so violent as to cause structural failures of components and attached equipment in a very short time, usually less than a second.

By increasing the pressure drop in the injector (higher injection velocities) or by changing the combustion chamber volume, vibration effects have been reduced. The method of mounting affected the frequency and amplitude in some cases. Certain injector designs, for example, ring slot injectors, which inject fuel and oxidizer through alternate concentric ring-shaped slots, have high frequency vibration tendencies.

Considerable research effort has been expended on the subject of thrust chamber vibration, and special techniques and special instrumentation have been developed to measure these oscillations. Pressure amplitudes seem to vary locally within the thrust chamber, and frequencies up to 20,000 cycles per second have been recorded. Several types of high frequency oscillation have been distinguished, one associated with the acoustic resonances of the chamber volume and shape, another related to injection phenomena. However, several vibration types still remain unexplained. The elimination of vibration in the operation of a rocket is still largely an empirical and experimental process.

9 Injectors

The functions of the injector are similar to those of a carburetor in an internal combustion engine. The injector has to introduce and meter the flow to the combustion chamber, and atomize and mix the propellants in such a manner that a correctly proportioned homogeneous fuel-oxidizer mixture will result, one that can readily be vaporized and burned.

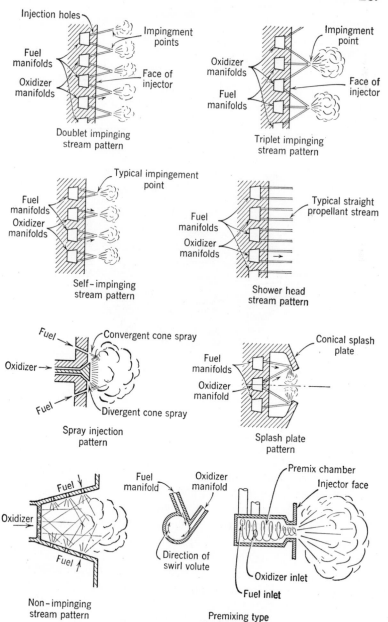

FIGURE 7–13. Schematic diagrams of several injector types.

Injector Types

Several general types of injectors are shown in Figure 7–13.

In the *impinging stream type, multiple hole injectors,* the propellants are injected through a number of separate small holes in such a manner that the fuel and oxidizer streams impinge upon each other. Impingement will aid atomization of the liquids into

FIGURE 7–14. Injector with 90° self-impinging (i.e., fuel-against-fuel and oxidizer-against-oxidizer) type, countersunk, doublet injection pattern. Large holes are inlets to fuel manifolds. (Courtesy General Electric Company.)

droplets and will also aid distribution. There are at least three categories: *doublet impinging stream injection patterns* employ a series of two impinging streams, one of which is fuel and the other oxidizer (see Figures 7–1 and 7–2). The use of two streams of one propellant impinging on a single stream of the other propellant is known as the *triplet* impinging stream pattern; in the *self-impinging pattern* fuel impinges only against another fuel stream, and each oxidizer stream impinges (separately from the fuel) against another oxidizer stream, thus avoiding intense combustion at the impingement points. An injector of this type is shown in Figure 7–14.

The *non-impinging or shower head injection* type employs non-impinging streams of propellant usually emerging normal to the face of the injector. It relies usually on turbulence and diffusion to achieve mixing. The V-2 rocket used this type of injector.

Splash plate type injectors are intended to promote propellant mixing in the liquid state and employ the principle of impinging the propellant streams against a surface. Certain nitric acid propellant combustions have successfully used this injection method.

FIGURE 7–15. Spray injector during water test. (Courtesy North American Aviation, Inc.)

Sheet or spray type injectors give cylindrical, conical, or other types of spray sheets of liquid rocket propellants; these sprays generally intersect and thereby promote mixing. A special type is the *ring slot injector*. A spray injector undergoing water tests is shown in Figure 7–15.

In *premixing injectors* the mixing of the liquid propellants is achieved before they are introduced into the combustion chamber. The time delay of the reaction dictates the dimensions and the flow rate of the premixing chamber, and generally the control of explosions of the premixed propellants inside the injector is critical.

Injector Calculations

The *hydraulic injector characteristics* can be evaluated accurately and can be designed to give the desired injection pressures, flows, and mixture ratio.

For a given thrust and a given effective exhaust velocity or specific thrust, the total propellant flow is given by $\dot{w} = Fg/c$. The relations between the mixture ratio, the oxidizer, and the fuel flow rates are:

$$\dot{w}_o + \dot{w}_f = \dot{w} \tag{7-9}$$

$$r = \dot{w}_o / \dot{w}_f \tag{7-10}$$

$$\dot{w}_o = \frac{r}{r+1} \dot{w} \tag{7-11}$$

$$\dot{w}_f = \frac{1}{r+1} \dot{w} \tag{7-12}$$

For the *flow* of an incompressible fluid through a hydraulic system,

$$Q = C_d A \sqrt{\frac{2g\,\Delta p}{\rho}} \tag{7-13}$$

or

$$\dot{w} = Q\rho = C_d A \sqrt{2g\rho\,\Delta p} \tag{7-14}$$

This relationship is general and can be applied to any one section of the propellant feed system, to the injector, or to the overall liquid flow system. In injectors it is used to determine the hydraulic characteristics of the propellant injection orifices. A typical variation of injection orifice flow and pressure drop is shown in Figure 7–16.

For any given pressure drops the propellant orifices determine the *mixture ratio* and the *propellant flows* of the rocket unit. From equations 7–10 and 7–14 the mixture ratio is

$$r = \frac{(C_d)_o A_o}{(C_d)_f A_f} \sqrt{\frac{\rho_o\,\Delta p_o}{\rho_f\,\Delta p_f}} \tag{7-15}$$

The quantities in the equations above have to be chosen so that the correct design mixture ratio is attained, even if the total flow is varied slightly. It is usually endeavored to select orifices whose discharge coefficients are constant over a large range of Reynolds numbers and whose ratio $(C_d)_o/(C_d)_f$ remains invariant. For a given injector it is usually difficult to maintain the mixture ratio constant at low flows or thrusts, such as in starting.

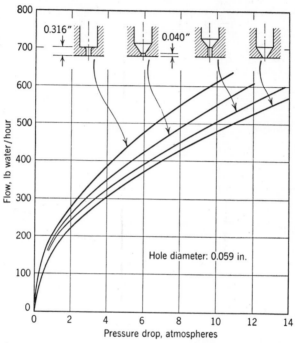

FIGURE 7–16. Hydraulic characteristics of four types of injector orifices.

The quality of injection is usually checked by *water tests,* which permit a direct observation of jet size and impingement pattern and also an evaluation of the mixture ratio for a given injector design. If $\rho_o = \rho_f$ and $\Delta p_o = \Delta p_f$, such as is the case in water tests of injectors, the formula above gives

$$r = \frac{(C_d)_o}{(C_d)_f} \frac{A_o}{A_f} \tag{7–16}$$

Therefore the mixture ratio measured in water tests can be converted into the actual propellant mixture ratio by multiplying it

TABLE 7–2. INJECTOR DISCHARGE COEFFICIENTS

Orifice Type	Diameter (inches)	Discharge Coefficient
Sharp-edged orifice	above 0.10	0.61
	below 0.10	0.65 approx.

Short tube with rounded entrance $L/D > 3.0$	0.040	0.88
	0.062	0.90
	0.040	
	(with $L/D \sim 1.0$)	0.70

Short tube with conical entrance	0.020	0.7
	0.040	0.82
	0.062	0.76
	0.100	0.84–0.80
	0.125	0.84–0.78

Short tube with spiral effect	0.04–0.25	0.2–0.55

Sharp-edged cone	0.040	0.70–0.69
	0.062	0.72

by the square roots of the density ratio of the propellant combination and the square root of the pressure drop ratio.

The mechanism of propellant atomization with simultaneous vaporization, partial combustion, and mixing is difficult to analyze, and performance of injectors has to be evaluated by experiment within a rocket thrust chamber. It is difficult to duplicate actual rocket conditions by subjecting injectors to water tests or checking their injection pattern with propellants without combustion.

The *injection velocity* equals

$$v = Q/A$$

$$= C_d \sqrt{2g\,\Delta p/\rho} \qquad (7\text{--}17)$$

Values of discharge coefficients for various types of injection orifices are shown in Table 7–2. The velocity will be a maximum for a given injection pressure drop when the discharge coefficient equals one. Ordinarily, the discharge coefficient C_d is expressed as the product of the velocity coefficient and a jet area contraction coefficient. In the short tube orifices of rocket injectors, the contraction coefficient and the velocity coefficient are considered equal to each other. Smooth and well-rounded entrances to the injection holes and clean bores give high values of the discharge coefficient (see Table 7–2).

When an oxidizer and a fuel jet impinge, the *resultant momentum* can be calculated from the following relation, based on the principle of conservation of momentum. Figure 7–17 illustrates

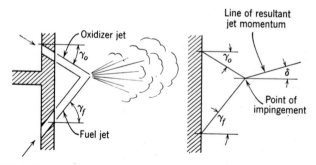

FIGURE 7–17. Angular relations of doublet impinging stream injection pattern.

a pair of impinging jets, and defines γ_o as the angle between the chamber axis and the oxidizer stream, γ_f as the angle between the chamber axis and the fuel stream, and δ as the angle between the chamber axis and the resultant stream.

If the total momentum of the two jets before and after impingement is equal,

$$\tan \delta = \frac{\dot{w}_o v_o \sin \gamma_o - \dot{w}_f v_f \sin \gamma_f}{\dot{w}_o v_o \cos \gamma_o + \dot{w}_f v_f \cos \gamma_f} \qquad (7\text{--}18)$$

Good performance is often obtained when the resultant momentum of impinging streams is approximately axial. If the resultant momentum is along the chamber axis, $\delta = 0$, $\tan \delta = 0$, and the angular relation for an axially directed jet momentum has to equal

$$\dot{w}_o v_o \sin \gamma_o = \dot{w}_f v_f \sin \gamma_f \qquad (7\text{--}19)$$

From these equations the relation between γ_f, γ_o, and δ can be determined. A sample calculation is shown at the end of this chapter.

Injector Design Considerations

A complete theory relating injector design parameters to rocket performance and combustion phenomena has not yet been devised, and therefore the approach to the design and development of liquid propellant rocket injectors has been largely empirical. Yet the available data indicate several important parameters which effect the performance and operating characteristics of injectors; some of these are briefly enumerated here.

Propellant Combination. The particular fuel and oxidizer combination determines such characteristics as the relative chemical reactivity, the vaporization, the ignition temperature, the diffusion of hot gases, the volatility or the surface tension, all of which are believed to affect injection behavior in rockets. Hypergolic (self-igniting) propellants generally require injector designs different from those required by propellants which must be ignited. If one of the propellants is readily gasified (liquid oxygen or ammonia), then the injector design can take advantage of this fact by not requiring splash plates or liquid mixing devices. Injector designs which perform well with one combination generally do not work too well with a different propellant combination.

Injection Orifice Pattern and Orifice Size. With individual holes in the injector plate, there appears to be an optimum condition for each of the following parameters: orifice size, angle of impingement, angle of resultant momentum, distance of the impingement locus from the injector face, number of injection orifices per unit of injector face surface, flow per unit of injection orifice, and distribution of orifices over the injector face. Most of these parameters are determined experimentally.

Transient Conditions. Starting and stopping may require special provisions (temporary plugging of holes, accurate valve timing, insertion of paper cups over holes to prevent entry of one propellant into the manifold of the other propellant, or check valves) to permit satisfactory transient operation. In large size injectors there is also a considerable time delay before all the orifices are fully supplied with propellant from the manifolds.

Hydraulic Characteristics. The orifice type and the pressure drop across the injection orifice determine the injection velocity. A low pressure drop is desirable to minimize weight of the feed system or the pumping power and improve the overall rocket efficiency, yet high pressure drops are used often to increase the rocket's resistance to combustion instability and to give an injection velocity for better atomization of the liquids.

Heat Transfer. It has been proved experimentally that injectors influence the performance and the heat transferred in rocket thrust chambers. Spray injectors in certain cases have been found to cause excessive heat transfer across the nozzle walls. Low heat transfer rates have usually been obtained when the injectors were designed so that the resultant momentum of the individual injection stream was pointed in the direction of the chamber axis or when the injection pattern resulted in an intentionally rich mixture near the chamber walls. In general, the higher the performance of an injector, the higher will be the heat transfer rate to the walls of the combustion chamber and the injector face, because the high efficiency usually leads to high turbulence and thin boundary layers.

Structural Design. The injector is highly loaded by pressure forces from the combustion chamber and the propellant manifolds. These pressure conditions during transition (starting or stopping) can cause stresses which sometimes exceed the steady state operating conditions by several times. The face of many modern injectors is flat and must be reinforced by suitable structure, in such a manner that there will be no unnecessary complications in the geometrical and hydraulic arrangement of the manifold passages; the structure must also be sufficiently flexible to avoid the applying of undue thermal stresses caused by heating the injector face by hot combustion gases. The injector design must also provide for positive seals between the fuel and the oxidizer manifold (an internal leak generally causes manifold explosion or internal fires) and a sealed attachment of the injector to the chamber.

10   Thrust Chambers with Variable Thrust

A variable thrust unit has a *regulated propellant flow,* which is controlled by means of variable throttling orifices or multiple injectors.

When the injection pressure is regulated, the pressure drop across the injector orifice and the flow will vary accordingly. If the flow varies over an appreciable range, the discharge coefficients and the injection velocities may change sufficiently to affect the flow pattern. The mixing, atomization, resultant momentum, and impingement pattern will, therefore, vary from those prevalent at rated conditions and combustion instability, and lower performance may result. The variation of flow through any fixed orifice injector hole should therefore be limited.

The *multiple injector* scheme avoids the difficulty of a variable flow through a fixed orifice by using several sets of injectors, each of which is connected to a separate manifold and a separate valve set. By turning individual injector sets on or off and by changing the flow through any one set only slightly, it is possible to obtain a smooth thrust variation and to maintain each injector at or near its optimum performance point. This injection scheme was actually used in the German 109–509 rocket unit, which powered the Me 163 fighter plane. There were, altogether, twelve individual spray type injectors in one combustion chamber. They were manifolded into three sets, two sets consisting of three individual injectors and one set consisting of six injectors. By means of appropriate control valves, it was possible to get a smooth variation of thrust (see Figure 3–10) from approximately 3700 pounds to 440 pounds without combustion instability and without any loss in performance due to poor injection. (For a given thrust chamber the chamber pressure, and therefore also the performance, will decrease with decreasing propellant flow.) This rocket is pictured in Figures 2–4 and 7–8.

Another way of preventing unstable operation and a drop-off in performance is to use *multiple rocket thrust chambers,* each of which operates always at or near rated conditions. This scheme utilizes the propulsion system most efficiently, because it operates the thrust chambers always at or near rated conditions. The thrust is varied by turning individual thrust chambers on or off. Such a scheme is successfully applied in the American 1500 N4C rocket engine, which uses four individual thrust chambers. This unit is shown in Figure 2–9.

11 Thrust Chamber Starting

One eminent British rocket engineer has been quoted as saying that the most difficult thing about running a thrust chamber is starting it. The starting procedure has to be accurately controlled so that a smooth and even combustion initiation is achieved. The starting condition is critical because it is easily possible to form an unignited *explosive mixture* of propellants in the combustion chamber. The violence of an explosion caused by a starting failure can be seen in Figure 13–1, which shows the remaining fragments of a rocket in which an explosive propellant accumulation was formed in the chamber prior to ignition.

The *initial propellant flow* is usually *less* than *full flow,* and the *starting mixture ratio* is different from the *operating mixture ratio.* A low initial flow prevents an excessive accumulation of unignited propellants in the chamber and tends to assure a smooth buildup of chamber pressure.

While the operating mixture ratio is selected to give a high specific impulse, the *starting mixture ratio* is selected within a wide range of mixture ratios, all of which have a short ignition delay and require little energy from an igniter to reach the temperature at which rapid burning can take place. Since the initial vaporization and mixing of propellants in a cold combustion chamber are not so thorough as the mixing during combustion, there will be more local regions of lean and rich mixtures. The optimum starting mixture is, therefore, only an average of a range of mixture ratios, all of which are readily ignited. Mixture ratios near the stoichiometric mixture ratio have a high heat release per unit of propellant and therefore permit bringing the chamber walls and the gases up to equilibrium faster than would be possible with other mixtures.

Each propellant has a certain *ignition delay,* which is the time necessary to bring an ignitable mixture from the initial condition in the thrust chamber to the temperature at which rapid burning takes place. This delay has been measured and is usually less than one-twentieth of a second. During this interval a quantity of unburned propellant accumulates in the chamber. If the delay is unduly long or if the starting propellant flow is excessive, explosions may result which may be severe enough to cause the destruction of the complete rocket engine.

In starting a thrust chamber one propellant always reaches the chamber a very short time ahead of the other propellant; it is almost impossible to synchronize exactly the fuel and oxidizer feed system so that the propellants reach the chamber simultaneously. Frequently a more reliable ignition is assured when one of the propellants is intentionally made to reach the chamber first. For a fuel-rich starting mixture the fuel is admitted first, while for a fuel-lean starting mixture the oxidizer is given the lead.

The propellant valves are therefore often so controlled that they operate in a definite sequence, thereby assuring an intentional lead of one of the propellants. Often the valves are only partially opened, avoiding an accumulation of hazardous unburned propellant mixture in the chamber. Once combustion is established, the valves are fully opened and full flow may reach the thrust chamber assembly. The initial reduced flow burning period is called the *preliminary stage.*

12   Ignition System

Non-spontaneously ignitable propellants need to be activated by absorbing energy prior to combustion initiation. This energy is supplied by the ignition system. The igniter has to be located near the injector in such a manner that it will receive a satisfactory starting mixture, yet it should not hinder or obstruct the steady combustion process. Five different types of successful propellant ignition systems have been used.

Spark plug ignition has been used successfully on liquid oxygen–gasoline and on nitromethane–oxygen thrust chambers. The spark plug is usually located in a region where initial fuel and

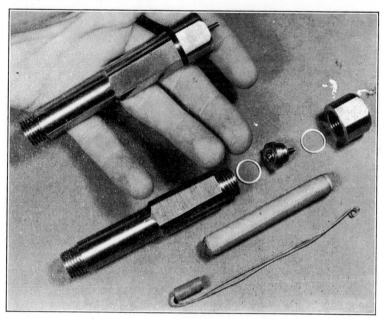

FIGURE 7–18. Pyrotechnic or powder charge igniter. (Courtesy North American Aviation, Inc.)

oxidizer vapors will form an ignitable mixture. This method seems to be particularly applicable to small rocket units. The spark plug is often built into the injector. Many of the early rocket thrust chamber designs used this ignition method.

Because of the high temperature and the erosive qualities of the hot chamber gases, the electrodes deteriorate quite rapidly, and the spark plug has to be replaced frequently.

Powder charge ignition uses a powder squib of a few seconds' burning duration. The powder charge is electrically ignited by a hot wire or other means, and burns with a hot flame within the combustion chamber. Almost all solid propellant rockets and also certain types of liquid rocket chambers are ignited in this fashion. The powder container may be designed to fit directly onto the injector, or the chamber (see Figure 7–18), or may be held in the chamber from outside through the nozzle. The German V-2 rocket is ignited in this last manner. This ignition method can only be used once; thereafter the charge has to be replaced. Powder igniters are discussed further in Chapter 11.

In *precombustion chamber ignition* a small chamber is built next to the main combustion chamber and connected through an orifice, similar to precombustion chambers used in some internal combustion engines. A small amount of fuel and oxidizer is injected into the precombustion chamber and ignited by a spark plug, catalyst, or other means. The burning mixture enters the main combustion chamber in a torch-like fashion and ignites the main propellant flow which is injected into the main chamber. This ignition procedure permits repeated starting and has proved successful with liquid oxygen–gasoline and oxygen–alcohol thrust chambers.

Auxiliary fluid ignition is a method whereby some liquid or gas, in addition to the regular fuel and oxidizer, is injected into the combustion chamber for very short periods during the starting operation. This fluid is hypergolic, which means it produces spontaneous combustion with either the fuel or the oxidizer. The combustion of nitric acid and some organic fuels can, for instance, be initiated by the introduction of a small quantity of aniline at the beginning of the rocket operation.

Catalytic ignition is a fifth method of ignition, utilizing a solid or liquid catalyst which initiates a chemical decomposition of the propellant.

13   Mounting Considerations

The thrust chamber has to be rigidly fastened to the vehicle frame, such as the missile or the airplane. The mounting bracket has to be capable of taking the thrust and other loads, such as acceleration, and vibration forces. Provision also has to be made to permit thermal expansion and correct alignment of the thrust chamber parts.

The V-2 thrust chamber is supported at four points on the outer skin of the chamber assembly as shown in Figures 2–3 and 7–6.

The support connections are so designed that the lateral and longitudinal alignment and adjustment of the nozzle axis are readily made during the assembly procedure. The thrust chambers shown in Figures 7–1, 7–7, and 7–8 are supported at the injector.

Vehicles which undergo quick maneuvers, such as antiaircraft missiles and rocket fighter planes, experience severe lateral accelerations. In these applications it is sometimes advantageous to support the thrust chamber close to its center of gravity, thereby reducing the bending moments at the support points.

14   Sample Thrust Chamber Design Calculation

No general rule can be given for designing thrust chambers, since each particular design will depend on the application, the selected propellant combination, the available data, and the experience of the designer. Tables 2–2, 2–3, 7–3, and 7–4 give typical design data. However, the usual approach for determining the performance, configuration, size, heat transfer, hydraulic characteristics, and injection parameters is general in nature, and the method of computation applies with but few exceptions to all types of liquid propellant thrust chambers. The following example illustrates the general application of these considerations and the use of some of the equations developed in this chapter.

Example 7–1. A thrust chamber is to be designed with these specifications:

Propellants	Nitric acid and aniline
Mixture ratio	2.75
Chamber pressure	300 psia
Atmospheric pressure	14.7 psia
Thrust	1000 lb

The thrust chamber is to be designed for a cylindrical combustion chamber, a helically wound cooling coil with one of the propellants as coolant, and a multiple hole injector with an injection pressure drop of 80 psi.

The specifications above can be considered the requirements to which the unit has to conform. The selection of the propellants, the mixture ratio, chamber pressure, and the chamber configuration are usually based on sound theoretical and experimental reasons which depend on the application, the availability of propellants and materials, and experience. Let it be assumed that the above are fixed and given.

Several other basic quantities, such as the specific impulse, the chamber temperature, the mean molecular weight of exhaust gases, and the specific

TABLE 7–3. DATA FOR THRUST CHAMBER ASSEMBLY OF 1500-LB THRUST

(*Reference:* H. S. Seifert, M. M. Mills, and M. Summerfield, "Physics of Rockets: Liquid Propellant Rockets," *American Journal of Physics*, Vol. 15, No. 2, pp. 121–140, 1947.)

Thrust at sea level	1500 lb
Combustion chamber pressure	300 psi
Specific impulse	193 sec
Exhaust velocity	6200 ft/sec
Duration of operation	45 sec
Thrust chamber weight	50 lb
Propellants	nitric acid and aniline
Mixture ratio	2.75
Specific heat ratio	1.25
Corrected thrust coefficient, C_F	1.35
Nozzle expansion ratio, ϵ	5.0
Throat area	3.7 in.^{2}
Exit area	18.5 in.^{2}
Combustion volume	272 in.^{3}
Characteristic length, L *	73.4 in.
Chamber area ratio	5.85
Chamber length	11 in.
Propellant flow rate	7.8 lb/sec
Oxidizer flow rate	5.72 lb/sec
Fuel flow rate	2.08 lb/sec
Heat of combustion of mixture	1800 Btu/lb
Heat transferred to coolant	50 Btu/sec
Coolant liquid	aniline
Chamber heat transfer rate	1.0 Btu/in.^{2} sec
Nozzle heat transfer rate	2.5–3.0 Btu/in.^{2} sec
Gas temperature in chamber	4500°F
Gas temperature at nozzle throat	3000°F
Gas temperature at nozzle exit	2000°F
Wall temperature on gas side	1000°F
Wall temperature on liquid coolant side	500°F
Coolant boiling temperature at 500 psi	650°F
Mean coolant temperature	300°F
Injector type	impinging stream
Number of jet pairs	8
Oxidizer hole diameter	0.1285 in.
Fuel hole diameter	0.096 in.
Oxidizer injection pressure drop	100 psi
Fuel injection pressure drop	67 psi
Angle of resultant jet momentum	5 degrees (outward)

TABLE 7–4. CHARACTERISTIC DATA FOR THRUST CHAMBER OF 13,500-LB THRUST USING A PRESSURIZED FEED SYSTEM *

Thrust at sea level	13,500 lb
Thrust at altitude	15,900 lb
Specific impulse	224 sec
Chamber pressure	300 psig
Oxygen flow rate	37 lb/sec
Fuel flow rate	23.4 lb/sec
Reactant ratio (oxidizer to fuel flow)	1.58
Oxygen injector pressure drop	84 psi
Fuel injector pressure drop	63 psi
Fuel cooling jacket pressure drop	42 psi
Coolant velocity (chamber)	21.8 ft/sec
Coolant velocity (throat)	34.4 ft/sec
Heat transfer rate (average)	0.7 Btu/in.^{2} sec
Throat diameter	6.4 in.
Chamber diameter	8.625 in.
Exit diameter	14.4 in.
Chamber length	7.25 in.
Throat to chamber area ratio	0.55
Exit to throat area ratio	5.0
Nozzle divergence angle	15 degrees
Thrust chamber overall dimension	33 in. long, 17 in. diameter at exit
Thrust chamber dry weight	135 lb
Thrust chamber wet weight	150 lb
Injector type	90° impinging like on like
Oxidizer	Liquid oxygen
Fuel	Denatured ethyl alcohol (92.5% by weight)
Nominal duration	54 sec

* Data through courtesy of General Electric Company.

heat ratio may now be determined. These quantities can be obtained from a thermochemical analysis of the acid-aniline propellant system for the mixture ratio and chamber pressure given above. The method of this analysis is given in Chapter 4. The results of such a calculation are:

Chamber temperature	4930° F = 5390° R
Mean molecular weight of exhaust gases	25 lb/mole
Ideal specific impulse	218 sec
Specific heat ratio	1.22

1. Nozzle Configuration

The required nozzle cross sections and nozzle shape will now be calculated. The nozzle coefficient is determined from equation 3–30

$$C_F = \sqrt{\frac{2k^2}{k-1}\left(\frac{2}{k+1}\right)^{(k+1)/(k-1)}\left[1 - \left(\frac{p_2}{p_1}\right)^{(k-1)/k}\right]} + \frac{p_2 - p_3}{p_1}\frac{A_2}{A_t}$$

Since the atmospheric pressure is equal to the nozzle exit pressure ($p_2 = p_3$), the last term of the equation above is equal to zero. Substituting $p_2 = 14.7$ psia, $p_1 = 300$ psia, and $k = 1.22$,

$$C_F = 1.41$$

C_F can also be determined from Figure 3–11.

The thrust correction factor is assumed to be 0.96.

Equation 3–35 is to be solved for the nozzle throat area.

$$A_t = \frac{\dfrac{F}{\zeta_F}}{C_F p_1} = \frac{\dfrac{1000}{0.96}}{1.41 \times 300} = 2.47 \text{ in.}^2$$

The nozzle throat diameter is therefore

$$D_t = \sqrt{\frac{4A_t}{\pi}} = 1.77 \text{ in.}$$

The ideal exhaust velocity can be found from the ideal specific impulse.

$$v_2 = I_s g = 218 \times 32.2 = 7020 \text{ ft/sec}$$

The actual effective exhaust velocity can be estimated by correcting the theoretical exhaust velocity by a velocity correction factor ($\zeta_v = 0.94$).

$$c = v_2\zeta_v = 7020 \times 0.94 = 6600 \text{ ft/sec}$$

The nozzle exit area can be found from the continuity equation 3–2.

$$A_2 = \frac{\dot{w}V_2}{v_2} = \frac{FgV_1}{(v_2)^2}\left(\frac{p_1}{p_2}\right)^{1/k} = \frac{FgT_1R'}{(v_2)^2 p_1\mathfrak{M}}\left(\frac{p_1}{p_2}\right)^{1/k}$$

$$= \frac{1000 \times 32.2 \times 5390 \times 1544}{(6600)^2 \times 300 \times 25}(20.4)^{0.82} = 9.66 \text{ in.}^2$$

The nozzle area expansion ratio is obtained from equation 3–18.

$$\epsilon = \frac{A_2}{A_t} = \frac{9.66}{2.47} = 3.9$$

The nozzle exit diameter is

$$D_2 = \sqrt{\frac{4A_2}{\pi}} = 3.51 \text{ in.}^2$$

The value of the area expansion ratio could also have been obtained from equation 3–25 or from Figure 3–7.

The nozzle is now determined as follows. Summarizing:

Throat area	2.47 sq in.
Exit area	9.66 sq in.
Throat diameter	1.77 in.
Exit diameter	3.51 in.
Nozzle diffuser half angle	15 degrees
Exhaust velocity	6600 ft/sec

2. Chamber Configuration

A cylindrical shape has been chosen for this chamber. Gas velocities and Mach numbers in the chamber are very low compared to nozzle velocities. Although their values are not readily calculated or measured, a reasonable chamber velocity is believed to be between 200 to 400 ft/sec. By assuming a value of 250 ft/sec, an estimate of the chamber cross section can be made.

$$A_1 = \frac{\dot{w}V_1}{v_1} = \frac{FgR'T_1}{v_2\mathfrak{M}p_1v_1} = \frac{1000 \times 32.2 \times 1544 \times 5360}{6600 \times 25 \times 300 \times 250} = 21.5 \text{ in.}^2$$

$$\text{Chamber diameter } D_c = \sqrt{\frac{4A_1}{\pi}} = 5.23 \text{ in.}^2$$

A similar result could also have been obtained by assuming a low chamber Mach number and using equation 3–13. A chamber volume to throat area ratio of approximately 60 appears desirable. ($L^* = 60$.)

$$V_1 = L^*A_t = 60 \times 2.47 = 148 \text{ in.}^3$$

Since the exact chamber dimensions are not so critical as the nozzle dimensions, variations in chamber configuration will not appreciably affect the performance. The exact chamber dimensions may, therefore, be chosen as follows:

Chamber diameter	5.0 in.
Convergence angle	30 degrees
Chamber volume	150 in.³
Length of cylindrical chamber portion	6.5 in.

A scaled sketch of the inside contour of the thrust chamber can now be drawn similar to Figure 7–1.

3. Injector Design

A multiple hole impinging jet injector is arbitrarily chosen for this rocket because such injectors have given good performance in the past. Let it be assumed that there will be eight pairs of injection streams, each consisting of an oxidizer and a fuel jet, and that the resultant momentum of each jet pair is in an axial direction.

The propellant weight flow can be found as follows:

$$\dot{w} = \frac{Fg}{c} = \frac{1000 \times 32.2}{6600} = 4.88 \text{ lb/sec}$$

The oxidizer and fuel flow, according to equations 7–11 and 7–12, are respectively

$$\dot{w}_o = \frac{\dot{w}r}{r+1} = \frac{4.88 \times 2.75}{2.75+1} = 3.58 \text{ lb/sec}$$

$$\dot{w}_f = \frac{\dot{w}}{r+1} = \frac{4.88}{2.75+1} = 1.30 \text{ lb/sec}$$

The following propellant quantities and properties are of concern:

Propellant	Aniline	Nitric Acid
Temperature of injected propellant	270° F	60° F
Specific gravity at injection temperature	0.97	1.5
Density at injection temperature	60.5 lb/cu ft	94 lb/cu ft
Heat of vaporization at standard conditions (Btu/lb)	187	207
Boiling point at 1 atm	364° F	191° F
Boiling point at 300 psia	650° F	. . .

The propellant injection volume flows are:

$$Q_o = \frac{\dot{w}_o}{\rho_o} = \frac{3.58}{94} \times 1728 = 65.9 \text{ in.}^3/\text{sec}$$

$$Q_f = \frac{\dot{w}_f}{\rho_f} = \frac{1.30}{60.5} \times 1728 = 37.1 \text{ in.}^3/\text{sec}$$

From equation 7–14 it is possible to calculate the injector hole areas. It is assumed that the injection pressure drops in the fuel and oxidizer lines are equal to 80 psi, and that both orifice discharge coefficients are equal to 0.75.

$$\Sigma A_o = \frac{\dot{w}_o}{C_d\sqrt{2g\,\Delta p\,\rho_o}} = \frac{3.58 \times 144}{0.75\sqrt{2 \times 32.2 \times 80 \times 144 \times 94}} = 0.0822 \text{ in.}^2$$

$$\Sigma A_f = \frac{\dot{w}_f}{C_d\sqrt{2g\,\Delta p\,\rho_f}} = \frac{1.30 \times 144}{0.75\sqrt{2 \times 32.2 \times 80 \times 144 \times 60.5}} = 0.0372 \text{ in.}^2$$

Since there will be eight pairs of injection streams, the individual hole areas and diameters will be

$$A_o = 0.0822/8 = 0.0103 \text{ in.}^2$$

$$A_f = 0.0372/8 = 0.00465 \text{ in.}^2$$

$$D_f = 0.077 \text{ in.—use Drill No. 48 (0.076 in.) } A_f = 0.0455$$

$$D_o = 0.1145 \text{ in.—use Drill No. 33 (0.1130 in.) } A_o = 0.100$$

If it is assumed that there is no jet contraction, the injection velocities will be

$$v = C_d \sqrt{\frac{2g \, \Delta p}{\rho}}$$

$$v_f = 0.75 \sqrt{\frac{2 \times 32.2 \times 80 \times 144}{60.5}} = 83 \text{ ft/sec}$$

$$v_o = 0.75 \sqrt{\frac{2 \times 32.2 \times 80 \times 144}{94}} = 66.7 \text{ ft/sec}$$

These velocities have magnitudes which promise to give good injection and justify the original assumption of 80 psi injection drop.

The injection angles are now to be chosen so that the resultant momentum will be in an axial direction. This is done in accordance with equation 7–19 and by arbitrarily selecting the angle of inclination of the oxidizer jet at 20 degrees. The symbols below are the same as in equation 7–19.

$$\sin \gamma_f = \frac{w_o v_o}{w_f v_f} \sin \gamma_o = 2.75 \frac{66.7}{83} \sin 20° = 0.75$$

$$\gamma_f = 48.5°$$

The following quantities have now been determined for the injector:

Injector Design Parameter	Fuel	Oxidizer
Flow (total propellant flow = 4.88 lb/sec)	1.30 lb/sec	3.58 lb/sec
Volume flow	37.1 in.^{3}/sec	65.9 in.^{3}/sec
Pressure drop through injector	80 psi	80 psi
Injection velocity	83 ft/sec	66.7 ft/sec
Number of injection holes	8	8
Diameter of each hole	0.076 in.	0.1130 in.
Angle of hole with nozzle axis	+48½°	−20°
Total injection area	0.0372 in.^{2}	0.0822 in.^{2}

4. Heat Transfer

This thrust chamber is to be regeneratively cooled. Although it has been possible to calculate approximate heat transfer film coefficients of the gas layer, their accuracy is questionable. They will, therefore, not be determined in this example. Accurate heat transfer data have to be determined by tests. The average wall temperature of the chamber will, however, be estimated and the cooling jacket will be designed so that the assumed average heat flow (1 Btu/in.^{2} sec) can safely be absorbed in the coolant. The total heat transfer is the product of the average heat transfer rate per unit area and the inside chamber and nozzle surface areas.

Total heat transfer $= Q = 1.0 \times 150 = 150$ Btu/sec

Either the oxidizer or the fuel can be used as coolant. In this case the fuel is to be preferred, because it is non-corrosive, because it requires a smaller and therefore lighter cooling jacket, and because, as will be shown below, its cooling capacity is adequate.

The transferred heat to be absorbed by the cooling fluid is from equation 5–9.

$$A\bar{q} = \dot{w}_f \bar{c}\, \Delta T$$

For aniline the average specific heat at the temperature in question has a value of 0.55 Btu/°F lb.

The mean coolant temperature rise is, therefore,

$$\Delta T = \frac{A\bar{q}}{\dot{w}_f \bar{c}} = \frac{150}{1.30 \times 0.55} = 210°\,\text{F}$$

This temperature rise is not excessive, and the fuel therefore appears to be satisfactory as a coolant. If the fuel was originally at 60° F, the temperature at which the fuel enters from the cooling jacket into the injector is therefore approximately $60 + 210 = 270°$ F. As can be seen, this temperature is well below the boiling point of the fluid, and there will be little danger of any local boiling within the cooling jacket. This temperature was used in estimating the proper specific gravity of the injected fuel.

The film coefficient for the coolant liquid will now be evaluated. The following values are needed for the coolant (aniline):

Density	60.5 lb/cu ft
Thermal conductivity	2.7×10^{-5} Btu/sec ft^2 °F/ft
Viscosity	3.1×10^{-5} lb-sec/sq ft
Specific heat	0.55 Btu/lb °F

The evaluation of this film coefficient depends on the Reynolds number and the Prandtl number. In order to evaluate it, the coolant velocity and the equivalent diameter of the cooling coil passage have to be known.

The cooling coil passage will be rectangular in cross section and will wind around the chamber in a helical fashion. By assuming an average coolant velocity of 15 ft/sec, the cross-sectional area for a single helix will be

$$A = \frac{Q}{v} = \frac{37.1}{12 \times 15} = 0.206 \text{ in.}^2$$

In order to have a low coolant pressure drop and a relatively simple shape to manufacture, a double helix coolant passage of rectangular cross section was chosen. The dimensions of a cross section through a single helix might then be approximately $\frac{1}{8} \times 1\frac{3}{16}$ in. The value of D to be used in the calculation of the Reynolds number equals four times the hydraulic radius.

From equation 5–12 the coolant film coefficient is

$$h_l = 0.023\, c_p\, \frac{\dot{w}}{A} \left(\frac{Dv\rho}{\mu g}\right)^{-0.2} \left(\frac{\mu gc}{\kappa}\right)^{-0.67}$$

$$= 0.023 \times 0.55 \times \frac{1.3}{0.206}$$

$$\times \left(\frac{0.0183 \times 15 \times 60.5}{3.1 \times 10^{-5} \times 32.2}\right)^{-0.2} \left(\frac{3.1 \times 10^{-5} \times 0.55 \times 32.2}{2.7 \times 10^{-5}}\right)^{-0.6.}$$

$$= 0.00154 \text{ Btu/in.}^2 \text{ sec } °R$$

The heat transfer across the liquid coolant film is obtained from equation 5–6

$$q = h_l(T_{wl} - T_l)$$

This relation is to be solved for the wall temperature on liquid side

$$T_{wl} = \frac{q}{h_l} + T_l = \frac{1.0}{0.00154} + \frac{60 + 270}{2} = 825° \text{ F}$$

and gives an average temperature estimate of the outside wall surface of the inner chamber wall. If the wall is assumed to be 0.075 in. thick, the equivalent film coefficient for the wall will be

$$h_w = \frac{\kappa_w}{t_w}$$

Stainless steel has been selected for chamber material because of its good erosion resistance.

For stainless steel $\kappa = 1.3$ Btu/in.^{2} hr °F/in.

$$h_w = \frac{1.3}{0.075 \times 3600} = 0.0048 \text{ Btu/in.}^2 \text{ sec } °F$$

The average wall temperature on the gas side of the chamber is, therefore,

$$T_{wg} = \frac{1.0}{0.0048} + 825 = 1062° \text{ F}$$

The average wall temperature on the gas side is considered safe for stainless steel. The throat section in an actual design should be checked separately to determine its heat transfer characteristics.

5. Cooling Coil Loss

In order to select the appropriate feed pressure for the fuel, it will be necessary to estimate the hydraulic losses in the cooling coil which surrounds the chamber and nozzle. According to equation 7–7, the loss is

$$\Delta p = f\, \frac{L}{D}\, \frac{\rho v^2}{2g}$$

where Δp is the friction loss (lb/ft^2), L is the length of coil (ft), f is the friction coefficient, D is the diameter or $4 \times$ hydraulic radius (0.22/12 ft), ρ is the density at jacket temperature (lb/cu ft), and v is the velocity in cooling passage (15 ft/sec).

There are two identical helix cooling coils in parallel. The length L is the total length of the cooling helix, when unwound from the chamber jacket and nozzle. Assuming that there is a wall 0.075 in. wide between individual cooling passages, there will be a total of twelve turns in each helix, giving an approximate total length of 83 in. These quantities can be more accurately determined when the cooling coil is developed from scaled drawings; for this example the above can be considered adequate for estimating the pressure drop.

The friction factor f is a function of Reynolds number and can be found from Figure 7–10 to be 0.038 for clean steel pipes at a Reynolds number of 16,600. The friction coefficient f has to be corrected for the curvature effect. An empirical formula has been developed for small thrust chamber, using aniline cooling:

$$\text{Friction correction factor} = 1 + 3.5 \frac{D}{D_c} = 1.0 + 3.5 \frac{0.22}{5.25} = 1.147$$

where D_c is the helix diameter and D is the equivalent passage diameter.

The friction loss is, therefore,

$$\Delta p_f = 0.038 \times 1.147 \times \frac{83}{0.22} \times \frac{60.5}{144} \times \frac{15^2}{64.4} = 24.1 \text{ psi}$$

The thrust chamber supply pressure is equal to the sum of the chamber pressure and the pressure losses in jacket and injector.

$$p_o = 300 + 80 = 380 \text{ psi}$$

$$p_f = 300 + 80 + 24.1 = 404 \text{ psi}$$

The fuel has to be supplied at 404 psi and the oxidizer at 380 psi. The feed system has to be so controlled that it will supply the propellants at these pressures and an oxidizer flow rate of 3.58 lb/sec and a fuel flow rate of 1.30 lb/sec.

6. Wall Thickness

The thickness of the cylindrical shell is chosen in conformance with stress values. For a cylinder under radial pressure:

$$\Delta p \, D = 2 t_w s$$

where Δp is the pressure difference across jacket, D is the mean diameter of cylinder, t_w is the thickness of cylinder wall, and s is the working stress.

For certain stainless steels at elevated temperatures the yield stress may be taken as 25,000 psi. Applying a safety factor of 2 to account for pressure surges during starting and stopping, for other loads and for uneven thermal expansion, the working stress can be taken as 12,500 psi.

The maximum pressure difference across the wall occurs during starting when the cooling jacket pressure is approximately 420 psi, while the chamber pressure is zero. This pressure tends to collapse the chamber. The worst condition will occur when a thrust chamber is restarted while the inner wall is still hot.

$$t_w = \frac{\Delta p \, D}{2s} = \frac{420 \times 5.1}{2 \times 12,500} = 0.086 \text{ in.}$$

This is the minimum tolerable thickness; actually, the thickness should be somewhat heavier to allow for welding factors, buckling tendency, and stress concentration. The thickness, for simplicity's sake, will be made uniform throughout, that is, also in the nozzle section. For larger thrust chambers the nozzle is usually heavier, because a larger pressure differential is exerted across the wall at that location. The value of 0.109 in. has been chosen arbitrarily.

A similar calculation should be carried out for the outer chamber shell; the thickness for the outer shell was found to be 0.062 in.

Problems

1. For a certain thrust chamber the throat diameter equals 3 in. and the characteristic length equals 7.0 ft. What will be the chamber volume? What are the dimensions of the chamber if a cylindrical shape is selected? The L/D ratio of the cylinder is 1.75, and the nozzle entrance cone has a half angle of 25° and an area ratio of 7.0.

2. Gasoline and oxygen are used as fuels in the rocket above at a chamber pressure of 300 psi and a mixture ratio of 2.5 (see Figure 4–9). What is the average stay time of the propellants in the chamber? What estimated percentage of time is spent by the gas in the nozzle (guess this)?

3. The following conditions are given for the cooling jacket of a rocket thrust chamber assembly:

Rated chamber pressure	210 psi
Rated jacket pressure	290 psi
Chamber diameter	16.5 in.
Nozzle throat diameter	5.0 in.
Nozzle throat gas pressure	112 psi
Average wall temperature	1000° F
Cooling passage height at chamber and nozzle exit	⅜ in.
Cooling passage height at nozzle throat	¼ in.
Nozzle exit pressure	14.7 psi
Nozzle exit diameter	9.0 in.
Wall material	1020 carbon steel
Safety factor on yield strength	2.5

Compute the outside diameters and the thickness of the inner and outer walls at the chamber, at the throat, and at the nozzle exit.

4. A cooling jacket of the following specifications is given:

Coolant: Aniline	
Coolant density	61 lb/cu ft
Coolant viscosity	3.1×10^{-5} lb sec/ft^2
Passage dimensions (average)	$\frac{1}{8} \times 1$ in.
Coolant flow	1.26 lb/sec
Single helix with mean diameter	5 in.
Length of unwound helix	125 in.

Determine (a) the hydraulic radius, (b) the Reynolds number, (c) the corrected friction factor, (d) the pressure loss.

5. Determine the hole sizes and the angle setting for a multiple hole, doublet impinging stream injector which uses alcohol and liquid oxygen as propellants. The resultant momentum should be axial, and the angle between the oxygen and fuel jets $(\gamma_o + \gamma_f)$ should be 60°. Assume the following:

$(C_d)_o$	0.87
$(C_d)_f$	0.91
ρ_o	71 lb/cu ft
ρ_f	51 lb/cu ft
Chamber pressure	300 psi
Fuel pressure	400 psi
Oxygen pressure	380 psi
Number of jet pairs	4
Thrust	250 lb
Actual specific impulse	218 sec
Mixture ratio	1.20

Answers: 0.0197 in.; 0.0214 in.; 35.2°; 24.8°.

Symbols

A	area, ft^2
b	constant
C_d	discharge coefficient
C_F	thrust coefficient
c	effective exhaust velocity, ft/sec
$\bar{c}$	average liquid specific heat, Btu/lb °F
D	diameter, ft
d	total derivative
E	modulus of elasticity, lb/in.^{2}
F	thrust, lb
f	friction loss coefficient
g	acceleration of gravity (32.2 ft^2/sec)

I_s specific impulse, lb/lb-sec

k specific heat ratio

L length, ft

L^* characteristic chamber length, ft

$\mathfrak{M}$ molecular weight, lb/mole

n constant

p absolute pressure, lb/ft^2

Q volume flow, ft^3/sec

R' universal gas constant (1544 ft-lb/°R mole)

r mixture ratio

T absolute temperature, °R

t_w wall thickness, in.

t_s stay time, sec

V specific volume, ft^3/lb

V_c combustion chamber volume (volume up to throat), ft^3

v velocity, ft/sec

$\dot{w}$ propellant weight flow rate, lb/sec

Greek Letters

α nozzle divergence half angle

β nozzle convergence half angle

γ_o angle between chamber axis and oxidizer stream

γ_f angle between chamber axis and fuel stream

Δ finite differential

δ angle between chamber axis and the resultant stream

ϵ nozzle area ratio ($\epsilon = A_2/A_t$)

ϵ_c chamber area ratio ($\epsilon_c = A_1/A_t$)

ζ_d discharge correction factor

ζ_F thrust correction factor

ζ_v velocity correction factor

η constant pressure cycle efficiency

λ coefficient of thermal expansion, in./in. °F

ν Poisson ratio

ρ density, lb/ft^3

σ stress, lb/in.^{2}

Subscripts

a actual value as differentiated from ideal value

1   nozzle inlet or chamber condition

2   nozzle exit

3	atmospheric conditions surrounding nozzle
co	cone
cy	cylinder
f	fuel
i	initial condition
o	oxidizer
t	throat
w	wall

Chapter 8

Liquid Propellant

Rocket Systems

1 General Requirements

The early rocket experimenters were elated about the fact that a rocket—they were referring to the early solid propellant rocket—was an exceedingly simple power source which did not embody a single moving part. However, the modern liquid rocket propulsion system has not only an intricate thrust chamber but also a complex feed mechanism, which may have some two dozen very sensitive precision valves and switches, in addition to some high power, high speed rotating machinery and a separate high output power supply.

The liquid propellant engine system generally consists of one or more *tanks* to store the propellants, a *feed mechanism* for forcing the liquids into the thrust chamber, a *power source* which furnishes the energy required by the feed mechanism, and a *control* device for regulating the propellant flow rates. The selection of a particular feed system and its components is governed primarily by the application of the rocket, its size, propellant, thrust, flight program, and duration, and by general requirements of simplicity of design, ease of manufacture, reliability of operation, and minimum weight. A classification of several of the more important types of feed systems is shown in Figure 8–1.

Since any one of the separate units which comprise a rocket system can be built in several different ways, the number of possible combinations is very large. In fact, the author does not know of any two liquid propellant rocket designs with identical systems. Rather than describe in detail the many different types,

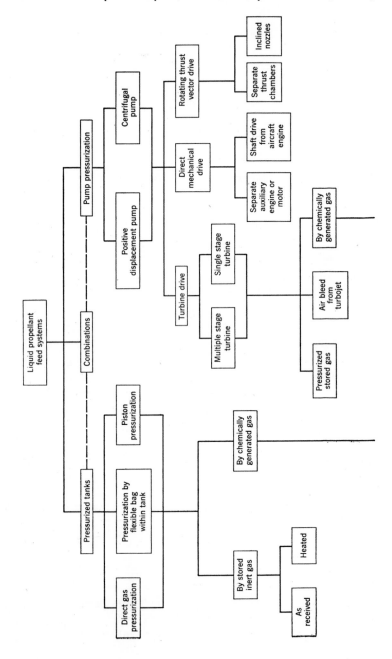

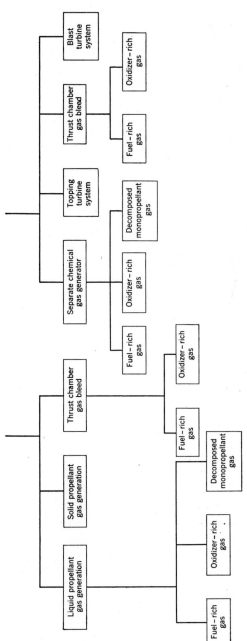

FIGURE 8-1. Classification of liquid propellant rocket feed systems.

which would not give a clear picture of the basic elements, this chapter will discuss the principles and components of several of the more representative and common types of rocket systems and their mechanisms. References to further study can be found in Sections 6.1, 6.3, 6.4, and 6.5 of the Reference Bibliography.

2   Gas Pressure Systems

One of the simplest and most common means of pressurizing the propellants is to force them out of their respective tanks by displacing them with high pressure gas. This gas is fed into the propellant tanks at a controlled pressure, thereby giving a controlled propellant discharge.

For certain rocket units, a gas pressure feed system is very light in weight. For low thrust and short duration, such as for many assisted take-off units, a feed system of this type is preferred. Although the propellant tanks in gas pressure feed systems have to be heavy to withstand the high internal pressures, the overall system weight is usually lower than that of a turbopump system for these applications.

A simple pressurized feed system is shown schematically in Figure 8–2. It consists essentially of a high pressure gas tank, a gas shut-off and starting valve, a pressure regulator, propellant tanks, propellant valves, and feed lines. Additional components, such as filling and draining provisions, check valves, and filters, are also often incorporated.

After all tanks are filled, the high pressure air valve (2) in Figure 8–2 is remotely actuated and admits air through the pressure regulator (3) at a constant pressure to the propellant tanks (5) and (6). The purpose of the check valves (4) is to prevent a mixing of the oxidizer with the fuel when the unit is not in an upright position. The propellants can be fed to the thrust chamber (13) by opening valves (11). When the propellants are completely consumed, the pressurizing air serves also as a scavenging agent and cleans lines and valves of liquid propellant residue.

The variations in this system, such as the combination of several valves into one or the elimination and addition of certain components, depend to a large extent on the application. If a unit is to be used over and over, such as an aircraft power plant rocket, it will include several additional features, such as possibly a thrust regulating device and a tank level gage; they will not be found in an expendable, single shot unit, which may not have even

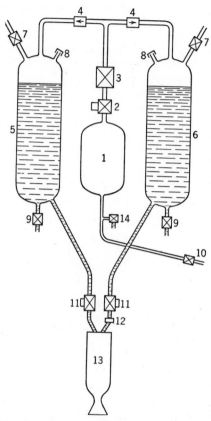

FIGURE 8–2. Schematic diagram of gas pressure feed system. (1) High pressure air supply tank, (2) high pressure air valve (remote control), (3) pressure regulator, (4) check valves, (5) oxidizer tank, (6) fuel tank, (7) tank vent valves, (8) filler necks, (9) drain valves, (10) air filler valve, (11) propellant valves (remote control), (12) restricting orifice, (13) rocket thrust chamber, (14) air bleed valve.

a tank drainage provision. More elaborate pressurized feed systems are listed in reference 6.102, and are discussed in the following sections of this chapter. A typical missile feed system is illustrated schematically in Figure 8–3.

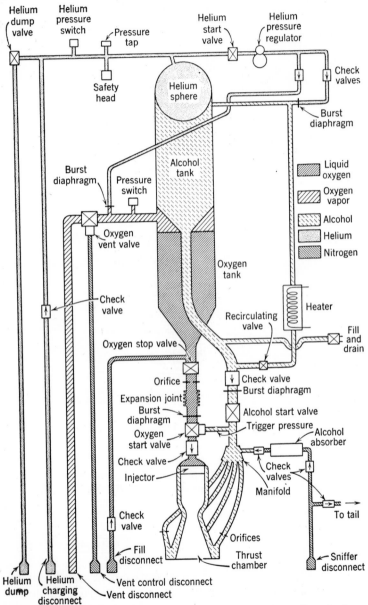

FIGURE 8–3. Schematic diagram of pressurized liquid propellant feed system for missile application. (Courtesy General Electric Company.)

The first part of gas leaving the high pressure storage tank is at or slightly below ambient temperature. The gas remaining in the tank undergoes essentially an isentropic expansion, causing the temperature of the gas to decrease steadily; the last portions of the pressurizing gas leaving the tank will be very much colder than the ambient temperature and will readily absorb heat from the piping and the tank walls. The Joule-Thompson effect will cause a further small temperature change. In an actual propulsion system installation the pressurized gas is required to perform other functions such as operation of valves and controls, according to the particular system requirements. Rather than to attempt a detailed analysis of a complicated system which would obscure the fundamental principles, the following simplified analysis is more representative of gas storage requirements.

A *simplified analysis* of the pressurization of a propellant tank can be made on the basis of the conservation of energy principle by assuming an adiabatic process (no heat transfer) and by assuming the initial weight of gas in the piping and the propellant tank to be small. Let the initial condition in the gas tank be given by subscript 0, the instantaneous conditions in the gas tank by subscript g, and in the propellant tank by subscript p.

$$W_g c_v T_g + W_p c_v T_p + \frac{p_p V_p}{J} = W_0 c_v T_0 \qquad (8\text{--}1)$$

The work done by the gas in displacing the propellants is given by $p_p V_p / J$. Using equations 3–3, 3–4, and 3–5, the initial storage gas weight W_0 may be found.

$$c_v \frac{p_g V_0}{R} + c_v \frac{p_p V_p}{R} + \frac{p_p V_p}{J} = W_0 c_v T_0$$

$$W_0 = \frac{p_g V_0}{R T_0} + \frac{p_p V_p}{R T_0} k$$

This may be expressed as

$$W_0 = \frac{p_g W_0}{p_0} + \frac{p_p V_p}{R T_0} k$$

$$= \frac{p_p V_p}{R T_0} \left(\frac{k}{1 - p_g/p_0} \right) \qquad (8\text{--}2)$$

The first term in this equation expresses the weight of gas required to empty a completely filled propellant tank, if the gas temperature is maintained at the initial storage temperature T_0. The second term expresses the availability of the storage gas as a function of the pressure ratio through which the gas expands. In most systems a constant propellant tank pressure is maintained by means of an automatic regulator, which requires a minimum pressure drop of $p_g - p_p$. In such cases the equation 8–2 may be more convenient to use in the form

$$W_0 = \frac{p_p V_p}{R T_0} \left[\frac{k}{1 - (p_g/p_p)(p_p/p_0)} \right] \qquad (8–3)$$

A heating of the pressurizing gas will reduce the storage requirements and can be accomplished by putting a heat exchanger into the gas line. Heat from the rocket thrust chamber, the exhaust gases, or from other devices can be used as energy sources. The reduction of storage gas weight will depend largely on the type and design of the heat exchanger.

The heating and cooling effects of the tank and pipe walls, the liquid propellants, and the valves on the pressurizing gas are difficult to evaluate analytically and need to be experimentally investigated. The design of storage tanks therefore allows a reasonable excess of pressurizing gas to account for the effects above, for ambient temperature variations, and for the absorption of gas by the propellant. Equations 8–2 and 8–3 are therefore valid only under ideal conditions.

Example 8–1. What air tank volume is required to pressurize the propellant tanks of a 2000-lb thrust rocket thrust chamber using 90 per cent hydrogen peroxide at a chamber pressure of 300 psia for 30 sec in conjunction with a solid catalyst? The air pressure is 2000 psia, the tank pressure is 450 psia, and the minimum pressure drop across the regulator is 100 psi.

Solution. The exhaust velocity is 4250 ft/sec and the required propellant flow can be found from equation 3–34 ($\zeta_d = 1.06$).

$$\dot{w} = \zeta_d \frac{Fg}{c} = 1.06 \frac{2000 \times 32.2}{4250} = 16.05 \text{ lb/sec}$$

The total propellant required is

$$W = \dot{w}t = 16.05 \times 30 = 482 \text{ lb}$$

The density of 90 per cent hydrogen peroxide is 86.7 lb/ft³. The propellant volume is 482/86.7 = 5.56 ft³. With 5 per cent allowed for ullage and excess propellants, equation 8–2 will give the required weight of air ($R = 53.3$, $T_0 = 520°$ R, $k = 1.40$).

$$W_0 = \frac{p_p V_p}{R T_0} \frac{k}{1 - \dfrac{p_g}{p_0}}$$

$$= \frac{450 \times 144 \times 5.56 \times 1.05}{53.3 \times 520} \frac{1.40}{1 - \dfrac{450 + 100}{2000}}$$

$$= 26.4 \text{ lb}$$

With additional 5 per cent allowed for excess gas, the high pressure tank volume will be, from equation 3–3,

$$V_0 = \frac{W_0 R T_0}{p_0} = \frac{1.05 \times 26.4 \times 53.3 \times 520}{2000 \times 144}$$

$$= 2.77 \text{ ft}^3$$

The pressures in the gas storage tank are usually chosen so as to permit a small and lightweight *gas tank design*. The weight of the tank for storing the compressed gas depends on the density of the gas, its maximum storage temperature, and its value of k, and is approximately inversely proportional to the molecular weight of the gas selected. The storage pressure ranges ordinarily between 1800 and 3500 pounds per square inch and is usually five to eight times as high as the propellant tank pressure.

Air is preferred as a *pressurizing gas* because it is readily available. For propellants which react with its pressurizing gas, an inert gas, for example nitrogen, must be used unless provisions are made to separate the chemically active gas from the propellant. This separation may be accomplished by means of a collapsible, flexible bag within the propellant tank or by means of a piston-cylinder arrangement.

In pressurizing liquid oxygen, some of the pressurizing gas, such as air or nitrogen, is condensed or dissolved and therefore not fully effective as a pressurizing agent. A low-freezing inert gas, such as helium, has been used for forcing liquid oxygen out of tanks. In general, about two and one half times as much nitrogen weight is needed for pressurizing liquid oxygen, if compared to the nitrogen needed for displacing an equivalent volume of water at the same pressure.

An interesting variation of the gas-pressurized system is one in which liquid oxygen pressurizes itself by means of its own vapor pressure. This system was frequently used in early rocket units, such as Goddard's first flying unit, shown in Figure 2-7. Although this system is simple in construction, it is difficult to control.

Chemical pressurization, which permits a small controlled reaction within the propellant tanks to produce high pressure gases, has often been proposed. By injecting a small amount of fuel or other suitable spontaneously ignitable chemical into the oxidizer tank, or vice versa, gases can be generated to pressurize the propellant. To date, these methods have not proved to be very satisfactory because the injection, combustion, and the accurate control of small flows of liquid propellant are difficult.

The *thrust* of a pressurized gas rocket propulsion system is determined by the magnitude of the propellant flow, which in turn is determined by the pressure regulator setting. The propellant *mixture ratio* in this type of feed system is controlled by the hydraulic resistance of the liquid propellant lines and can usually be adjusted by means of variable or interchangeable restrictors. Further discussion of the adjusting of thrust and mixture ratio can be found in Section 10 of this chapter.

Example 8-2. The following data are given for a liquid rocket unit with a pressurized feed system. The correct mixture ratio is to be adjusted by orifices.

Propellants	Acid and aniline
Aniline density	63.5 lb/ft^3
Nitric acid density	96 lb/ft^3
Desired mixture ratio	2.75
Fuel injection pressure	440 psia
Oxidizer injection pressure	385 psia
Regulated pressure	480 psia
Pressure loss in fuel line and valve	27 psi
Pressure loss in oxidizer line and valve	23 psi
Thrust	1000 lb
Actual specific impulse	200 sec

Determine the size of the restrictor orifices, assuming that they are disk inserts with sharp-edged holes, the discharge coefficient of which is 0.61.
Solution. The general flow equation 7-14 can be applied.

$$w = C_d A \sqrt{2g \, \Delta p \, \rho}$$

The pressure drop across the orifice is to be determined from the difference between tank pressure, which is equal to the regulated pressure and the thrust chamber injection pressure, diminished by the line and valve losses.

$$\Delta p_f = 480 - 440 - 27 = 13 \text{ psi}$$

$$\Delta p_o = 480 - 385 - 23 = 72 \text{ psi}$$

The flows can be determined from equations 1–8, 7–11, and 7–9.

$$\dot{w} = \frac{F}{I_s} = \frac{1000}{200} = 5 \text{ lb/sec}$$

$$\dot{w}_o = \frac{r\dot{w}}{r + 1} = \frac{2.75 \times 5.0}{3.75} = 3.67 \text{ lb/sec}$$

$$\dot{w}_f = 1.33 \text{ lb/sec}$$

The restrictor areas can now be determined:

$$A_o = \frac{\dot{w}_o}{C_d \sqrt{2g \, \Delta p_o \, \rho_o}}$$

$$= \frac{3.67 \times 144}{0.61 \sqrt{2 \times 32.2 \times 72 \times 144 \times 96}} = 0.108 \text{ in.}^2$$

Restrictor orifice diameter in oxidizer line = 0.372 in.

$$A_f = \frac{1.33 \times 144}{0.61 \sqrt{2 \times 32.2 \times 13 \times 144 \times 63.5}} = 0.114 \text{ in.}^2$$

Restrictor orifice diameter in fuel line = 0.382 in.

3 Piston Type Tank Rocket

Figure 8–4 is a schematic drawing of a piston type tank rocket system. Its propellant tanks are made into cylinders, each of which is provided with a floating piston. The piston is actuated by combustion chamber gas and forces the propellant out of the tank under pressure. Since the chamber pressure is lower than the tank pressure, the area of the piston exposed to the chamber gases is made intentionally larger than that exposed to the propellants. By mechanically combining the floating pistons in the oxidizer and fuel tanks, it is possible to predetermine the operating mixture ratio very accurately, making any mixture ratio controls such as restricting orifices unnecessary.

A number of systems similar to the one shown in Figure 8–4 have been proposed, and a few have actually been built. Although this system is simple, it is relatively heavy, for it requires not only thick-walled propellant tanks, but also one or two heavy gas actuating cylinders. The chamber gases, used as a pressurizing agent, are very hot and often cause erosion, as well as thermal expansion and warping difficulties. The sealing of large, high pressure pistons to prevent the mixing of fuel and oxidizer is difficult.

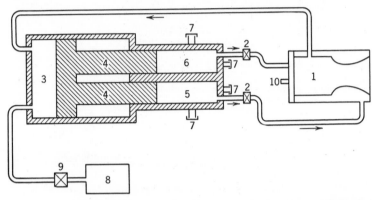

FIGURE 8–4. Schematic diagram of a piston type feed system. (1) Rocket thrust chamber, (2) propellant valves, (3) pressurizing cylinder filled by chamber gases, (4) floating piston, (5) fuel cylinder, (6) oxidizer cylinder, (7) fill, flush, and drain fittings, (8) small starting air supply, (9) starting air valve, (10) igniter.

4 Turbopump System

The turbopump rocket system pressurizes the propellants by means of *pumps,* which, in turn, are driven by *turbines.* The turbines derive their power from the expansion of hot gases. A separate *gas generator* ordinarily produces these gases in the required quantities and at the desired turbine inlet temperature by means of a chemical reaction similar to the reaction in the combustion chamber. A turbopump feed system is shown schematically in Figures 8–5 and 8–6. Typical turbopump units are shown in Figures 8–7, 8–8, and 8–9. Further information on turbopumps can be found in the references listed in Section 6.3 of the Reference Bibliography.

Turbopump rocket systems are usually used on high thrust and long duration rocket units; they are usually lighter than other types for these applications. Their weight is essentially independent of duration. The thrusts and durations at which a turbopump or a gas-pressurized feed system will give a *minimum propulsion system weight* are shown in Figure 8–10.

Several American rocket units contain turbine-driven pumps for pressurizing propellants to the rocket thrust chamber. They

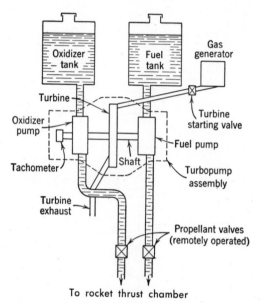

FIGURE 8–5. Simplified schematic diagram of turbopump feed system.

include the rockets used in the Bell X1-A supersonic research plane shown in Figure 1–4 and the Navy Viking research missile (High Altitude Sounding Rocket).

Turbines

The design and analysis of rocket turbines are essentially identical to those of conventional steam and gas turbines and can be found in various textbooks. Rather than describing the design and discussing the conventional theory of turbines, which would have to be lengthy to be explicit and would be a repetition of existing literature, this section is devoted primarily to giving data and describing pertinent features of rocket turbine applications and to pointing out some of the significant differences between rocket turbines and conventional turbines.

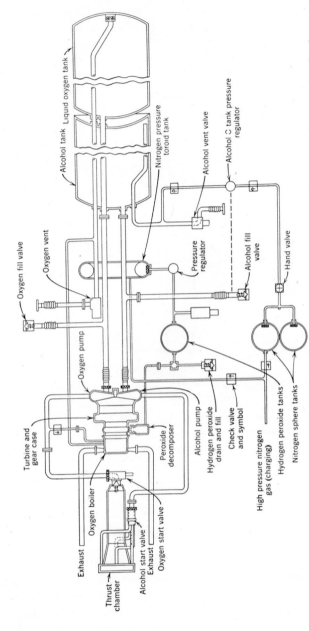

FIGURE 8–6. Schematic diagram of missile rocket system using a turbopump. The turbine is driven by the decomposition products of hydrogen peroxide, which in turn comes from a pressurized tank. (Courtesy General Electric Company.)

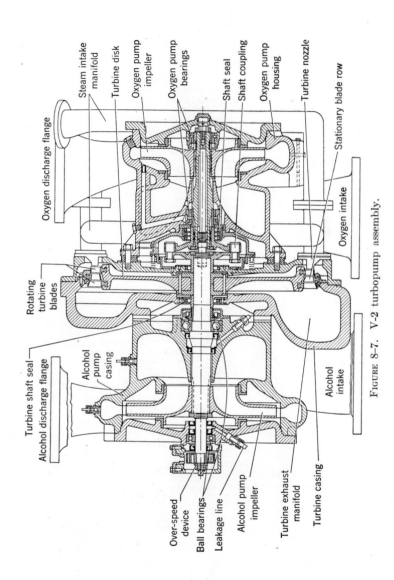

Oxygen discharge flange

Steam intake manifold

Turbine disk

Oxygen pump impeller

Oxygen pump bearings

Shaft seal

Shaft coupling

Oxygen pump housing

Turbine nozzle

Stationary blade row

Oxygen intake

Rotating turbine blades

Turbine shaft seal

Alcohol discharge flange

Alcohol pump casing

Alcohol intake

Turbine casing

Over-speed device

Ball bearings

Leakage line

Alcohol pump impeller

Turbine exhaust manifold

FIGURE 8-7. V-2 turbopump assembly.

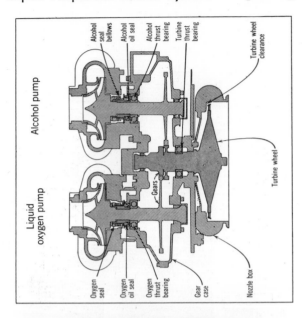

FIGURE 8–8. Developmental turbopump assembly with geared turbine drive, centrifugal propellant pumps, and oil pump for gear case lubrication for use with liquid oxygen and alcohol. Section through the assembly shows location of principal parts. The steel alloy turbine wheel (lower left) and the disassembled oxidizer pump (lower right) show typical detail construction. The pump components from left to right are: the pump case, aluminum impeller, seal ring assembly, cover plate shaft assembly with gear; in foreground is the neck heater assembly. (Courtesy General Electric Company.)

Classification and Description. For rocket applications *impulse turbines* are used almost exclusively, primarily because they are simpler and weigh less per unit horsepower than other turbine types in the range of 75 to 2000 horsepower with high pressure ratios. A single stage impulse turbine is shown in Figure 8–8.

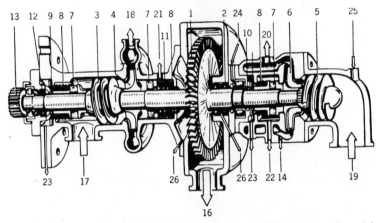

FIGURE 8–9.   Turbopump for German Walter 109-509 rocket unit.   (1) Turbine wheel, (2) carbon seal rings, (3) oxidizer booster pump impeller, (4) oxidizer pump impeller, (5) fuel booster pump impeller, (6) fuel pump impeller, (7) carbon face seal, (8) seal spring, (9) synthetic rubber membrane, (10) felt seal ring, (11) metal bellows, (12) oil seal plate, (13) starter drive spur gear, (14) fuel discharge pressure tap, (15) steam inlet (not shown), (16) steam outlet, (17) oxidizer suction flange, (18) oxidizer discharge flange, (19) fuel suction flange, (20) fuel discharge flange, (21) oxidizer leakage return to tank, (22) fuel leakage return to tank, (23) leakage drain, (24) grease passage, (25) fuel drain from control unit, (26) steam leakage drain.

Several variations of impulse turbines are used for driving rocket feed systems. They include the *velocity stage turbine,* often called *Curtis type turbine,* which is used on the German V-2 rocket. A cross section of this turbopump is shown in Figure 8–7. The disassembled turbine is shown in Figure 8–11, and its performance and design data are listed in Table 8–1. The enthalpy of the working fluid is converted into kinetic energy within the turbine nozzles. High velocity gases are delivered to the rotating blades, and blade rotation takes place as a result of

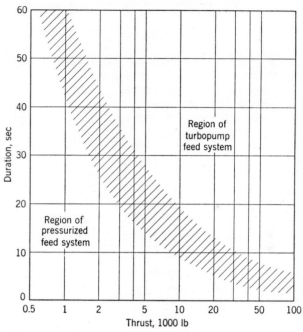

FIGURE 8–10. Durations and thrusts for which pressurized or turbopump feed system will give minimum propulsion system weight.

TABLE 8–1.   PERFORMANCE AND DESIGN DATA

V-2 TURBOPUMP

Weight of assembly	331 lb
Turbine	
Power output	465 hp
Gas consumption	4.7 lb/sec
Gas inlet pressure	375 psia
Gas inlet temperature	725°F
Gas outlet pressure	25 psia
Number of nozzles	16
Turbine type	Curtis stage
Shaft speed	3800 rpm
Mean blade diameter	17.6 in.
Gas type	Reaction products of concentrated 80 per cent hydrogen peroxide

TABLE 8-1. PERFORMANCE AND DESIGN DATA (*Continued*)

V-2 TURBOPUMP

Fuel Pump

Liquid	75 per cent alcohol with 25 per cent water
Density	54 lb/ft^3 at 60°F
Flow	123.5 lb/sec
Discharge pressure	310 psi
Suction pressure	15 psi
Power input	270 hp
Shaft speed	3800 rpm
Impeller diameter	12.6 in.
Number of impeller vanes	7

Oxidizer Pump

Liquid	Liquid oxygen
Density	71.2 lb/ft^3 at −298°F
Flow	152.5 lb/sec
Discharge pressure	250 psi
Suction pressure	30 psi
Power input	190 hp
Shaft speed	3800 rpm
Impeller diameter	10.3 in.
Number of impeller vanes	7

Materials

Part	Tensile Strength	Composition
All castings, turbine and pump casings, pump impellers	28,500 psi	Aluminum alloy 10–13 per cent Si 0.2–0.5 Mg 0.3–0.7 Mn
Turbine disk forging	25,500 psi	Aluminum alloy 2.0–2.5 per cent Mg 1.0–2.0 Mn 0.0–0.2 Sb
Turbine blades	35,500 psi	Aluminum alloy 0.5–1.5 per cent Mg 0.5–1.5 Si 0.3–1.3 Mn
Shafts, bolts	90,000 psi	Steel 0.45 per cent C Less than 0.10 P & S
Turbine nozzle block	31,300 psi	Gray cast iron
Oxygen pump bearings		Lead bronze 18–26 per cent Pb 0.3 Sb 0.3 Sn Remainder Cu

the impulse imparted by the momentum of the fluid stream of high kinetic energy to the rotating blades which are mounted on the turbine disk. The Curtis turbine has a stationary set of blades, which changes the flow direction after the gas leaves the first set of rotating blades, and a subsequent second set of rotating

FIGURE 8–11. German V-2 turbine. (North American Aviation Photograph.)

blades in which the working fluid gives up further energy to the turbine wheel. In the V-2 both sets of rotating blades are mounted on the same turbine disk, as shown in Figures 8–7 and 8–11.

The turbine exhaust gases pass through a *De Laval nozzle* at the exit of the exhaust pipe (see Figures 8–25 and 8–27). The high turbine outlet pressure gives critical flow conditions at the venturi throat and thereby assures a constant turbine outlet pressure and a constant turbine power, which will not vary with altitude.

The V-2 rocket turbine disk, the blades, and the housing are constructed of aluminum alloy, which is permissible with the low gas temperatures. Only the nozzles, the inlet manifold, the shaft, and a few small parts are made of ferrous material.

Another type of rocket impulse turbine is the *re-entry turbine,* which was used on the *German 109–509 rocket propulsion system* in the German Me 163 rocket fighter plane. This unit is described in Figure 8–9 and in Table 8–2. The nozzles are not uniformly

TABLE 8–2. WALTER 109–509A ROCKET ENGINE

Weight of assembly	68.4 lb
Turbine	
Power output	90 hp
Gas consumption	0.84–0.93 lb/sec
Gas inlet pressure	398 psi
Gas inlet temperature	725°–825°F
Number of nozzles	1
Turbine type	Re-entry type, single row wheel
Shaft speed (max.)	16,500 rpm
Mean blade diameter	7⅛ in.
Number of blades	78
Fuel Pump	
Liquid	"C Stoff" $\begin{cases} 57 \text{ per cent methanol} \\ 30 \text{ per cent } N_2H_4 \cdot H_2O \\ 13 \text{ per cent water} \end{cases}$
Density at room temperature	57.4 lb/ft³
Flow (max.)	4.94 lb/sec
Discharge pressure (max.)	540 psi
Shaft speed (max.)	16,500 rpm
Number of impeller vanes	8
Impeller diameter	3.87 in.
Oxidizer Pump	
Fluid	$\begin{cases} 80 \text{ per cent hydrogen peroxide} \\ 20 \text{ per cent water} \end{cases}$
Density	84.3 lb/ft³
Flow (max.)	16.46 lb/sec
Discharge pressure (max.)	569 psia
Shaft speed (max.)	16,500 rpm
Number of impeller vanes	8
Impeller diameter	3.27 in.

distributed along the circumference of the turbine casing, and the gases are admitted only along certain parts of the periphery.

After flowing through the moving blades, the steam is collected in a passage and directed to re-enter the same moving blades at other parts of the periphery, thereby giving up further energy to the shaft. This turbine is interesting because it operates over a wide range of load and speed conditions, for a thrust variation from 440 to 3700 pounds. Although the turbine housing is constructed of an aluminum alloy, the disk, shaft, and blades are of stainless steel. The inlet gas temperature (750° F) of this unit is also low, if compared to commercial and aircraft gas turbines.

The gas used for driving these two German turbines was the decomposition products of concentrated hydrogen peroxide, which consist of superheated water vapor and hot gaseous oxygen.

Turbine Performance and Design Considerations. The power supplied by the turbine is proportional to the enthalpy drop of the working fluid and the turbine efficiency.

$$P_T = \eta_T \dot{w} \, \Delta h \tag{8-4}$$

From equations 3–1 and 3–6, this is

$$P_T = \eta_T \dot{w} c_p T_1 \left[1 - \left(\frac{p_2}{p_1} \right)^{(k-1)/k} \right] \tag{8-5}$$

The power delivered by the turbine P_T is proportional to the turbine efficiency η_T, the flow through the turbine $\dot{w}$ (which usually is also the gas generator flow), and the available enthalpy drop per unit of flow Δh. The units in the equation above have to be consistent (1 Btu = 778 ft-lb). This enthalpy is a function of the specific heat c_p, the nozzle inlet temperature T_1, the pressure ratio across the turbine, and the ratio of the specific heats of the turbine gases. The power delivered by the turbine P_T has to be equal to the power required by the propellant pumps, the auxiliaries mounted on the turbopump (such as hydraulic pumps, electric generators, tachometers, etc.), and power losses in bearings, gears, seals, and wear rings. Usually these losses are small and can be neglected. The effect of the turbine gas flow on the specific impulse of the rocket engine system is discussed in Section 7 of this chapter.

The rocket designer is interested in obtaining a high turbine efficiency, in order to reduce the flow of the turbine working fluid, raise the overall effective specific impulse, and therefore reduce the propellant weight required for driving the turbine.

The *turbine efficiency* of impulse turbines is an optimum for a certain ratio of the gas velocity issuing from the turbine nozzle to the blade velocity, as shown in Figure 8–12. The turbine nozzle exit velocity can be determined from equation 3–14, and the blade

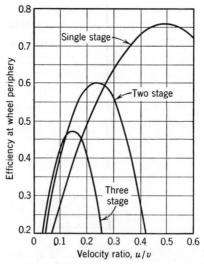

FIGURE 8–12. Impulse turbine efficiency with buckets having equal inlet and exit angles (nozzle angle = 17 degrees). (*Reference:* A. Stodola, *Steam and Gas Turbines,* McGraw-Hill Book Co., Inc., 1927.)

velocity is the product of the mean blade radius and the shaft speed. Existing single stage rocket turbines operate at efficiencies of 20 to 40 per cent at velocity ratios of 0.07 to 0.15, as shown in Figure 8–12.

This low efficiency in most rocket turbines is dictated by centrifugal *pump design considerations,* which *limit the shaft speed* for turbopumps in which the pump and turbine are mounted on a common shaft, as discussed in the next section. A low shaft speed together with minimum weight requirements, which prohibit a very large turbine wheel diameter, give a low blade speed, which in turn reduces the efficiency according to Figure 8–12.

A multiple stage impulse turbine (Curtis type) will often permit a higher turbine efficiency at the expense of increased turbine weight and design complications, but at the benefit of a reduction in the turbine gas requirements.

An increase in the enthalpy drop of the turbine gas by increasing the turbine inlet pressure or temperature or by using superior gas generator propellants will give a higher turbine nozzle exit velocity, but the gain in power output will be small, since the turbine efficiency will decrease and the design will usually become more complex. Therefore little is to be gained in existing rocket turbines by increasing the turbine inlet temperature; on the contrary, low gas temperatures (750° F) may permit an aluminum turbine design with an appreciable weight saving and a reduction of the distortion, warping, and rubbing of parts due to severe temperature shock.

The advantage of increased turbine efficiency (less gas generator propellant requirement) can be realized only if the turbopump design will allow high blade speeds, such as by gearing the turbine to the pumpshaft or by using pumps which permit high shaft speeds. See Figure 8–6.

The *peripheral speed* of turbine blades is limited by material strength considerations at elevated temperatures. Some alloy steel turbines have reached blade speeds above 1300 feet per second at temperatures above 1600° F. Aluminum turbine wheels have been operated satisfactorily at a tip speed of over 500 feet per second at 750° F and up to 1200 feet per second at room temperature. Because the total number of cycles is relatively small, the designer may neglect creep and fatigue considerations in many instances and permit the inlet temperatures and blade speeds to exceed the values established for conventional, long duration turbines.

There is *no warm-up time* allowed in rocket turbines. The sudden admission of hot gases at full flow causes severe shock and thermal distortion, and increases the chances for rubbing between metal parts.

Weight is at a premium in all flying installations, and the feed system is selected to have a minimum combined weight of turbines, pumps, gas generator valves, and gas generator propellants. In short duration rocket units the total amount of gas turbine propellant carried is usually small, and it is sometimes more profitable, from a weight standpoint, to make the turbine installation small and light at the expense of poorer turbine efficiency, which increases the amount of required gas-generating propellants.

The design of rocket turbines is closely related to that of the pumps. Very often the turbine and several pumps are on the same shaft and use the same bearings. (See Figures 8–7 and 8–9.) The design is complicated by the fact that many of the rocket propellants present handling difficulties. In the V–2, for instance, extremely cold liquid oxygen is fed through one of the pumps. The design must provide not only for heat insulation between the hot turbine and the liquid oxygen, but also for seals to prevent any propellants from entering the turbine casings.

The *vibration* problems of a rocket turbine are more complicated than those of ordinary gas turbines because of the proximity of a very potent vibration source, namely, the rocket thrust chamber. This requires that the critical speed of the turbine and pump assembly be not only different from the operating speed, but also at a low point of the vibration amplitude-frequency spectrum of the rocket thrust chamber.

Pumps

Classification and Description. Of the numerous types of pumps available, the *centrifugal pump* is generally considered the most suitable for pumping propellant in large rocket units, since, for the large flows and high pressure involved, it is efficient as well as economical in terms of weight and space requirement. For small flows, such as are required for units of less than 5000-pound thrust, other types of pumps may prove advantageous. Piston, vane, gear, wobble plate pumps, and other positive displacement pumps are in this category.

Piston pumps and *gear pumps* are particularly suitable for high viscosity propellants at low flow and high discharge pressures. Liquid oxygen and other liquefied gases should be pumped only in centrifugal propellant pumps, unless special design provisions are made to prevent the liquefied gas from being trapped in an enclosed pump space. Almost every type of positive displacement pump not only pressurizes the fluid but also meters the flow because a predetermined quantity of fluid is displaced with each revolution of the pump. Flow controls for units using such pumps are therefore relatively simple.

Figure 8–13 is a schematic drawing of a centrifugal pump. Fluid entering the *impeller*, which is essentially a wheel with vanes rotating within a *casing*, is accelerated within the impeller channels and leaves the impeller periphery with a high velocity to enter the *volute*, or collector, and thereafter the *diffuser*, where

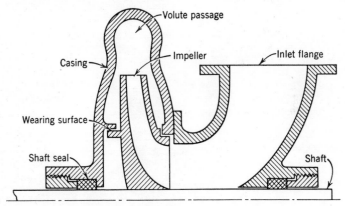

FIGURE 8–13. Schematic presentation of a typical centrifugal pump.

conversion from kinetic energy (velocity) to potential energy (pressure) takes place. Internal leakage, or circulation between the high pressure (discharge) side to the low pressure (suction) side, is held to a minimum by maintaining close clearances between the rotating and stationary parts at the *wearing surfaces*. External leakage along the shaft is prevented by the use of a *stuffing box* or *shaft seal*. Single stage pumps (one impeller only) are sometimes limited in the pressure rise they can impart to the liquid, and multiple stage pumps are therefore needed for high pressure rises.

Figure 8–9 shows the turbopump of the German 109–509 propulsion system. The pump characteristics are included in Table 8–2. An interesting feature of its pump design is the application of a spiral type *booster pump* or *inducer*, which increases the pressure at the inlet to the centrifugal impeller (see Figure 8–9). The centrifugal pumps of the German V-2 rocket are shown in

Figures 8–7, 8–14, and 8–15, and their performance data are given in Table 8–1.

There is a free passage of flow through the pump at all times, and no positive means for shut-off are provided. The pump characteristics, that is, the pressure rise, flow, and efficiency, are func-

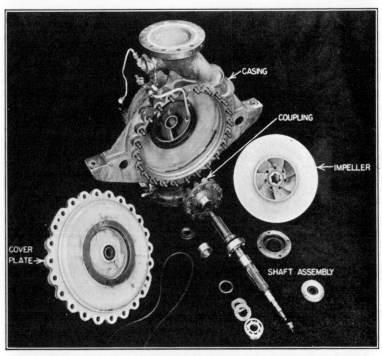

FIGURE 8–14. V-2 fuel pump. (North American Aviation Photograph.)

tions of the pump speed, the impeller, the vane shape, and the casing configuration. Figure 8–16 shows a typical set of curves for the centrifugal pumps of the German V-2 rocket.

When pumping liquefied gases, such as liquid oxygen, special provisions have to be made to insulate the pump passages carefully so that little heat will be absorbed from the atmosphere or from the bearings. In the V-2 rocket even the oxygen pump shaft is insulated from the fuel pump shaft by means of an insulated coupling. Pictures of the oxygen pump, when empty and filled on a test stand, are shown in Figures 8–17 and 8–18. Atmospheric moisture forms ice on the cold pump casing. In one design (Figure 8–8) an electric heater is employed on one side of the liquid oxygen pump to prevent freezing of oil in the gear case.

Pump Parameters. The basic analysis and design of conventional pumps are applied also to rocket propellant pumps. This

FIGURE 8–15. V-2 oxygen pump. (North American Aviation Photograph.)

section outlines primarily some of the important parameters and features which have to be considered in rocket propellant pumps. For a detailed performance and design analysis, reference should be made to textbooks on the subject (see references 6.301 and 6.302).

The *required pump flow* is established by the rocket design for a given thrust, effective exhaust velocity, propellant densities, and mixture ratio. In addition to the flow required by the thrust

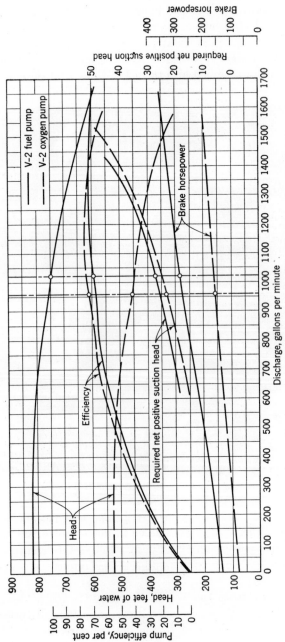

FIGURE 8–16. Water test performance curves of V-2 centrifugal pumps.

FIGURES 8–17 and 8–18. Liquid oxygen pump on test when filled and empty. One-half-in. frost formation is due to condensation of moisture. (Courtesy North American Aviation, Inc.)

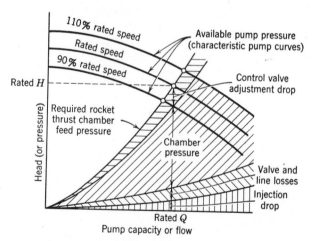

FIGURE 8–19. Available and required feed pressure versus propellant flow for a turbopump system.

chamber, the propellant consumption of the gas generator and auxiliaries has to be considered in determining the pump flows (see Section 6). The *pump discharge pressure* is determined from the chamber pressure and the hydraulic losses in valves, lines, cooling jacket, and injectors. Figure 8–19 shows the variation of the required and the available pump pressure with flow. In order to obtain the rated flow at the rated pressure, an additional adjustable pressure drop for a control valve or orifice is usually included which permits an adjustment or change in the required feed pressure. A regulation of the pump speed will reduce the required adjustable pressure drop. This adjustment of head * and flow is necessary to allow for hydraulic and performance tolerances on pumps, valves, injectors, etc.

In addition to the basic parameters of *speed, discharge flow,* and *pump head,** several other derived quantities and experimental coefficients are important.

It is possible to predict the pump performance at various speeds if the performance is known at any given speed. Since the fluid velocity in a given pump is proportional to the pump speed, the flow quantity or discharge will also be proportional to the speed and the head will be proportional to the square of the speed. This gives the following relations:

$$Q \text{ (flow)} \sim N \text{ (rpm)}$$

$$H \text{ (pump head)} \sim N^2 \qquad (8\text{–}6)$$

$$P_P \text{ (pump power)} \sim N^3$$

From these relations it is possible to derive a parameter called the *specific speed.*

$$N_s = \frac{21.2N\sqrt{Q_e}}{(\Delta H)_e^{3/4}} \qquad (8\text{–}7)$$

The symbols in the equations above are defined in the listing at the end of this chapter. For each range of specific speed, a

---

* By pump head (often called total dynamic head) is always meant the difference between pump discharge and pump suction head. Its units are feet. The conversion from pounds per square inch into feet of head is: (X) psi $= 144(X)/$density (lb/ft³).

certain shape and impeller geometry has proved most efficient, as shown in Table 8–3.

TABLE 8–3. PUMP TYPES

Impeller Type	Radial	Francis	Mixed Flow	Axial
Basic shape	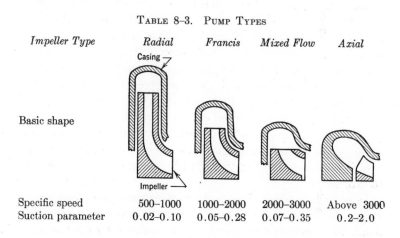			
Specific speed	500–1000	1000–2000	2000–3000	Above 3000
Suction parameter	0.02–0.10	0.05–0.28	0.07–0.35	0.2–2.0

The *impeller tip speed* in centrifugal pumps is limited by design and strength considerations to 200 to 1000 feet per second. For cast impellers this limiting value is lower than for machined and welded impellers. This maximum impeller tip speed determines the maximum head that can be obtained from a single stage. The impeller vane tip speed is the product of the shaft speed, expressed in radians per second, and the impeller radius and is related to the pump head by

$$u = \psi \sqrt{2g\,\Delta H} \qquad (8\text{–}8)$$

where ψ has values between 0.90 and 1.10 for different designs. For many pumps, $\psi = 1.0$.

The flow quantity defines the impeller inlet and outlet areas according to the equation of continuity. The diameters obtained from this equation should be in the proportion indicated by the diagrams for a given specific speed in Table 8–3. The continuity equation is

$$Q = A_1 v_1 = A_2 v_2 \qquad (8\text{–}9)$$

where the subscripts refer to the impeller inlet and outlet sections, all areas being measured normal to their respective flow velocity.

The inlet velocity ranges usually between 10 to 20 feet per second and the outlet velocity between 10 and 50 feet per second.

The pump performance is limited by *cavitation,* a phenomenon which occurs when the static pressure at any point in a fluid flow passage becomes less than the fluid vapor pressure. The formation of vapor bubbles causes cavitation. These bubbles collapse when they reach a region of high pressure, that is, when the static pressure in the fluid is above the vapor pressure. In centrifugal pumps cavitation is most likely to occur in the pump impeller inlet because this is the point at which the lowest absolute pressure is encountered. The excessive formation of vapor causes the pump discharge to fluctuate and makes the combustion erratic and dangerous; this may lead to severe thrust chamber vibrations or even to explosions.

In order to avoid cavitation the *suction head* above vapor pressure *required* by the pump $(H_s)_R$ must always be *less* than the *available* or *net positive suction head* furnished by the line up to the pump $(H_s)_A$; that is $(H_s)_R \leq (H_s)_A$. The required suction head above vapor pressure can be determined from the pump suction or Thoma parameter and the suction specific speed

$$\sigma = \frac{(H_s)_R}{\Delta H} \tag{8-10}$$

$$S = \frac{N_s}{\sigma^{3/4}} \tag{8-11}$$

$$= \frac{21.2N\sqrt{Q_e}}{(H_s)_R^{3/4}} \tag{8-12}$$

The suction parameter σ depends on the quality of design and the specific speed, as shown in Table 8–3. The suction specific speed S is a constant between 5000 to 30,000. For pumps with poor suction characteristics it has values near 5000, for the best pump designs without cavitation it has values near 10,000 and 15,000, and for pumps with local cavitation it has values up to 30,000.

In equation 8–11 the required suction head $(H_s)_R$ is usually defined as the critcial suction head at which the developed pump discharge head has been diminished arbitrarily by 1 per cent in a pump test with increasing throttling in the suction side. Figure

8–20 shows the typical shape of the curves resulting from such a test.

The head that is available at the pump suction flange is called the *net positive suction head* or *available suction head above vapor pressure.* It is an absolute head value determined from the tank pressure (the absolute gas pressure in the tank above the liquid level), the elevation of the propellant level above the pump inlet, the friction losses in the line between tank and pump, and

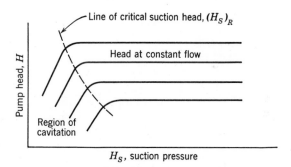

FIGURE 8–20. Typical variation of head loss with suction pressure for a cavitating pump. These experimental curves are usually obtained by running the pump and by gradually reducing the suction head with a valve.

the vapor pressure of the fluid. When the flying vehicle is undergoing accelerations, the head due to elevation must be corrected accordingly. These various heads are defined in Figure 8–21. The net positive suction head is the maximum head available for suppressing cavitation at the inlet to the pumps.

$$(H_s)_A = H_{tank} + H_{elevation} - H_{friction} - H_{vapor} \quad (8\text{–}13)$$

In order to avoid pump cavitation, $(H_s)_A$ has to be higher than $(H_s)_R$. If additional head is required by the pump, the propellant may have to be pressurized by external means, such as by the addition of another pump in series (called booster pump) or by gas pressurization of the propellant tanks. This latter method requires not only thicker tank walls, and therefore heavier tanks, but also a separate and often a complicated gas-pressurizing system. For example, the oxygen tank of the German V-2 was pressurized to 2.3 atmospheres, partly to avoid pump cavitation.

For a given value of $(H_s)_A$, propellants with high vapor pressure require correspondingly high tank pressures and heavier installations. For a given available suction head $(H_s)_A$ a pump with a low required suction pressure will usually permit designs with high shaft speeds, small diameter, and low weight. A small value

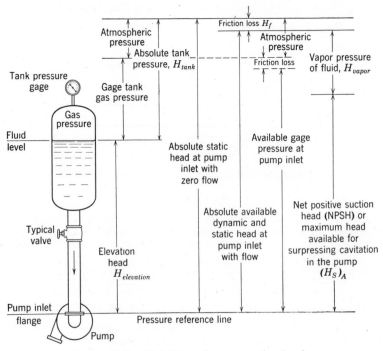

FIGURE 8–21. Definition of pump suction heads.

of $(H_s)_R$ is desirable because it may permit a reduction of the requirements for tank pressurization and therefore a lower installation weight. For a given head and flow requirement the value of $(H_s)_R$ will be small if the hydrodynamic pump design of the impeller and fluid passages is favorable (low value of σ) and if the shaft speed N is low. A very low shaft speed will, however, require a large diameter pump, which will be excessively heavy. The trend in selecting centrifugal pumps for rocket application has been to select the highest shaft speed which will give pumps with low values of $(H_s)_R$, will not require excessive tank pressurization or other design complications, and thereby will permit a relatively light weight pump design. This places a premium on pumps with good suction characteristics.

The maximum possible *efficiency* of a centrifugal pump depends on the specific speed and the flow capacity. The pump efficiency is reduced by the surface roughness of casing and impellers, by the power consumed by seals, bearings, and stuffing boxes, and by excessive bearing leakage and poor design.

The pump efficiency is defined as

$$\eta_P = \frac{\text{Fluid power}}{\text{Shaft power}} = \frac{\rho Q\ \Delta H}{550 P_P} \qquad (8\text{--}14)$$

It can readily be seen that the pump power when using propellants has to be multiplied by the density ratio if the required power for water tests is to be determined.

Example 8–3. Determine the shaft speed and basic impeller dimensions for a liquid oxygen pump which is to deliver 100 lb of propellant per sec at a discharge pressure of 300 psia. The oxygen tank is pressurized to 35 psia; the friction loss in the suction piping and the head due to acceleration are negligible. The initial tank level is 10 ft above the pump.

Solution. Since the density of liquid oxygen is 71.2 lb/ft^3 at its boiling point of $-298°$ F, the flow will be $100/71.2 = 1.405$ ft^3/sec. The vapor pressure of liquid oxygen at its boiling point is 1 atm $= 14.7$ psi $= 29.8$ ft. The head tank is $35 \times 144/71.2 = 71$ ft. The available suction head above vapor pressure is then $(H_s)_A = 71 + 10 - 0 - 29.8 = 51.2$ ft. The available suction head is $71 + 10 = 81$ ft. The discharge head is $300 \times 144/71.2 = 607$ ft. The pump head is then $607 - 81 = 526$ ft.

The required suction head will be taken as 80 per cent of the available suction head in order to provide a margin of safety for cavitation. From equation

$$\sigma = \frac{(H_s)_R}{\Delta H} = \frac{0.80 \times 51.2}{526} = 0.0779$$

For the pump design under consideration assume $S = 7000$. (This is a conservative value if experimental data are lacking.) From equation 8–11

$$N_s = S(\sigma)^{3/4} = 7000 \times (0.0779)^{0.75} = 1030$$

According to Table 8–3, the impeller shape will be of a Francis type. The shaft speed can be evaluated from the definition of the specific speed of equation 8–7,

$$N_s = \frac{21.2 N \sqrt{Q}}{(\Delta H)^{3/4}} = \frac{21.2 N \sqrt{1.405}}{(526)^{0.75}} = 1030$$

$$N = 4480 \text{ rpm} = 470 \text{ radians/sec}$$

The impeller diameter can be evaluated from the tip speed by equation 8–8,

$$u = \psi \sqrt{2g \, \Delta H} = 1.0 \sqrt{2 \times 32.2 \times 526} = 184 \text{ ft/sec}$$

$$D_2 = \frac{184 \times 2}{470} = 0.783 \text{ ft} = 9.42 \text{ in.}$$

The impeller inlet diameter can be found from equation 8–9 by assuming an inlet velocity of $v_1 = 15$ ft/sec and a shaft cross section of $1\frac{1}{2}$ sq in.

$$A_1 = \frac{Q}{v_1} = \frac{1.405}{15} = 0.0938 \text{ ft}^2 = 13.5 \text{ in.}^2$$

$$\frac{\pi}{4} D_1^2 = 13.5 + 1.5$$

$$D_1 = 4.37 \text{ in.}$$

Rocket Application of Pumps. In flying vehicles *light weight* is of great importance. A pump which is inefficient, but appreciably lighter than an efficient design, may sometimes be preferred if the necessary increase in weight of the turbine, gas generator, and gas generator propellant is less than the weight saving in the pump.

Since many of the propellants are dangerous to handle, special provision has to be made to prevent any leakage through the shaft seals or stuffing box. With spontaneously ignitable propellants a leakage will lead to fires in the pump compartment and may cause explosion hazards. Multiple seals are often used with a drainage provision that safely disposes of any propellants which flow past the first seal by piping them away as shown in Figure 8–9. The sealing of corrosive propellants puts very severe requirements on the sealing materials and design.

Rocket pumps usually start without priming, but they rely on gravity to fill the pumps. In commercial pump installation care is often taken to fill or prime the pump with fluid prior to starting.

As in turbines and in all other high speed rotating machinery, due consideration has to be given to critical speed, axial and radial bearing loads, and stresses in rotating parts. Since rocket pumps are usually not rigidly mounted on heavy foundations, but are supported elastically, and since a powerful vibration source, namely the thrust chamber, is often adjacent to or near the pump, vibrations may have serious effects, such as shaft failures or local rubbing of rotating and stationary parts.

The flight program of the flying vehicle will determine the flight accelerations, which in turn affect the suction head. Particularly in vehicles that undergo severe accelerations, such as antiaircraft missiles and fighter planes, special provisions have to be made to maintain the minimum required pump suction head, such as the addition of ejectors to take vapor and air bubbles out of the pump suction line.

Gas Generators

The power necessary to drive the turbine is usually obtained from the gas generator, which generates gases by a chemical reaction of propellants similar to those in thrust chambers. The generated gases have to be relatively cool compared to thrust chamber reaction gases, because excessive temperatures will cause a failure of the turbine buckets, the turbine nozzles, and sometimes the turbine wheel. The propellants used for this purpose are intentionally mixed in such proportions that the resultant gas temperature will be relatively low.

There are many possible methods for generating gases. The following more common types are discussed here: (1) *Gas-pressurized generator,* having own propellant supply. (2) *Feed system pressurized generator,* using same propellants as rocket from same feed system, but with separate combustion chamber. (3) *Gas bleeding* directly from main combustion chamber. (4) *Solid propellant charges* burning at a slow rate and giving off gases. (5) *High pressure stored gas.*

1. *Gas-pressurized generator systems* are very similar to conventional gas-pressurized rocket systems, with the exception of the nozzle. Instead of a rocket thrust chamber nozzle which will give reaction, the gases are fed in a manifold or pipe to the turbine and are there expanded in the turbine nozzles. Such a gas-pressurized generator contains high pressure propellant tanks, a high pressure gas supply, a pressure regulator, valves, and a reaction chamber. This generator type is entirely self-starting and does not require special starting provisions.

This type of system, which was used on the German V-2, is shown in Figure 8–22. The elliptical hydrogen peroxide tank is located at the top, the gas generator decomposition chamber is at the lower center, and the catalyst tank containing liquid sodium

FIGURE 8–22. V-2 gas generator. The elliptical hydrogen peroxide tank is on top, and the liquid catalyst tank is next to the generator chamber in lower left. Controls, gages, and valves are mounted directly to the supporting structure. (North American Aviation Photograph.)

permanganate is at the lower right. A flow circuit for this system
is shown in the upper right of Figure 8–27. The unit, when installed on the propulsion system, can be seen in Figure 2–3.

Gas-pressurized generators using the following propellants have
been used: (a) hydrogen peroxide and catalyst; (b) nitric acid,

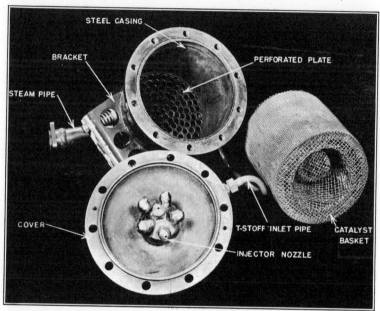

FIGURE 8–23. Gas generator decomposition chamber of German Walter 109-
509 rocket unit. Chamber must be filled with catalyst-impregnated stones.

aniline, and water (water used to lower temperature); (c) liquid
oxygen, alcohol, and water.

2. *Feed system pressurized gas generators* use the same propellants and the same feed system as the main rocket thrust chamber.
A small portion (about 2 per cent) of the total propellant is bled
off at the discharge of the main propellant pumps. Such a scheme
is actually used on rocket fighter power plants, such as the German 109–509 used in the Me 163 plane. The hydrogen peroxide
decomposition chamber for the Me 163 unit is shown in Figures
8–23 and 2–4. It is filled with catalyst-impregnated stones, which
are not shown in these pictures. Another solid catalyst generator

using hydrogen peroxide is shown in the flow diagram of Figure 8–6.

A special *starting device* is needed for feed system gas generators. It may be a means to rotate the turbine, such as an electric starter motor, or a small gas-pressurized auxiliary propellant supply which starts to furnish reactants to the generator, or a small charge of compressed air which starts the rotation of the turbine. The gas generator system using the main propellants for the feed system is lighter than the gas-pressurized self-contained generator for reasonably long durations (above approximately one minute) and for motor thrusts above approximately 20,000 pounds. Special provisions have to be made to control the flow of propellant to the turbine independently of the pump discharge characteristics.

3. *Gas bleeding* takes hot gases from the main rocket combustion chamber for driving the turbine. Because turbine materials cannot withstand the extremely high temperatures of combustion gases (above 4000° F), it is necessary to cool these gases before admission into the turbine or into an uncooled turbine manifold. The gas generator is replaced by a cooling chamber in which hot gases are cooled by mixing them with controlled amounts of one of the propellants. This scheme is also known as a *bleed turbine* system.

4. *Solid propellant charges* used for generating turbine gases have a performance which is very different from that of solid propellants used in rocket units as given in Chapters 9, 10, and 11. While rocket propellants usually burn above 4000° F for durations of less than 45 seconds, gas generator propellant mixtures have to burn for several minutes at temperatures between 700° and 1800° F. The powder burning rates are therefore slow and measure between $\frac{1}{32}$ and $\frac{1}{8}$ inch per second of flame travel in the solid propellant mixture. This gas-generating system is simple and contains all the propellant and an igniter in a pressure vessel. It is, however, heavy and often more bulky than other types of gas-generating systems.

5. *High pressure gas* can and has been used for driving rocket turbines. This system design is essentially similar to the air supply system of a gas-pressurized propellant system and consists of a high pressure storage tank, valves, and a regulator. A saving

of gas requirements and weight can be achieved if the air can be heated prior to admission to the turbine.

Rocket units operating in vehicles which also have turbojets can obtain rocket turbine gases by bleeding from the turbojet.

Gas generators have been used for *other applications* besides supplying power to rocket feed systems. They have a use wherever there is a need for a large amount of power for a relatively short time, because they are simpler and lighter than conventional short duration power equipment. Typical applications are gas generators for driving torpedo turbines and gas generators for actuating airplane catapults. Some of the launching ramps used for the German V-1 pulse jet missile were powered by a hydrogen peroxide gas generator, which forced a piston over the length of the launching ramp.

5   Other Pressurizing Systems

A number of other schemes for pressurizing propellants have been proposed. One method proposes the use of jet pumps similar to a steam injector. A part of the propellant is evaporated in the thrust chamber cooling jacket and then forced into the jet pump, actuating the remainder of the propellant and forcing it into the rocket injector. This scheme has no moving parts but requires a separate starting device and is quite inefficient.

In aircraft installations, where rockets are used as a power boost to a conventional engine, it is practicable to take the power necessary for driving the propellant pumps directly from the main aircraft engine, eliminating the necessity for a turbine and gas generator. A rocket of this type is shown in Figure 8–24.

Another scheme uses a combustion chamber on a *rotating shaft*, which in turn is geared to the propellant pumps. A torque is obtained by inclining a pair of nozzles a few degrees to the shaft axis and displacing them from the shafts. Most of the rocket thrust acts then in an axial direction, except for a small component, which delivers the torque necessary for driving the pumps and auxiliaries. The principle is the same as that of a rotating lawn sprinkler. Several such units have been built in various countries but have been abandoned in favor of turbopump feed systems.

The use of a *separate internal combustion engine* instead of a gas turbine for furnishing power to the propellant pumps has been successful at low flight altitudes.

The *topping turbine* drive system has a low pressure ratio turbine built directly into the thrust chamber, so that most of the gases are used for power before they are fully burned in the chamber. In the *blast turbine* scheme, a turbine wheel (with

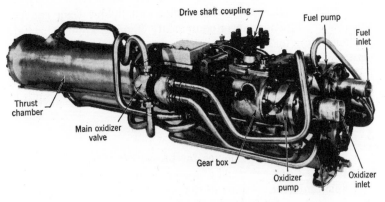

FIGURE 8–24. Patterned after an earlier German BMW rocket engine, the French-made SEPR-25 aircraft rocket operates on nitric acid and furaline. Its propellant pumps are mounted on a gear case and are driven through a jack shaft directly from the main aircraft engine. This rocket has a rated thrust of 3300 lb, a dry weight of 245 lb including accessories, a sea level specific impulse of 196 sec, a mixture ratio of 2.7, and a shaft speed of 5170 rpm. The unit is 60 in. long and 17 in. high. (Courtesy S.E.P.R., Paris.)

cooling provisions) is partly immersed in the jet blast of the thrust chamber nozzle exhaust gases.

6 Auxiliary Uses of Propellants

In a typical liquid rocket propulsion system, the propellant supply from the missile tanks is often used for other purposes in addition to producing thrust. These uses will, to some extent, affect the overall missile performance, but in general these effects will be small since the required propellant consumption is small when compared to that which is used directly for producing thrust. Liquid propellants have been used for one or more of the following, in addition to producing thrust.

Driving Turbopump Feed System

A small portion of the propellants is often burned in a separate gas generator chamber or bled from the thrust chamber and used to drive the turbopumps. This scheme has already been discussed in the previous section. Depending on the exact engine system, the required feed pressures, and the turbine efficiency, the gas flow to the turbine consumes approximately 1 to 5 per cent of the propellant flow to the thrust chamber. In order to prevent damage to the turbine materials, the gas leaving the gas generator must be at a lower temperature than that existing in the thrust chamber. This can be accomplished by utilizing a different mixture ratio for the gas generator. Often the low pressure turbine gas is exhausted through a low area ratio nozzle to produce a small amount of additional thrust.

Driving Auxiliary Power System

In some engines an auxiliary source of power may be obtained from the turbine drive. A typical system might include hydraulic pumps and/or an electric generator. In cases where the electric generator is driven directly by the main turbopump, additional flow of propellants to the main gas generator will be necessary to supply the power requirements for driving the electric generator in addition to the main propellant pumps.

Tank Pressurization

In some applications, a small amount of one or both of the propellants is utilized for the pressurization of the main propellant tanks. In a turbopump feed system it is still necessary to pressurize the tanks slightly (10 to 40 pounds per square inch) in order to prevent pump cavitation. By bleeding some of the propellant off at the high pressure pump discharge, vaporizing it in a heat exchanger, and piping it back to the tanks, the necessary pressurization can be achieved. This is done in the V-2 oxygen tank pressurizing system (see Section 8).

A typical schematic flow diagram illustrating these various propellant uses is shown in Figure 8–25. Figure 8–26 shows a propellant flow balance for this typical rocket engine.

The implication of these propellant uses for purposes other than production of thrust in a thrust chamber is threefold:

1. The extra propellant flow affects the overall performance in that the specific impulse of the rocket engine is usually slightly lower than that of the thrust chamber alone.

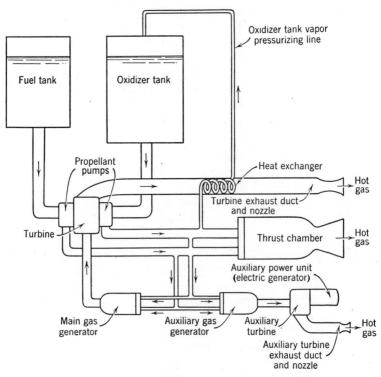

FIGURE 8-25. Simplified schematic diagram of several auxiliary uses of propellants in a typical rocket power plant. The valves and controls are not shown here.

2. The overall mixture ratio of the propellants supplied from the tanks is usually slightly different from the mixture ratio of the propellants flowing to the thrust chamber or the gas generator.
3. The propellant tank volumes must allow not only for the propellants consumed by the thrust chamber, but also for the propellants used for other purposes.

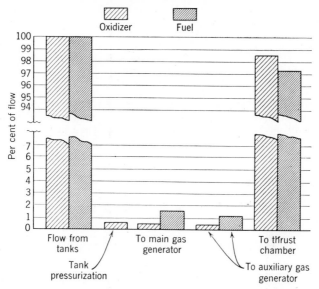

FIGURE 8–26. Typical propellant flow balance diagram.

7 Calculating Specific Impulse for a Complete Rocket Engine System

The simplified relations which follow give the basic method for determining the overall specific impulse, the total propellant flow, and the overall mixture ratio as a function of the corresponding component performance terms for the complete rocket engine system.   Let the subscripts oa, o, and f designate the overall engine system, the oxidizer, and the fuel, respectively.   Then

$$(I_s)_{oa} = \Sigma F / \Sigma \dot{w} \tag{8–15}$$

$$\dot{w}_{oa} = \Sigma \dot{w} \tag{8–16}$$

$$r_{oa} = \Sigma \dot{w}_o / \Sigma \dot{w}_f \tag{8–17}$$

These same equations should be used for determining the overall performance when more than one rocket engine is contained in a vehicle propulsion system.

Example 8–4. For the engine system shown in Figure 8–25, determine a set of equations which will express (1) the overall engine performance, and

(2) the overall mixture ratios of the propellant flows from the tanks. Let the following subscripts be used:

tc thrust chamber
gg gas generator
ap auxiliary power
tp tank pressurization

Solution. Only the oxidizer tank is pressurized by vaporized propellant. Although this pressurizing propellant must be considered in determining the overall mixture ratio, it should not be considered in determining the overall specific impulse since it stays with the vehicle and is not exhausted overboard.

$$(I_s)_{oa} = \frac{F_{tc} + F_{gg} + F_{ap}}{\dot{w}_{tc} + \dot{w}_{gg} + \dot{w}_{ap}} \tag{8-18}$$

$$r_{oa} = \frac{(\dot{w}_o)_{tc} + (\dot{w}_o)_{gg} + (\dot{w}_o)_{ap} + (\dot{w}_o)_{tp}}{(\dot{w}_f)_{tc} + (\dot{w}_f)_{gg} + (\dot{w}_f)_{ap}} \tag{8-19}$$

If the auxiliary power is variable during flight, a variation in specific impulse and mixture ratio will occur as the power demand changes. This variation is in addition to the normal variation due to altitude or flight acceleration.

It is interesting to note that the thrust produced by the exhaust gases from the gas generator (when exhausted through a supersonic nozzle) and auxiliary power system increases materially with altitude (by a factor of 1 to 3) while that produced by the thrust chamber improves by only 10 to 20 per cent. This difference in thrust increase is directly related to the difference in area ratios and pressure ratios of the thrust chamber nozzle and of the turbine exhaust gas nozzle, the latter usually being very small. Thus the performance penalty for using propellants to drive turbines usually decreases with increasing altitude.

8 Controls

All liquid propellant rockets have controls to accomplish some or all of the following tasks.

1. Start rocket operation.
2. Shut down rocket operation.
3. Restart.
4. Maintain programed operation (predetermined constant or varied thrust, preset propellant mixture ratio or flow) by calibration of feed system, or by automatic controls.

5. Make emergency shutdown when safety device senses a malfunction or a critical condition.
6. Fill with propellants.
7. Drain excess propellant after operation.
8. Check out proper functioning of critical components without actual operation.

In the earlier sections of this chapter several typical systems which incorporated some of these elements above were described. The *complexity* of these elements and the complexity of the systems depend very much on the nature of the mission of the rocket. In general, rockets which are used only once (single shot devices), which are filled with propellants at the factory, and which have to operate over a narrow range of environmental conditions tend to be simpler than rockets which are intended for repeated use, for applications where satisfactory operation must be demonstrated prior to use, and for manned vehicles. Because of the nature of the liquid propellants, most of the control functions are achieved by valves, regulators, and flow controls. These are discussed further in the next few sections of this chapter.

In the *starting* and *stopping* process of a rocket engine, it is possible for the mixture ratio to vary considerably from the rated design mixture ratio value since the flow increases in a very short time from zero to rated propellant flow value. During this transition period it is possible for the rocket engine to pass through regions of chamber pressure and mixture ratio, which can permit combustion instability. The starting and stopping of a rocket engine is very critical in timing, valve sequencing, and transient characteristics. A good control system must be designed to avoid undesirable transient operation.

A close *control* of the *flow* of propellant, of the *pressure,* and of the *mixture ratio* is necessary to obtain reliable and repeatable rocket performance. Fortunately, most rocket units operate with a constant propellant consumption and a constant mixture ratio, which simplifies the operating control problem.

Stable operation of a liquid propellant rocket can be accomplished without automatic control devices because the liquid flow system in general tends to be inherently stable. This means that the system reacts to any disturbance in the flow of propellant (a sudden flow increase or decrease) in such a manner as to reduce the effect of the disturbance. The system therefore usually has a natural tendency to control itself. However, in some cases the natural resonances of the system and its components can have frequency values which tend to destabilize the system.

The principles used in calibrating and adjusting a liquid propellant rocket engine to the desired steady state operating condition (proper thrust, mixture ratio, etc.) are given in Section 10 of this chapter. *Safety controls* are intended to protect personnel and equipment in case of malfunction. For example, the control system is usually so designed that a failure of the electrical power supply to the rocket will cause a non-hazardous shutdown (all electrical valves automatically return to their normal position) and no explosion of unreacted propellant can occur. Another example is an electrical interlock device, which prevents the opening of the main propellant valves until the igniter has functioned properly.

Check-out controls permit a simulation of the operation of critical control components without actual operation of the rocket unit. For example, many rockets have provisions for permitting actuation of the principal valves without having propellant or pressure in the system.

The *flow control system of the V-2 propulsion engine* is shown schematically in Figure 8–27. The sequence of operation of this system illustrates the use of each particular valve. The sequence is outlined here.

Operation Sequence of V-2 Propulsion Unit

(a) *Preparation Prior to Launching*

1. Thorough inspection and functional checking of all valves and switches.
2. Tanking of propellant in correct amounts in the following order: alcohol, liquid oxygen, hydrogen peroxide, permanganate, and air at 200 atmospheres.
3. Momentary opening of preliminary fuel valve and pilot control valve (29) and (26) to permit filling of cooling jacket, fuel pump, and lines.
4. Adjustment of air pressure reducer (4) to desired value. (Regulated operating pressure is 30.8 atmospheres.)

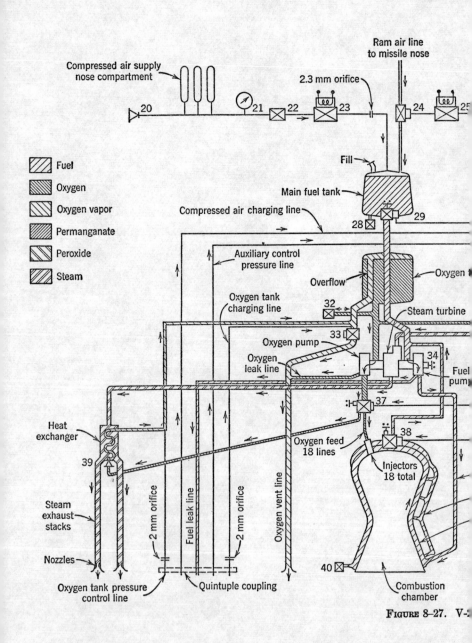

Compressed air supply
nose compartment

Ram air line
to missile nose

2.3 mm orifice

20 21 22 23 24 25

Fuel
Oxygen
Oxygen vapor
Permanganate
Peroxide
Steam

Fill

Main fuel tank

Compressed air charging line

28 29

Auxiliary control
pressure line

Overflow

Oxygen

Oxygen tank
charging line

32

Steam turbine

33

Oxygen pump

Oxygen
leak line

34 Fuel
pump

37

Heat
exchanger

38

39

Oxygen feed
18 lines

Injectors
18 total

Steam
exhaust
stacks

2 mm orifice

Fuel leak line

2 mm orifice

Oxygen vent line

Nozzles

40

Oxygen tank pressure
control line

Quintuple coupling

Combustion
chamber

FIGURE 8–27. V–2

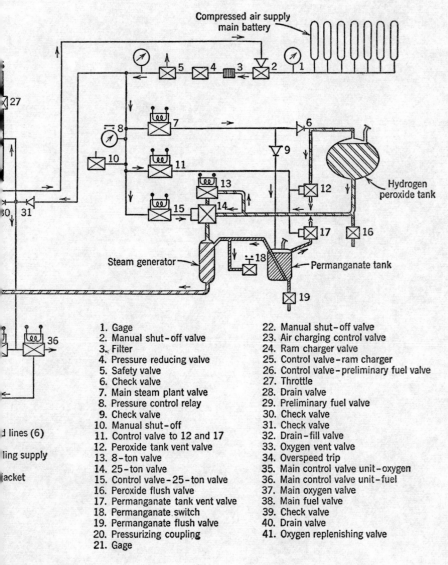

Compressed air supply
main battery

Hydrogen
peroxide tank

Steam generator

Permanganate tank

1. Gage
2. Manual shut-off valve
3. Filter
4. Pressure reducing valve
5. Safety valve
6. Check valve
7. Main steam plant valve
8. Pressure control relay
9. Check valve
10. Manual shut-off
11. Control valve to 12 and 17
12. Peroxide tank vent valve
13. 8-ton valve
14. 25-ton valve
15. Control valve-25-ton valve
16. Peroxide flush valve
17. Permanganate tank vent valve
18. Permanganate switch
19. Permanganate flush valve
20. Pressurizing coupling
21. Gage

22. Manual shut-off valve
23. Air charging control valve
24. Ram charger valve
25. Control valve-ram charger
26. Control valve-preliminary fuel valve
27. Throttle
28. Drain valve
29. Preliminary fuel valve
30. Check valve
31. Check valve
32. Drain-fill valve
33. Oxygen vent valve
34. Overspeed trip
35. Main control valve unit-oxygen
36. Main control valve unit-fuel
37. Main oxygen valve
38. Main fuel valve
39. Check valve
40. Drain valve
41. Oxygen replenishing valve

d lines (6)

ling supply

acket

ant flow diagram.

5. Auxiliary control air pressure from ground is disconnected (used for tests only).

6. Oxygen tank pressurized from ground by air to approximately 1.1 to 1.5 atmospheres. This is necessary to prevent cavitation in oxygen pump at the start.

7. Preliminary fuel valve (26 and 29) opens and admits fuel up to main fuel valve.

(b) *Preliminary Burning Stage*

1. The powder igniter is energized. The igniter consists of multiple powder charges mounted on a wheel which is pivoted inside the combustion chamber on a stick fastened to the launching platform. The whirling distributes the ignition flame evenly.

2. Main oxygen valve (37) opens partially by releasing control pressure air through the control valve (35), which is solenoid operated. Oxygen at reduced flow is admitted to the combustion chamber.

3. Main fuel valve (38) opens partially by releasing pressurized air through control valve (36). Fuel flows by gravity through partially opened propellant valve into thrust chamber, ignites, and burns with oxygen. If burning is satisfactory, the operator gives an electric signal for the main stage.

(c) *Main Burning Stage*

1. Air charging of oxygen tank from ground is stopped.

2. Valve (11) is energized, closing the peroxide and permanganate tank vent valves (17 and 12).

3. Main steam plant valve (7) is energized, which pressurizes the permanganate and peroxide tank.

4. Permanganate flows to steam generator chamber and closes a pressure switch (18). This pressure switch controls the operation of valves (13) and (15) and insures arrival of permanganate prior to peroxide in the generator.

5. Valves (13) and (15) are then energized, permitting peroxide to flow through the 8-ton valve and the 25-ton valve (14) into the steam generator. This generates peroxide steam by catalysis (water vapor and gaseous oxygen) at about 400 psi and 725° F at a rate of 4.66 pounds per second.

6. Steam drives turbopump, thus delivering the propellant to the thrust chamber under pressure. Steam is exhausted through the heat exchanger and two exhaust pipes.

7. The pump pressure opens the main oxygen and fuel valves (37 and 38) to the wide open positions, and full propellant flow enters the thrust chamber. The missile will now lift itself off the ground.

(*d*) *Flight Operation*

1. A small amount of liquid oxygen flows through restricting check valve (39) and is evaporated in a heat exchanger. This permits slight pressurization of oxygen tank (2 to 2.3 atmospheres).
2. Oxygen tank vent valve (33) prevents overpressurization.
3. During part of flight, fuel is pressurized by ram air through valve (24), which is actuated according to a fixed program through pilot valve (25).

(*e*) *Cut-off Sequence*

1. Twenty-five-ton valve (14) is closed approximately 3 seconds prior to cut-off. This reduces the thrust and permits more accurate cut-off determination. As explained in Chapter 2, the exact cut-off is determined by electronic means.
2. Eight-ton valve (13) is closed.
3. Preliminary fuel valve (29), main fuel valve (38), main oxygen valve (37), and main steam plant valve (7) are closed.
4. All vent values remain closed.
5. During last part of trajectory, fuel tank is pressurized by air from separate air supply through valve (23). This prevents collapsing of fuel tank when missile re-enters atmosphere.

Programed control operations are possible by controlling the desired variable (e.g., flow) through a signal (usually an electric voltage from an automatic guidance system). *Variable thrust rockets* are often used in manned rocket aircraft, and the thrust level is usually controlled by the pilot to suit his flight program. In *variable thrust units,* control is achieved by special propellant valves. In some cases such controls consist of rotating sleeve valves, with variable sleeve cut-out sections so as to give a variable throttle effect when the sleeve is rotated. The amount of rotation can be manually controlled by the operator or by some automatic control means, such as the differential pressure of a flow meter. The manual control scheme is used on the German Me 163 power plant and permits a thrust variation from 440 to 3700 pounds. The rotating sleeve valve with cut-outs serves as a pilot valve to other propellant valves.

In the *multiple thrust chamber rocket unit* (more than one thrust chamber for one feed system) controls are necessary for shutting off or turning on individual chambers at will or in a certain sequence. This problem can be solved by using individual valves for each thrust chamber and by assembling the respective pilot valves into a composite unit. Such controls are complicated by the fact that the turbopump power supply has to be simultaneously regulated. If, for example, another thrust chamber were turned on suddenly, without immediately augmenting the turbine input, the turbopump would be unable to furnish the required propellant. The turbine control, therefore, has to be coupled with the thrust chamber controls. Typical multiple thrust chamber rocket units are shown in Figures 2–9 and 8–28.

FIGURE 8–28. This YLR-45-AJ-1 rocket unit, shown here on its assembly fixture, has two thrust chambers (at left) fed from a single turbopump. This rocket operates on nitric acid and jet fuel and is used in assisting the take-off of heavy airplanes. This unit shows some of the typical electrical, pneumatical, and other controls necessary to insure proper starting, operating, and safety. (Courtesy Aerojet-General Corporation.)

Automatic controls are discussed further in Section 11 of this chapter.

9 Valves

The art of designing and making valves is based to a large extent on experience. No one chapter could do justice to it by describing valve design and operation. The types of valves used in propellant feed systems are various. A general classification of the more important types is given here.

(a) *Classification as to fluid*
    Fuel
    Oxidizer

Air or other pressurized gas
Turbine gas

(b) *Classification as to mode of actuation*
Automatically operated (by solenoid, pilot valve, trip mechanism, etc.)
Manually operated
Pressure-operated by air, gas propellant, or hydraulic fluid (for example, check valve, tank vent valve, pressure regulator, relief valve)

(c) *Classification as to use*
Main propellant control
Bleed
Drain
Fill
By-pass
Preliminary stage flow
Pilot valve
Safety valve
Overboard dump
Regulator
Regulator loader
Gas generator control

(d) *Classification as to valve position*
Normally open
Normally closed
Normally partially open

(e) *Classification as to number of ports*
Simple shut-off valve (2 ports)
Three-way valve
Four-way valve

Although the general design of rocket valves is relatively straightforward, the design details, such as clearance, seat materials, and opening time delay, present development difficulties. The valves in rockets have to be foolproof, for any valve failure will, very often, cause a failure of the rocket unit itself. A leak in a propellant valve or a delay in opening at an inopportune time may have disastrous effects.

All valves are tested for two qualities prior to installation; they are tested for leaks—through the seat and also through the glands—and for functional soundness.

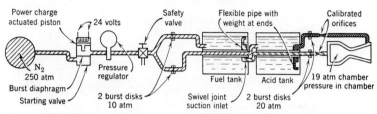

FIGURE 8–29. Schematic flow diagram of "Wasserfall," German antiaircraft missile developed during World War II.

The propellant valves handle relatively large flows at high service pressures. Therefore, the forces necessary to actuate the valves are large. Hydraulic or pneumatic pressure, controlled by pilot valves, operate the larger valves; these pilot valves are, in turn, actuated by a solenoid or a mechanical linkage. Essentially this is a means of power boost. In order to actuate the propellant valves directly, excessively large actuators, very heavy solenoids, or elaborate and heavy mechanical linkages would be required.

A very simple and a very light type of valve is a *burst diaphragm*. It is essentially a circular disk of material which blocks a pipeline and is designed so that it will fail and burst at a predetermined pressure differential. Burst diaphragms are positive seals and prevent leakage, but they can be used only once. The German *Wasserfall* antiaircraft missile uses four burst disks; two

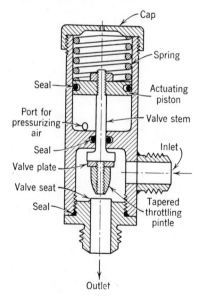

FIGURE 8–30. Propellant valve in open position.

FIGURE 8–31. Main propellant valve assembly for small nitric acid–aniline rocket. (Official U. S. Navy Photograph.)

FIGURE 8–32. The same main propellant valve for small nitric acid–aniline rocket shown disassembled. (Official U. S. Navy Photograph.)

are in high pressure air lines and are designed to fail at 10 atmospheres, two are in the propellant lines and designed to fail at 20 atmospheres. Figure 8–29 is a schematic flow diagram of the "Wasserfall."

A valve with a *tapered pintle,* shown in Figure 8–30, provides a simple means for controlling the propellant flow during the start-

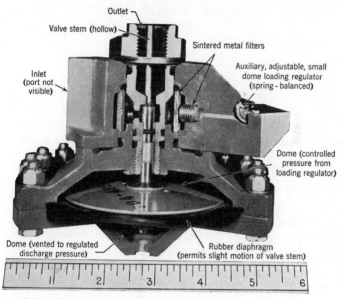

FIGURE 8–33. High pressure gas regulator valve is suitable for high flow and automatically throttles flow to maintain constant, preset outlet pressure. Large piston area in dome is required to obtain sufficient force to move valve stem with small pressure differential between controlled dome pressure and regulated outlet pressure. (Courtesy North American Aviation, Inc.)

ing period. As the valve stem is withdrawn from the seat, the outlet port area is continually increased and the taper on the pintle determines the throttling program. The rate of opening has to be controlled by regulating the actuating fluid. The main propellant valve units of a nitric acid–aniline rocket are shown in Figures 8–31 and 8–32. This valve assembly consists of two tapered pintle valves coupled to a single actuating cylinder. A small oil accumulator sphere prevents the actuating air from entering the cylinder, thereby assuring a smooth and steady travel motion of the valve.

Pressure regulators are special valves which are used frequently in liquid propellant rockets. Here usually the discharge pressure is regulated to a predetermined standard pressure value by continuously throttling the flow. Examples of places where they are useful can be found in Figures 8–2, 8–27, and 8–29. A typical gas-controlled pressure regulator is shown in Figure 8–33.

10   System Calibration

Because of fabrication and control tolerances, it is to be expected that the actual performance parameters of a rocket engine, as determined by test, will deviate somewhat from the design values. Since $I_s = F/\dot{w}$, any deviations in factors which affect thrust or weight flow rate will affect performance. Also, since I_s is a maximum at only one particular ratio of oxidizer to fuel flow for any given propellant, the performance is a function of mixture ratio.

It will be shown in Chapter 12 that the terminal velocity of a missile in flight is a function of the I_s and the logarithm of the ratio of take-off weight to burnout weight. If propellant flow were to take place at a mixture ratio which deviated from the design value, one of the propellants would be exhausted before the other, with some propellant remaining in the tank and with a resulting increase in the effective burnout weight of the missile. This would have a detrimental effect on the terminal velocity, attainable range, and trajectory of the missile. Furthermore operation at off-mixture ratio will usually cause losses by lowering of the pump and turbine efficiencies, and cause changes in the system pressure drops.

The accuracy to which these performance objectives must be controlled determines the extent of the action to be taken and the tolerances in the calibration of a liquid propellant rocket engine system. For many liquid propellant applications these tolerances are severe.

Two methods are available for precise control of thrust and mixture ratio. One uses an automatic system to control the deviations and the other relies on static calibration of the engine system. The latter approach is the simpler of the two and is usually preferred. Calibration of a liquid propellant rocket engine system to a high degree of accuracy requires the following three steps:

The individual calibration of hydraulic and pneumatic components is the first step. For these components (e.g., pressure regulators, pneumatic lines, valves, propellant feed lines, flowmeters, and calibration orifices), curves showing the pressure drop versus flow characteristics are required. These curves are generally plotted in terms of head loss and volumetric flow so as to eliminate the fluid density as an explicit variable. The flow system characteristic curve is obtained by adding the individual component head versus flow curves to the chamber pressure curve. Such a balance of head and flow must be made for both fuel and oxidizer systems. Figure 8–34 shows such a balance for a pressurized system.

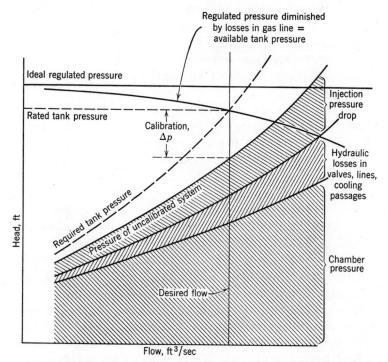

FIGURE 8–34. Balance of head and flow in one of the propellant lines of a typical calibrated, gas-pressurized liquid propellant feed system.

The calibration of components which operate at extremes of temperature is the next step. These components include thrust chamber assemblies, hot gas generators, and turbopumps. It has been found that characteristics of these components which are determined by water flow calibration at room temperature differ from those determined under operating conditions because the actual flows in these components are not adiabatic. Hot gases and cold propellants (such as liquid oxygen) give slightly different pressure drops than those obtained with water, which is normally used for calibrations. Thus, the pressure drop versus flow characteristics of main propellant injectors, gas generator injectors, and thrust chamber cooling jackets are best determined by a series of test firings of the individual components.

Likewise, pump head-flow-speed relationships should be determined using the actual propellants for which the pumps are designed rather than water. It is often considered best to calibrate the pumps while operating the turbopump as a unit on a test stand fitted with actual or simulated missile feed lines. Operating the complete turbopump also serves to establish the efficiency of the turbine, and, if missile exhaust ducting is used, its operating pressure ratio.

The third step is the matching of propellant flows and pressure drops. Here calculations are made for determining the proper adjustment, such as the size of a calibration orifice, the setting of a pressure regulator, or the adjustment of a control valve. The exact adjustment depends on the specific system which is used. The two principal means of feeding propellants are pressurized tanks and turbopumps. The actual calibration procedure is usually more complex for a turbopump system, because the pump calibration curves (flow-head-power relation) cannot readily be estimated without good test data and cannot be approximated by simple analytical relations. In this case the turbine shaft torque has to equal the torque required by the pumps. Thus a power balance has to be made in addition to the matching of pressures and the individual propellant flows. A typical flow-pressure balance curve for one of the two propellant systems (either fuel or oxidizer, but not both) is shown in simplified form in Figure 8–19. Here the pump characteristics of several pump speeds have to be considered. Because of the complexity of calibration calculations of turbopump feed systems, and because of the many differences between individual feed systems, no detail discussion will be given here on this subject. The fundamental relations used in calibrations are those developed in Chapters 3, 7, and 8.

Example 8–5. The following component data and design requirements are given for a pressurized liquid propellant rocket system similar to that in Figure 8–2:

Fuel	75% Ethyl alcohol
Oxidizer	Liquid oxygen
Desired mixture ratio	1.30
Desired thrust	5000 lb

Component test data:

Pressure losses in gas system were found to be negligible. Fuel valve and line losses were 9.15 psi at a flow of 9.63 lb/sec of water. Oxidizer valve and line losses were 14.2 psi at a flow of 12.8 lb/sec of liquid oxygen. Fuel cooling jacket pressure loss was 52 psi at a flow of 9.61 lb/sec of water. Oxidizer side injector pressure drop was 90.0 psi at 10.2 lb/sec of oxygen flow under thrust chamber operating conditions. Fuel side injector pressure drop was 48.3 psi at 10.2 lb/sec of fuel flow under thrust chamber operating conditions. Average results of several sea level thrust chamber tests were: Thrust = 5410 lb; Mixture ratio = 1.29; Specific impulse = 222 sec; Chamber pressure = 328 psia; Nozzle area ratio = 4.0.

Determine regulator setting and size and location of calibration orifices.

Solution. First the corrections necessary to obtain the desired thrust chamber conditions have to be determined. The experimental thrust chamber data must be adjusted for deviations in mixture ratio, thrust, and specific impulse. The variation of specific impulse with *mixture ratio* is determined from experimental data or (on a relative basis) from theoretical calculations similar to those which are the basis of Figure 4–4. Since the desired mixture ratio is so close to the actual test data, any mixture ratio correction will be neglected here.

The correction of the *specific impulse* for chamber pressure is made next. The specific impulse is essentially proportional to the thrust coefficients as determined from equation 3–30. For $k = 1.22$ (obtained from Table 4–3) and the pressure ratios $p_1/p_3 = 328/14.7 = 22.2$ and $300/14.7 = 20.4$, the values of C_F can be calculated as 1.420 and 1.405 respectively. In this calculation p_2 has to be determined for isentropic conditions, such as those in Figure 3–7, for the given nozzle area ratio. The sea level specific impulse is therefore corrected by

$$I_s = 222 \times 1.405/1.420 = 220 \text{ sec}$$

The *chamber pressure* has to be reduced from 328 psi to a lower value in order to bring the thrust from its test value of 5410 lb to the design value of 5000 lb. In accordance with equation 3–31 and 1–8

$$F = C_F A_t p_1$$

The chamber pressure is inversely proportional to the thrust coefficient C_F and proportional to the thrust and therefore

$$p_1/p'_1 = (F_1/F'_1)(C'_F/C_F)$$

The primes refer to the component test condition.

$$p_1 = 328(5000/5410)(1.42/1.405) = 306 \text{ psi}$$

The desired total *propellant flow* is

$$\dot{w} = F/I_s = 5000/220 = 22.7 \text{ lb/sec}$$

For a mixture ratio of 1.3, the desired *fuel and oxidizer flows* are obtained from equations 7–11 and 7–12.

$$\dot{w}_f = 9.9 \text{ lb/sec}$$

$$\dot{w}_o = 12.8 \text{ lb/sec}$$

Next the various component pressure drops are corrected to the desired flow values and with the corrected propellant densities in accordance with equation 7–14, which applies in general to all hydraulic devices. By neglecting variations in discharge coefficients, this equation can be rewritten into a convenient form.

$$\frac{\dot{w}}{\dot{w}'} = \sqrt{\frac{\rho}{\rho'}}\sqrt{\frac{\Delta p}{\Delta p'}}$$

With this equation and the specific gravity values of 1.14 for oxygen, 0.85 for diluted alcohol, and 1.0 for water, the new pressure drops for the corrected flow conditions can be found, and these are tabulated below with flow values given in lb/sec and pressure values in psi.

	Component Test Data			Design Conditions		
Component	Fluid	$\dot{w}$	Δp	Fluid	$\dot{w}$	Δp
Fuel injector	fuel	10.2	48.3	fuel	9.9	45.3
Oxidizer injector	oxygen	14.0	90.0	oxygen	12.8	75.0
Fuel cooling jacket	water	9.61	52.0	fuel	9.9	57.5
Fuel valve and line	water	9.63	9.15	fuel	9.9	10.1
Oxidizer valve and line	oxygen	12.8	14.2	oxygen	12.8	14.2

The total pressure drop in the fuel system is $45.3 + 57.5 + 10.1 = 112.9$ psi, and in the oxidizer system it is $75.0 + 14.2 = 89.2$ psi.

The tank pressures required to obtain the desired flows are calculated by adding the chamber pressure to these pressure drops.

$$(p)_o = 306 + 89.2 = 395.2 \text{ psi}$$

$$(p)_f = 306 + 112.9 = 418.9 \text{ psi}$$

In order to equalize the tank pressures, so that a single gas pressure regulator can be used, an *additional pressure loss must be introduced into the oxygen system*. The correction to this simple pressurized liquid propellant system is accomplished by means of an orifice, which must be placed in the propellant piping between the tank and the thrust chamber. This will cause an energy loss and the pressure drop in a calibration orifice will be $\Delta_p = 418.9 - 395.2 = 23.7$ psi. The *regulator setting* should be adjusted to give a regulated pressure of 418.9 psi under flow conditions.

The orifice area (assume $C_d = 0.60$ for a sharp-edged orifice) can be obtained from equation 7–14.

$$A = \frac{\dot{w}}{C_d \sqrt{2g\rho \, \Delta p}} = \frac{12.8 \times 144}{0.60 \sqrt{2 \times 32.2 \times 1.14 \times 62.4 \times 23.7 \times 144}}$$

$$= 0.889 \text{ in.}^2 \text{ (or 1.06 in. diameter)}$$

Example 8–2 shows another typical calibration problem for a pressurized feed system.

11 Automatic Controls

Automatically monitored controls are frequently used in liquid propellant rockets to accomplish one or more of the following purposes:

1. Stabilizing a complex pumping feed system (preventing flow surges).
2. Controlling internal rocket variables to attain a specified steady state performance, such as predetermined thrust, mixture ratio, or desired chamber pressure (for example, by control of pump speed or gas generator output).
3. Controlling variable initial conditions to attain a specified rocket performance (corrections for variable ambient temperature, propellant densities, or production tolerance buildups).
4. Programing in a controlled manner the performance of a rocket (variable thrust, or predetermined relation of chamber pressure and altitude).
5. Controlling the direction of the thrust with respect to the vehicle (hinged or gimbal thrust chamber).

Most of these controls use a servomechanism principle and generally consist of three basic elements: a *sensing mechanism* which measures or senses the variable quantity to be controlled; secondly, a *computing or controlling mechanism*, which compares

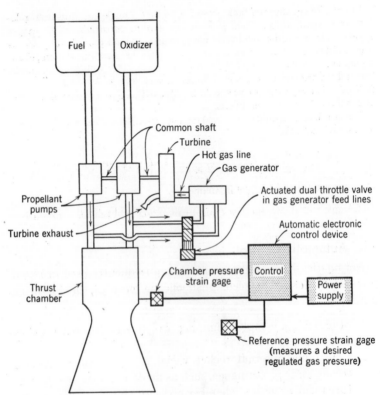

FIGURE 8-35. Simplified schematic diagram of a servomechanism type chamber pressure control of a liquid propellant rocket with a turbopump feed system and bootstrap type (self-pumping) gas generator.

the output of the sensing mechanism with a reference value and also gives a control signal to the third component, namely, the *actuating device* which manipulates the variable to be controlled.

Figure 8-35 illustrates a typical simple thrust control system aimed at regulating the chamber pressure (and therefore also the thrust) during the flight to a predetermined value. A pressure measuring device with an electric output is used for the sensing element, and an automatic control device compares this gage output signal with a signal from the reference gage and thus computes an error signal. This error signal is amplified, modulated, and fed to the actuator of the throttle valve. By controlling the propellant flow to the gas generator, the generator pressure is regulated and therefore also the pump speed and the main propellant flow; indirectly the chamber pressure in the thrust chamber is regulated and therefore also the thrust. These quantities are varied until such time as the error signal approaches zero. This system is vastly simplified here, for the sake of illustration, and in actual practice the system may have to be integrated with other automatic controls.

Any of the three principal components of an automatic control system can have many different forms. Typical sensing devices include those which measure chamber pressure, propellant pressures, pump rotational speeds, tank level, or propellant flow. Many of the instruments used in measuring these quantities on experimental rockets often lend themselves to modifications for control sensing devices. The actuating device can throttle propellant flow and control a bypass device or the gas generator discharge. There are many operating mechanisms for the controller such as direct electrical devices, electronic amplifiers (vacuum tube or transistors), magnetic amplifiers, magnetic clutches, hydraulic devices (useful for high actuator power and fast response), pneumatic devices, or mechanical devices (flyball governor and direct clutches).

There are basically four types of control principles: (1) a simple "on" and "off" type of control; (2) a proportional type control, where the control signal is essentially proportional to the error; (3) a derivative type control, where the signal is a function of the time derivative of the error (used principally for system stability); and (4) an integral type of control where the signal is proportional to the accumulative integral of the error. The actuators can be driven by electrical, hydraulic, pneumatic, or mechanical power. The exact type of component, the nature of the power supply, the system type, and the operating mechanism for the specific control depend on the details of the application and the requirements.

12   Propellant Tanks

The optimum shape for propellant tanks is spherical, for it gives a tank with the least weight and the least stress concentration. Unfortunately, spheres are not very desirable for flying vehicles because they fill the available space uneconomically. Propellant tanks are often made integral with the vehicle fuselage or wing and are usually irregular in shape.

Since the propellant tank has to fly, its weight is at a premium and the tank material is therefore highly stressed. Detail stress considerations will be omitted in this discussion because stresses for irregular tank shapes are beyond the scope of this book and because other loads besides internal pressure should be taken into consideration.

There are essentially two types of propellant tanks. (1) High pressure tanks: (a) gas supply tanks (1000 to 3000 pounds per square inch); (b) pressurized propellant tanks (300 to 700 pounds per square inch). (2) Low pressure tanks: propellant tanks for pump feed systems (zero to 50 pounds per square inch gage).

The first class is rather heavy and uses materials of high strength to weight ratio, usually heat treatable alloy steels. The proper welding and heat treatment of these high pressure tanks is a difficult process, requiring very great engineering and craftsman skill. The second variety is a thin-walled tank, often made of aluminum. Such tanks are sometimes so thin that they are difficult to handle, for they have a tendency to collapse under external loads. They can, however, be stabilized by a slight internal pressure (similar to a football).

The emptying of the propellant is sometimes difficult under flight and acceleration conditions. In some pressurized propellant tank designs the pressure gas mixes violently with the propellant, forming gas bubbles within the liquid, thereby causing erratic rocket operation. Antiaircraft missiles, fighter planes, or other vehicles which undergo heavy accelerations need special propellant tank-emptying provisions to prevent the tank outlet from being bare of liquid during operational maneuvers. The German "Wasserfall" antiaircraft missile uses swiveled flexible filler necks at the tank outlets, as shown schematically in Figure 8–29. These necks have a weight at their loose ends and therefore follow the liquid when the missile is laterally accelerated. Special provisions have to be made to minimize the formation of a vortex in a tank which is being emptied.

The extra volume of gas above the propellant is referred to as *ullage*. It is a necessary space which allows for thermal expansion of the propellant liquids and for the ejection of dissolved gases or the accumulation of gaseous products of slow reactions within the propellant during storage.

Problems

1. Estimate the weight and volume of air required to pressurize an acid-aniline feed system for a 1000-lb thrust chamber of 25 sec duration. ($\zeta_v = 0.92$.) The chamber pressure is 300 psia, and the mixture ratio is 2.75. The propellant tank pressure is 450 psia, and the air tank pressure is 2200 psia. Allow for 3 per cent excess propellant and 6 per cent excess air. The air regulator requires that the air tank pressure does not fall below 575 psia.

2. What would be the mixture ratio if a mechanic erroneously reversed orifices in the fuel and oxidizer lines in the gas-pressurized rocket unit given in Example 8–2? Assume the chamber pressure to be changed from 300 psia to 295 psi and assume that all hydraulic pressure losses, injection loss, cooling coil loss, valve and line loss, etc., vary as the square of the flow and inversely with the propellant density.

3. What would be the cross-sectional areas of the fuel, oxidizer, and gas pressure piston in a piston type feed system for a nitric acid–aniline unit of 1000-lb thrust with a mixture ratio of 2.00? The oxidizer pressure tank has an L/D ratio of 1.00. The rocket has a duration of 30 sec, a chamber pressure of 300 psia, a gas tank pressure of 275 psia, and a propellant tank pressure of 400 psia.

4. What are the specific speeds of the V-2 pumps? (See data given in Table 8–1.) What are the pump efficiencies?

5. Compute the turbine power output for a gas consisting of 64 per cent by weight of H_2O and 36 per cent by weight of O_2, if the turbine inlet is at 30 atm and 725° F with the outlet at 1.4 atm with 2.7 lb flowing each second. The turbine efficiency is 37 per cent.

6. Plot the head and power curves if the speed of the fuel pump shown in Figure 8–16 was decreased 20 per cent.

7. Compare the pump discharge gage pressures and the required pump powers for five different pumps using water, gasoline, alcohol, liquid oxygen, and nitric acid respectively. The corresponding specific gravities are 1.00, 0.720, 0.810, 1.14, and 1.37. Each pump delivers 100 gallons per minute, a head of 1000 feet, and arbitrarily has a pump efficiency of 84 per cent.

Answers: 433, 312, 350, 494, and 594 psi; 30.0, 21.6, 24.3, 34.2, and 41.1 hp.

8. The following data are given on a liquid propellant rocket engine:

Thrust	40,200 lb
Thrust chamber specific impulse	210.2 sec
Fuel	Gasoline (sp gr 0.74)
Oxidizer	Red fuming nitric acid (sp gr 1.57)
Thrust chamber mixture ratio	3.25
Turbine efficiency	58 per cent
Required pump power	580 hp
Power to auxiliaries mounted on turbo-pump gear case	50 hp
Gas generator mixture ratio	0.39
Turbine exhaust pressure	37 psia
Turbine exhaust nozzle area ratio	1.4
Enthalpy available for conversion in turbine per unit of gas	180 Btu/lb
Specific heat ratio of turbine exhaust gas	1.3

Determine the engine system mixture ratio and the system specific thrust.
Answers: 3.07 and 208.

9. The engine performance data for a turbopump rocket system are as follows:

Engine system specific impulse	212 sec
Engine system mixture ratio	2.52
Engine system thrust	5000 lb
Oxidizer vapor flow to pressurize oxidizer tank	0.003 per cent of total oxidizer flow
Propellant flow through turbine	2.1 per cent of total propellant flow
Gas generator mixture ratio	0.23

Determine performance of the thrust chamber (I_s, r, F).

Symbols

A	area, ft^2
C_d	discharge coefficient
C_F	thrust coefficient (see equation 3–30)
c_p	specific heat at constant pressure, Btu/lb °R
c_v	specific heat at constant volume, Btu/lb °R
D	diameter, ft
F	thrust, lb
g	acceleration of gravity, 32.2 ft/sec^2
H	head, ft

$(H_s)_A$	available pump suction head above vapor pressure, often called net positive suction head, ft
$(H_s)_R$	required pump suction head above vapor pressure, ft
ΔH	pump head differential, ft
Δh	enthalpy change, Btu/lb
I_s	specific impulse, lb-sec/lb
J	mechanical equivalent of heat, 778 ft-lb/Btu
k	specific heat ratio
N	shaft speed, rpm
N_s	specific speed of pump
P	power, hp
p	pressure, lb/ft^2
Δp	pressure differential, lb/ft^2
Q	volume flow rate, ft^3/sec
R	gas constant, ft-lb/°F lb
r	weight flow mixture ratio (oxidizer to fuel)
S	suction specific speed of pump
T	absolute temperature, °R
t	time, sec
u	tip speed or blade speed, ft/sec
V	volume, ft^3
v	gas or liquid flow velocity, ft/sec
W	weight, lb
$\dot{w}$	weight flow rate, lb/sec

Greek Letters

ζ_d	discharge correction factor
η	efficiency
ρ	density
σ	pump suction parameter
ψ	constant

Subscripts

ap	auxiliary power
e	maximum efficiency
f	fuel
g	gas tank
gg	gas generator
o	oxidizer

oa	overall engine system
P	pump
p	propellant tank
T	turbine
tc	thrust chamber
tp	tank pressurization
0	initial condition
1	inlet
2	outlet or exhaust
3	atmosphere

Chapter 9

Solid Propellant

Rocket Fundamentals

1 Principal Components of Solid Propellant Rockets

The outstanding feature of solid propellant rockets is their inherent simplicity and lack of moving parts such as valves, turbopumps, and controls. They are relatively easy to use and require little servicing. A typical solid propellant unit (Figure 9–1) has the following principal components: *propellant, hardware* such as chamber, nozzle, or mounting pads, and *igniter*.

Propellant

Solid propellants usually have a plastic-like, caked appearance and burn on their exposed surfaces to form hot exhaust gases which in turn produce a reaction force. A physical mass or body of the propellant is referred to as the *grain*. Some rockets have more than one grain in the same chamber.

A solid propellant contains all the materials necessary for sustaining chemical combustion. It may be a heterogeneous mixture of several chemicals, for example, a mixture of oxidizing crystals of perchlorate in a matrix of an organic plastic-like fuel such as asphalt. Or it may be a homogeneous charge of special chemicals such as modified nitrocellulose type gunpowder.

Once the propellant charge is ignited, a well-designed grain will burn smoothly on its exposed surfaces without severe surges or detonations. The combustion will consume the propellant grain material at a smooth rate in a direction normal to the burning

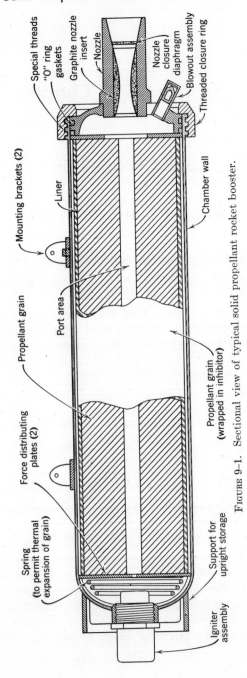

FIGURE 9–1.   Sectional view of typical solid propellant rocket booster.

surface. Further discussion of solid propellants, their physical and chemical properties, and their fabrication methods is to be found in Chapter 10.

The shape, size, exposed burning surface, and geometrical form of the grain influence the burning characteristics of the rocket and largely determine the operating pressure, thrust, and duration. The same propellant, that is, the same chemical formulation, can therefore be made into many different grain configurations. Some of the principal mathematical relations for determining the operating characteristics and the grain configuration are described in this chapter and in Chapter 11.

Hardware

The solid propellant is confined in a *combustion chamber* (usually of metal construction) and the reaction gases are exhausted through an *exhaust nozzle*. Combustion chambers are usually cylindrical in shape with elliptical or spherical ends. In addition, the hardware portion of the solid propellant rocket often includes some or all of the following: provisions for assembly (loading of grain) or disassembly of the unit; mounting lugs or pads; burst diaphragms or other safety provisions to prevent overpressurization of the chamber; and means for holding the propellant grain in place. These hardware components are usually uncooled and have to withstand severe heating. The design of typical hardware components is discussed in Chapter 11.

Igniter

The initiation of the combustion of the propellant grain is accomplished by means of a pyrotechnic igniter, which in turn is usually started by means of electrical current or percussion action. Igniters are described further in Chapter 11.

References for further study on solid propellant rockets can be found in Sections 3.6, 4.5, and 6.7 of the Reference Bibliography.

2 Grain Configuration

The thrust of a rocket is equal to the product of the mass flow rate and the effective exhaust velocity (see equation 1–4a). If a large thrust is desired, the mass flow has to be large. This can be achieved by a large burning surface, a fast burning rate, or both.

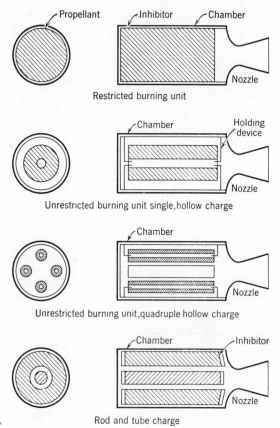

Restricted burning unit

Unrestricted burning unit single, hollow charge

Unrestricted burning unit, quadruple hollow charge

Rod and tube charge

FIGURE 9-2. Typical solid

Conversely, a low thrust for a correspondingly longer duration can be obtained with a given propellant if the exposed burning area is small. Since a given combustion chamber will be able to hold only a limited amount of propellant, the variation of thrust for any specific propellant has to be obtained by varying the geometric form and therefore the exposed burning surface of the propellant charge.

In addition to varying the shape of the grain, it is possible to limit the exposed burning surface by *inhibitors*. These are chemicals which are essentially inert or which burn very slowly. They are applied to those surfaces of the grain where burning is to be

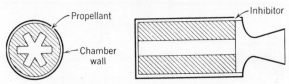

Typical internal burning star configuration

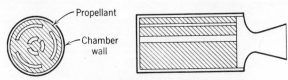

Typical internal burning multi-perforated configuration

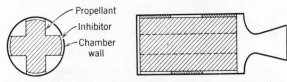

Typical partially restricted external burning cruciform configuration

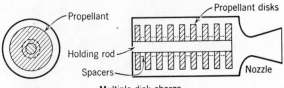

Multiple disk charge

propellant grain configuration.

prevented. Some inhibitors can be applied by dipping of the grain; others, by bonding sheets of inhibitor material to the surfaces which are to be restricted, or sometimes, by wrapping with a special tape. When an *inhibitor* is applied to the inner surface of the chamber it acts to reduce the heat transfer to the wall. This type of inhibitor is often referred to as a *liner*. Because an inhibitor restricts the burning of a grain, the solid propellant units with inhibitors are called *restricted burning rockets* and thus are differentiated from *unrestricted burning rockets*. Typical examples of several types of grain configurations are shown in Figure 9–2.

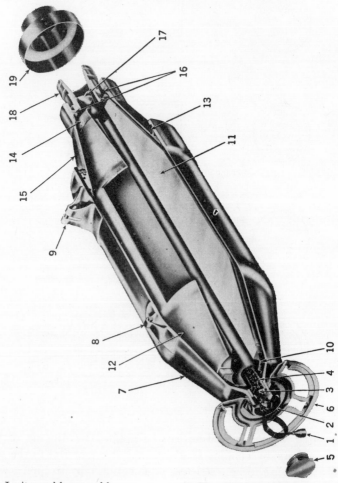

1. Igniter cable assembly
2. Igniter adapter
3. Igniter powder case
4. Igniter basket assembly
5. Plastic shipping cap
6. Handle
7. Chamber assembly
8. Forward mounting lug
9. Aft mounting lug
10. Grain spacer (sponge rubber)
11. Propellant grain
12. Chamber insulator (boot and baffle)

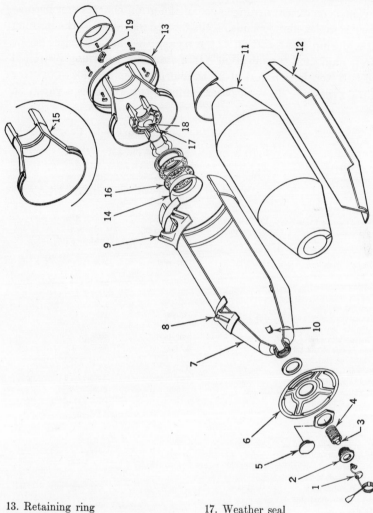

13. Retaining ring
14. Safety diaphragm deflector cone
15. Aft cap chamber
16. Diaphragm assembly

17. Weather seal
18. Nozzle body
19. Nozzle cover

FIGURE 9–3. Cutaway and exploded views of jet assisted take-off rocket engine 15KS-1000 A1. This unit delivers 1000-lb thrust for 15 sec at 60° F. Its empty weight is 115 lb and its loaded weight is 200 lb. The unit is 35⅜ in. long with a diameter of 10³⁄₁₆ in. (Courtesy Aerojet-General Corporation.)

The geometrical arrangement of the grain charges can become very complex and depends on the desired variation of the burning area during the operation of the rocket, the characteristics of the propellant, and the duration. In a simple end-burning restricted rocket (top left, Figure 9–2) the burning surface does not vary during the run. In most other configurations there is a variation

TABLE 9–1. PROPERTIES OF

Propellant Type Propellant system	Castable Composite		
	Oxidizer/fuel = $KClO_4/C_2H_4O$ †	Oxidizer/fuel = NH_4ClO_4/C_2H_4O †	Oxidizer/fuel = NH_4NO_3/C_2H_4O‡/catalyst
Typical ingredient variation, per cent	$KClO_4$ (50–80) C_2H_4O (50–20)	$KClO_4$ (50–80) C_2H_4O (50–20)	Typical $NH_4NO_3 = 80$ $C_2H_4O = 18$ Catalyst = 2
Adiabatic flame temperature, °F	2800–5000	2800–4500	2700
Average molecular weight, lb per mole	25–35	22–25	22
Specific heat ratio	1.24–1.27	1.22–1.26	1.26
Typical sea level specific impulse, sec	165–210	175–240	195
Characteristic velocity, ft/sec	3600–4000	3800–4800	4000
Burning rate at 1000 psi and 70° F, in./sec	0.5–1.2	0.1–0.5	0.1
Burning rate exponent, n	1.0–0.7	0.1–0.4	0.4
Specific weight, lb/in.^{3}	0.06–0.07	0.055–0.063	0.056
Maximum volume impulse at 1000 psi, lb-sec/ft^3	22,500	25,000	18,000
Temperature sensitivity of pressure (psi/psi °F), per cent	2–0.2	0.4–0.1	0.3
Lower combustion limit, psi	200–1000	<200	<100
Pressure limit, psi	>6000	>6000	>3000
Probable allowable operating temperature limits, °F	−70 to 170	−70 to 170	−50 to 160
Storage stability,§ temperature/humidity	Good/good	Good/fair	Good/bad
Smoke	Abundant	Much at low oxidizer; little at high oxidizer; mist at relative humidity greater than 80 per cent	None
Mechanical properties	Soft and resilient to hard and tough	Soft and resilient to hard and tough	Soft and resilient to hard and tough

* This table is intended only as a guide and is not meant to be absolutely correct. Data furnished in part by C. E. Bartley, Grand Central Aircraft Company, and in part by U. S. Naval Ordnance Test Station, China Lake.

† C_2H_4O is taken as typical in per cent composition for many solid propellant fuels.

of burning area with time. Figures 9–1 and 9–3 show internal burning grains.

There are basically three types of variations of burning area with time. If the grain is so designed that the burning area, and therefore also the gas evolution rate, the chamber pressure, and the thrust increase with burning time, then the rocket is said to

SOME SOLID PROPELLANT SYSTEMS *

Molded Composites	Extruded Double Base	Cast Double Base	Asphalt Base Thermoplastic
Ammonium picrate (AP)	Nitrocellulose (NC)	Nitrocellulose (NC)	Asphalt/perchlorate
Potassium nitrate	Nitroglycerin (NG)	Nitroglycerin (NG)	
Fuel	Miscellaneous	Plasticizer (Pl)	
		Miscellaneous	
AP (70–40)	NC (50–60)	NC (45–55)	Asphalt (22–30)
KNO_3 (20–50)	NG (30–45)	NG (25–40)	$KClO_4$ (78–70)
C_2H_4O (10–10)	Misc. (1–10)	Pl (12–22)	
		Misc. (1–2)	
Average about 3200	3800–5200	2600–4000	3800–3300
Average about 30	22–28	22–28	30
Average about 1.25	1.21–1.25	1.24–1.26	Average 1.25
160 to 200	205–230	160–220	180–195
3500–3800	4500–5000	3500–4200	3700–4200
0.24–1.0	0.6–0.9	0.22–0.37	1.3–1.7
Average about 0.5	0.1–0.8	0.1–0.8	0.7–0.8
0.059–0.064	Average 0.058	Average 0.057	0.063
19,500	23,500	19,500	21,000
0.16–0.3	0.1–0.8	0.1–0.8	Average 1
<500	<500	<500	500
<3000	>10,000	>5000	10,000
−40 to 140	−20 to 140	−30 to 140	+20 to +120
Good/poor	Bad/fair	Bad/fair	Good/bad
Abundant	None	None	Abundant
Hard and brittle	Hard and tough	Hard and tough	Variable with temperature, poor when warm

‡ All data for ammonium nitrate–C_2H_4O system are given as typical. This system has not been explored fully enough to give ranges.

§ Storate stability is rated bad if the propellant cannot be stored indefinitely at temperatures greater than 150° F.

have *progressive burning characteristics*. If the grain design produces a decrease in these quantities, then the rocket has *regressive
burning characteristics*. For example, an uninhibited cylindrical
propellant grain exhibits regressive burning characteristics. A
grain which maintains approximately constant burning area and
constant thrust is said to have *neutral burning characteristics*.
An end-burning, restricted grain is of this type.

Many grains have *perforations*, that is, holes in the propellant
charge to increase the burning surface. Depending on the purpose and use of the rocket, there are star-shaped configurations,
cruciform grains, and many others. In perforated grains, the
propellant burns on all exposed and unrestricted (uninhibited)
surfaces. The gases created in the forward end have to flow past
a portion of the propellant grain to the nozzle. The flow of combustion gases at high velocities over a burning propellant surface
may result in *erosion* at these gas-swept locations. Erosion is a
mechanical-chemical phenomenon which causes a change in burning rate at locations where it occurs; further discussion of erosion
is given in Chapter 11.

With many rocket configurations and particularly with unrestricted burning rockets there is a large portion of void space
in the combustion chamber. This empty volume is necessary to
permit the escape of combustion products from some portions of
the burning surface to the nozzle exit, to permit certain types of
grain mounting provisions, and to provide room for thermal expansion. Depending on the ingenuity of the grain design, this
void space can be made very small. For restricted burning units
the space factor (defined as the ratio of propellant volume to
chamber volume) has values between 0.6 to 0.90. For some unrestricted burning units this space factor may be as low as 0.3.
The large space factors permit a more compact and lighter design.
In the computation of the space factor, the volume occupied by
liners, inhibitors, and igniters is usually considered to be ineffective and is not included in the volume of the propellant.

3   Burning Rate

The velocity at which a solid propellant is consumed during
operation is called the *burning rate*. It is measured in a direction
normal to the propellant surface and is usually expressed in inches

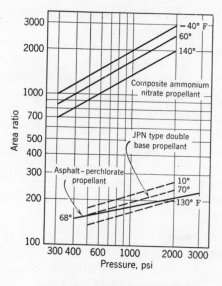

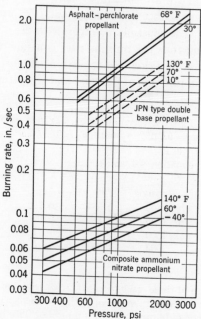

FIGURE 9–4. Burning characteristics of several typical solid rocket propellants. (Data furnished in part by U. S. Naval Ordnance Test Station, China Lake, California.

per second. For most ordinary propellants, the burning rate at 2000 pounds per square inch chamber pressure is between 0.03 and 2.5 inches per second. A unit which has, for example, a burning rate of 1.5 inches per second would have to be 45 inches long, if it is to burn for half a minute in cigarette fashion (with an end-burning propellant grain). Typical burning rates and other performance data are listed in Table 9–1.

For some restricted burning units and for certain propellant combinations, the burning rate can be approximated by the following empirical relation, in which the influence of all performance parameters is small compared to the chamber pressure and the initial grain temperature.

$$r = ap_c{}^n \tag{9-1}$$

The burning rate or velocity of propellant consumption r is usually given in inches per second, the chamber pressure p_c in pounds per square inch; a and n are constants. For most restricted burning propellants, n has values between 0.4 and 0.85, and a is between 0.05 and 0.002. The constant, a, varies with the initial propellant temperature, and thus the burning rate is a function of the temperature of the grain prior to combustion. Figure 9–4 shows the burning rate as a function of pressure and temperature for typical propellants.

Example 9–1. Plot the variation of burning rate with pressure for two propellants with $a_1 = 0.00137$, $n_1 = 0.9$, $a_2 = 0.060$, and $n_2 = 0.4$ with p expressed in psi and r in in./sec.

Solution. Use equation 9–1 and solve for several conditions as shown below.

Pressure	r_1	r_2
500	0.367	0.720
1000	0.685	0.95
1500	0.994	1.11
2000	1.28	1.26
2500	1.56	1.33

From inspection of these results and also from equation 9–1 it can be seen that the burning rate is very sensitive to the exponent n. High values of n give a rapid change of burning rate with pressure. This implies that even a small change in chamber pressure will produce substantial changes in the amount of hot gas produced.

Actually the burning rates are determined empirically and usually cannot be expressed by a simple mathematical relation, such as equation 9–1. For this reason, empirical data are used in computations instead of simplified burning rate relations. Further discussion of the burning rate is given in Chapter 11.

The *weight of propellant burned* can be determined from the burning area, A_b; the burning rate, r; and the propellant density, ρ_b;

$$\dot{w} = \frac{dW_u}{dt} = A_b\rho_b r \qquad (9\text{–}2)$$

and

$$W_u = \rho_b \int A_b r\, dt \qquad (9\text{–}3)$$

where W_u is the total weight of effective propellant and $\dot{w}$ is the propellant flow rate.

4 Basic Relation of Parameters Affecting Performance

The basic performance relation is derived from the principle of conservation of matter. The propellant mass burned per unit time has to equal the sum of the increase in gas mass per unit time in the combustion chamber and the mass flowing through the exhaust nozzle per unit time.

$$A_b r \rho_b = \frac{d}{dt}(\rho_c V_c) + A_t p_c \sqrt{\frac{gk}{RT_c}\left(\frac{2}{k+1}\right)^{(k+1)/(k-1)}} \qquad (9\text{–}4)$$

The term on the left side of the equation gives the rate of gas generation. The first term on the right gives the change in propellant mass in the combustion chamber, and the last term gives the nozzle flow according to equation 3–25. The burning rate of the propellant is r; A_b is the propellant burning area; ρ_b is the propellant density; ρ_c is the chamber gas density; V_c is the chamber volume, which becomes larger as the propellant is expended; A_t is the throat area; p_c is the chamber pressure; T_c is the absolute chamber temperature, which is usually assumed to be constant; and k is the specific heat ratio of the combustion gases. The equation above can be simplified and is useful in some numerical solutions of transient conditions, such as during the start.

If the change of the gas mass in the chamber volume is neglected, $d(\rho_c V_c)/dt = 0$, a relation for steady burning conditions can be obtained from equations 9–1 and 9–4.

$$\frac{A_b}{A_t} = \frac{p_c \sqrt{gk \left(\frac{2}{k+1}\right)^{(k+1)/(k-1)}}}{\rho_b r \sqrt{RT_c}}$$

$$= \frac{p_c^{1-n} \sqrt{gk \left(\frac{2}{k+1}\right)^{(k+1)/(k-1)}}}{\rho_b a \sqrt{RT_c}} \tag{9-5}$$

As an approximation, the chamber pressure can be expressed as a function of the area ratio of the burning surface to the nozzle throat cross section for a given propellant.

$$p_c \sim \left(\frac{A_b}{A_t}\right)^{1/(1-n)} = K^{1/(1-n)} \tag{9-6}$$

The ratio of the burning area to the nozzle throat area is an important quantity in solid propellant engineering and is often given the separate symbol K. Equations 9–5 and 9–6 show the relation between burning area, chamber pressure, throat area, and propellant properties. For example, this relation permits an evaluation of the variation necessary in the throat area, if the chamber pressure (and therefore also the thrust) is to be changed.

These relations are based on the very simple mathematical dependence of burning rate on chamber pressure. However, for many propellants, this simplification is not sufficiently valid. For accurate evaluation, experimental values must be found. Typical experimental results are shown in Figure 9–4.

5 Thrust, Exhaust Velocity, and Specific Impulse

The *ideal nozzle exhaust velocity* of a solid propellant rocket is dependent on the thermodynamic theory as presented in Chapter 3. For convenience, the result of the derivation (equation 3–15) is repeated here:

$$v_2 = \sqrt{\frac{2gk}{k-1} RT_c \left[1 - \left(\frac{p_e}{p_c}\right)^{(k-1)/k}\right]} \tag{9-7}$$

where v_2 is the ideal nozzle exhaust velocity, g is the acceleration of gravity, k is the ratio of specific heats, R is the gas constant, T_c is the combustion temperature of the reaction gases, and p_e/p_c is the ratio between the nozzle exit gas pressure and the effective nozzle inlet (stagnation) pressure.

In deriving this equation, it was assumed that the approach velocity of gases upstream of the nozzle is small and can be neglected. This is true if the port area A_p (i.e., the flow area of gases between and around the propellant grains) is relatively large compared to the nozzle throat area A_t. When the port to throat area ratio A_p/A_t is less than approximately 4, then a correction must be made to the effective exhaust velocity.

The thrust for solid propellant rockets is given by the identical definitions developed in Chapters 1 and 3, namely equations 1–4a and 3–29.

The *effective exhaust velocity*, c, and the *specific impulse*, I_s, are defined by equations 1–3, 1–4, and 1–8 and are repeated here for convenience.

$$c = v_2 + \frac{(p_e - p_a)A_e g}{\dot{w}} \tag{9–8}$$

$$I_s = c/g = \frac{F}{\dot{w}} = \frac{I_t}{W_u} \tag{9–9}$$

It is experimentally difficult to obtain an instantaneous propellant flow rate, $\dot{w}$, or the effective exhaust velocity. However, total impulse and total propellant weight consumed during the test can be measured. The propellant weight is determined by weighing the rocket before and after a test. The effective propellant weight is often slightly less than the total propellant weight, because some grain designs permit small portions of the propellant to remain unburned during combustion, as will be explained in a later chapter. It has been found that the *total impulse* can be accurately determined in testing by integrating the area under a thrust time curve. For this reason the average specific impulse is usually calculated from total measured impulse and effective propellant weight. The total impulse, I_t, is defined as the integration of thrust, F, over the operating duration, t_b;

$$I_t = \int_0^{t_b} F \, dt = \bar{F} t_b \tag{9–10}$$

where $\bar{F}$ is an average value of thrust over the burning duration, t_b.

The *effective burning time* is an arbitrary quantity and is defined in several ways by different manufacturers. Usually the thrust buildup period (time from ignition up to a certain percentage of rated thrust) and the thrust decay interval (usually defined as the time after the thrust drops below a specific value)

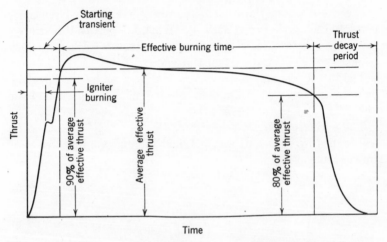

FIGURE 9-5. Typical solid propellant thrust-time diagram. The definitions of these durations and thrust values are arbitrary.

are not included in the effective burning duration. In many cases the total impulse during the thrust buildup and decay period is neglected in computing average performance values. A typical definition is shown in Figure 9-5.

The ratio of the ideal effective exhaust velocity (computed from the theoretical propellant characteristics and equation 9-7) to the measured average value of the effective exhaust velocity (determined from the total impulse and the effective propellant weight) gives an indication of the quality of a specific rocket's design.

Other Performance Parameters

In addition to the parameters of thrust and specific impulse discussed above, a number of performance parameters are used to evaluate solid propellant rockets and to compare the quality of design of one rocket with another. They are the *total impulse to loaded weight ratio* (I_t/W_G), and the *thrust to weight ratio* (F/W_G). Typical values of these performance parameters are given in Table 9–2.

TABLE 9–2. TYPICAL SOLID PROPELLANT PARAMETERS

Parameters	Symbol	Typical Values
Total impulse to loaded weight ratio	I/W_G	50 lb-sec/lb for poorly designed rockets 100 to 130 lb-sec/lb for highly stressed hardware and effective volume utilization
Thrust to weight ratio	F/W_G	200 for high thrust units 10 for low thrust units
Specific impulse (at sea level)	I_s	170 to 230 sec depending on propellant combination, chamber pressure, ambient pressure, and nozzle area ratio

The total impulse to loaded weight ratio approaches ideally the value of the specific impulse. When the weight of hardware, metal parts, inhibitors, etc., becomes very small in relation to the propellant weight, then the ratio I_t/W_G approaches I_t/W_u, which is the definition of the average specific impulse (equation 9–9). The higher the value of I_t/W_G, the better is the design of a rocket unit.

Another parameter used for comparing propellants is the *volume impulse;* it is defined as the total impulse per unit volume of propellant grain, or I_t/V_b.

Example 9–2. The following requirements are given for a solid propellant rocket:

Sea level thrust	2000 lb
Duration	10 sec
Chamber pressure	1000 psia
Operating temperature	Ambient (approx. 70° F)
Propellant	Ammonium nitrate–hydrocarbon (properties given in Table 9–1)

Determine the specific impulse, the throat and exit areas, the flow rate, the total propellant weight, the total impulse, the burning area, and an estimated weight assuming moderately efficient design.

Solution.   From Table 9–1:

$$k = 1.26$$

$$T_c = 2700° \text{ F} = 3160° \text{ R}$$

$$r = 0.10 \text{ in./sec at } 1000 \text{ psi}$$

$$c^* = 4000 \text{ ft/sec}$$

$$\rho = 0.056 \text{ lb/in.}^3$$

Molecular weight $= 22$ lb/mole

Gas constant $= 1544/22 = 70.3$ ft-lb)/(lb °R

From Figures 3–11 and 3–7

$$C_F = 1.57 \quad \text{(for } k = 1.26, \text{ with optimum expansion at sea}$$
$$\text{level and a pressure ratio of } 1000/14.7 = 68)$$

$$\epsilon = A_2/A_t = 7.8$$

The ideal thrust coefficient has to be corrected for nozzle losses.   Assume a correction of 0.98

$$C_F = 0.98 \times 1.57 = 1.54$$

The *specific impulse* is (equation 3–32)

$$I_s = \frac{1}{g} c^* C_F = (4000 \times 1.54)/32.2 = 191 \text{ sec}$$

The *required throat* area is obtained from equation 3–31.

$$A_t = \frac{F}{p_c C_F} = 2000/(1000 \times 1.54) = 1.30 \text{ in.}^2$$

The *exit area* is $7.8 \times 1.30 = 10.1$ in.^{2}

The *nozzle weight flow rate* is obtained from equation 1–8.

$$\dot{w} = F/I_s = 2000/191 = 10.47 \text{ lb/sec}$$

The *effective propellant weight* for a duration of 10 sec is therefore approximately 105 lb.   Allowing for residual propellant and for inefficiencies on thrust build-up the *total loaded propellant weight* is assumed to be 4 per cent larger, namely $105 \times 1.04 = 109$ lb.

The *total impulse* is from equation 9–10.

$$I_t = \overline{F} t_b = 2000 \times 10 = 20,000 \text{ lb-sec}$$

This can also be obtained from equation 9–9.

$$I_t = W_u \times I_s = 105 \times 191 = 20,000 \text{ lb-sec}$$

The propellant burning surface can be found by using equation 9–5.

$$A_b = \frac{A_t p_c \sqrt{gk \left(\dfrac{2}{k+1}\right)^{(k+1)/(k-1)}}}{\rho_b r \sqrt{RT_c}}$$

$$= \frac{1.30 \times 1000}{0.056 \times 0.10} \sqrt{\frac{32.2 \times 1.26}{(1544/22) \times 3160}} (0.885)^{8.7}$$

$$= 1840 \text{ in.}^2$$

This result can also be obtained from equations 9–2 or 9–3. The area ratio

$$K = A_b/A_t = 1840/1.30 = 1420$$

The *loaded gross weight* can only be estimated after a detail design has been made. However, an approximate guess can be made by chosing an impulse weight ratio of perhaps 85 (not a highly stressed design) from Table 9–2. These weights can be only approximations.

$$W_G = I_t \left(\frac{W_G}{I_t}\right) = 20,000 \times \frac{1}{85} = 235 \text{ lb}$$

Since the propellants account for 109 lb, the hardware parts can be estimated as $235 - 109 = 126$ lb.

6 Performance Limitations

Solid rocket propellants have certain limitations which prevent a wider application of these units. The performance of the propellant charge is very sensitive to ambient temperature variations. Also, their operation is not usually stable beyond certain limiting chamber pressure values. The characteristics of the individual propellants limit the thrust, burning, duration, and shape of the rocket.

Temperature Sensitivity

Experience has shown that the initial temperature of the grain will materially affect the performance. On a hot day a given solid propellant rocket will operate at a higher chamber pressure and thrust than on a cool day. The firing duration will be shorter, but the total impulse will not be changed significantly. This indicates that the initial temperature of the grain has a decided effect on the burning rate and that weather conditions have to be considered when exacting performance requirements are to be met.

The temperature sensitivity of liquid propellant rockets is usually not as severe and can easily be corrected. The methods of accurately controlling the thrust of a given propellant grain with varying ambient grain temperatures are: (1) variation of burning surface or the length and shape of the propellant grains or (2) replacement of the nozzle with one having a corrected throat area and expansion ratio.

The temperature sensitivity for different solid propellants is usually expressed as the percentage change of thrust per unit of temperature change. Ordinarily the temperature sensitivity has values ranging from a 0.0025-pound to 0.014-pound change in thrust per degree Fahrenheit per pound of original thrust. The temperature sensitivities of some molded composite and double base propellant are relatively low, measuring down to 0.001 $(°F)^{-1}$. Restricted double base propellant can have a sensitivity of 0.006 $(°F)^{-1}$, while unrestricted double base propellant may have a very high temperature sensitivity of 0.015 $(°F)^{-1}$. Typical values are given in Table 9–1.

Temperature changes affect the equilibrium pressure and the burning rate. The definitions of the temperature coefficients are usually given by

$$\pi_K = \left(\frac{\delta \ln p}{\delta T}\right)_K = \frac{1}{p_c}\left(\frac{\delta p}{\delta T}\right)_K \qquad (9\text{–}11)$$

$$\sigma_p = \left(\frac{\delta \ln r}{\delta T}\right)_p = \frac{1}{r}\left(\frac{\delta r}{\delta T}\right)_p \qquad (9\text{–}12)$$

Here π_K is the temperature sensitivity coefficient of equilibrium pressure at a particular value of K (K is the ratio of the burning surface to the throat area), expressed in per cent pressure change per degree temperature change. Mathematically it is defined as the partial derivative of the natural logarithm of the equilibrium chamber pressure p with respect to temperature T. The other temperature sensitivity coefficient σ_p refers to the change in burning rate r of a solid propellant with respect to temperature T at a particular value of chamber pressure p_c. It is also known as the burning rate temperature coefficient, while π_K is known as the temperature sensitivity of pressure.

Temperature Limits

Some solid propellants are limited to a fixed and rather small operational temperature range for reasons other than temperature sensitivity. At very cold temperatures some of the propellant charges become brittle and subject to cracking, particularly if the change in ambient temperature is rapid. An uneven temperature distribution or differential expansion between chamber, liner material, and propellant charge can cause such cracking. In geographical locations where the nights are cold and the days relatively very warm, solid propellant charges are particularly subject to temperature effects. Any crack in the grain increases the burning area and, therefore, the mass flow and the chamber pressure. This leads to an overloading of the chamber walls and often to a subsequent violent chamber failure.

Overheating of the propellant charge prior to firing will often cause the propellants to become weak and plastic, so that they are unable to withstand the sudden high chamber pressure or the acceleration which the vehicle might undergo. The subsequent failure is again due to an undesired increase in the burning area. The temperature under which most ordinary propellants can function is therefore limited. Typical temperature limits are given in Table 9–1. In some instances, additives and special design provisions permit a wider temperature range. Methods of increasing these temperature limits have been the subject of extensive research and new, improved propellant combinations show promise in this direction.

Pressure Limits

There is also a practical upper and lower pressure limit for the satisfactory operation of a solid propellant. Below a certain pressure the combustion becomes unstable; in fact, certain propellants will not sustain burning at atmospheric pressures. This, of course, means that the operating chamber pressure of solid units must be relatively high and always safely above this *lower pressure limit*. On the other hand, this lower combustion pressure limit represents an inherent safety feature in some solid propellants, for they will not ignite inadvertently at ambient pressure. Also, should the chamber explode, any fragments of these certain solid propellants will be relatively harmless since they will not sustain combustion at ambient pressure. This safety feature is not generally true of most liquid propellants.

Because many grains have regressive burning characteristics during the thrust decay period, there is often a propellant residue left (particularly with grains of irregular cross section) which will cease to burn once the chamber pressure falls below the lower pressure limit. Depending on the specific design, this remaining propellant may amount to perhaps 2 to 8 per cent of the initial propellant charge and is not effective in giving impulse to the rocket. In some designs this residue is referred to as "slivers."

The pressure is, as was explained previously, determined by the throat area. When the throat area exceeds a certain value, the combustion pressure will approach the lower pressure limit and the burning process will have a tendency to become unstable. This throat area is called the critical throat area; the actual throat area must always be smaller. The chamber pressure is usually selected so as to be safely above this limiting lower combustion pressure. A much higher operating pressure would require excessive wall thickness and an unduly heavy chamber weight.

Above a certain *upper pressure limit,* the burning rate will increase so rapidly that normal burning will no longer be possible and a detonation will occur which will usually shatter the chamber. This pressure is very high for most propellants (above 6000 pounds per square inch).

Deterioration

Many solid propellants deteriorate with storage. Some propellants experience a low order chemical reaction during storage, which changes the energy potential and the properties of the grain. Certain chemicals are often added to inhibit this decomposition. Other propellants absorb moisture which softens and weakens the charge. The decomposition of various double base propellants is self-catalyzing. Chemicals (such as diphenylamine added to Ballistite propellant) are usually added to neutralize the effect of the initial decomposition products.

Handling Precautions

As was mentioned previously, the formation of cracks in the grain is undesirable because it causes uncontrolled increases in the effective burning surface. Cracks in propellant grains are very difficult to detect. For these reasons it is necessary to handle solid propellant rockets carefully and avoid impact or shock loads on the rocket during storage and handling.

Size and Duration Limitation

The duration of solid propellant rockets is limited because of the practical problems of constructing very large and heavy

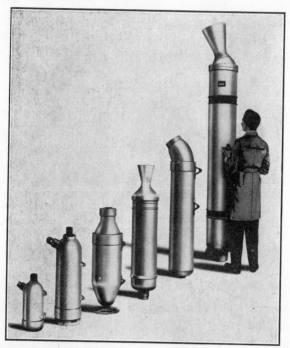

FIGURE 9–6. Solid propellant booster and assisted take-off rockets come in many different sizes and shapes. Reading from right to left these are rated at 250-lb thrust, 1000 lb for 14 sec, 1000 lb for 15 sec, 11,000 lb for 2.2 sec, 4500 lb for 5 sec, and 33,000 lb for 2.2 sec. For easy installation in aircraft, some of the nozzles are inclined with respect to the chamber axis. (Courtesy of Aerojet-General Corporation.)

chambers and because of excessive heating of critical and structural hardware parts in prolonged operation.

For any given propellant charge size there is also an upper limit to the maximum thrust, set by disproportionately large nozzles in relation to port area and propellant volume. Within this limitation, many different designs are possible; some typical shapes are shown in Figure 9–6.

7 Comparison between Solid Propellant and Liquid Propellant Rockets

It is very difficult to draw generalized conclusions on the relative merits of liquid and solid propellant rockets. Each particular application must be examined individually for the best exploitation of the inherent characteristics of the two types. Table 9–3 gives some of the more apparent advantages for each one.

TABLE 9–3. COMPARISON, LIQUID VS SOLID PROPELLANTS

Liquid Propellants	*Solid Propellants*
1. Can be less sensitive to temperature.	1. Simpler in construction and design.
2. Can be turned on and off.	2. Usually the lighter unit for low total impulse applications.
3. Usually lighter unit for long duration or high thrust.	3. Few servicing problems.
4. Often gives higher specific impulse.	4. Believed to be more reliable.
5. Thrust may be varied readily.	5. Sometimes difficult to handle.
6. Often involves simpler propellant preparation.	

Problems

1. What is the ratio of the burning area to the nozzle area for a solid propellant unit with these characteristics?

Propellant density	107 lb/cu ft
Chamber pressure	2000 psia
Burning rate	1.5 in./sec
Exhaust velocity	6000 ft/sec
Temperature sensitivity	0.004 $(°F)^{-1}$
Specific heat ratio	1.27
Gas constant	70 ft-lb/lb °F
Chamber gas temperature	4000° R

2. Plot the burning rate against chamber pressure for the unit above, using equation 9-1. Assume $n = 0.75$, $(1500 < p_1 < 3000)$, and $v_b = 1.5$ in./sec at $p_1 = 2000$ psia.

3. What would the area ratio A_b/A_t in problem 1 be if the pressure were increased by 10 per cent? (Use curve from problem 2.)

4. Assuming a space factor of 1.10, a duration of 15 sec, and a thrust of 1000 lb, what would be the chamber length and diameter for the unit in problem 1 if it were a restricted burning rocket?

5. Assume flat cylinder ends, a nozzle weight of 4 lb, an igniter weight of 1.5 lb, and mounting fittings of 1 lb. What is the total weight of the unit? What percentage is occupied by propellants? Assume an average hoop tension working stress of 30,000 psi and conditions similar to those of problem 1.

6. For the simple burning rate law (equation 9-1), find and plot the variation of burning rate for the following propellants between chamber pressures of 700 and 2000 psi.

Propellant	Burning Rate at 1000 psi	Exponent n
Castable composite	0.80 in./sec	0.80
Castable composite	0.12 in./sec	0.40
Double base	0.85 in./sec	0.70

Symbols

a	burning rate constant
A_b	solid propellant burning area, ft^2
A_p	port area (flow area of gases between and around propellant grains), ft^2
A_t	nozzle throat cross-sectional area, ft^2
C_F	thrust coefficient
c	effective exhaust velocity, ft/sec
F	thrust, lb
$\bar{F}$	average thrust, lb
g	acceleration due to gravity, ft/sec^2
I_s	specific impulse, sec or lb-sec/lb
I_t	total impulse, lb-sec
K	ratio of burning surface to throat area, A_b/A_c
k	specific heat ratio
n	burning rate exponent
p	pressure, lb/ft^2
R	gas constant, ft-lb/lb °R
r	propellant burning rate (velocity of consumption), ft/sec or in./sec

T absolute temperature, °R

t time, sec

V_c chamber volume, ft³

v_2 theoretical exhaust velocity, ft/sec

W_G total loaded rocket weight, or gross weight, lb

W_u total effective propellant weight, lb

$\dot{w}$ weight rate of flow, lb/sec

Greek Letters

δ partial derivative

π_K temperature sensitivity coefficient of equilibrium pressure, (°F)⁻¹

ρ density, lb/ft³

σ_p temperature sensitivity coefficient of burning rate, (°F)⁻¹

Subscripts

b solid propellant burning conditions

c chamber conditions

e nozzle exit conditions

t throat conditions

Chapter 10

Solid Propellants

1 Classification

This chapter describes some typical solid propellants, their physical and chemical characteristics, and their fabrication methods. This subject is extremely complex, and this chapter is intended to serve primarily as an introduction to some of the problems.

Solid propellants are chemicals which produce hot, high pressure gases by means of a combustion process, and these gases can therefore be used to provide the reaction force for rocket propulsion. Any one solid propellant usually includes two or more of the following:

1. *Oxidizer* (nitrates or perchlorates).
2. *Fuel* (organic resins or plastics).
3. *Chemical compound* combining fuel and oxidizer qualities (nitrocellulose or nitroglycerin).
4. *Additives* (to control fabrication process, burning rate, etc.).
5. *Inhibitors* (bonded, taped, or dip-dried onto propellant) to restrict burning surface.

There are two principal types of propellants. The first, often called *composite propellant* type, has two important ingredients, a fuel and an oxidizer, neither of which would burn satisfactorily without the presence of the other. Often these consist of crystalline, finely ground oxidizers dispersed in a matrix of a fuel compound. The second type contains unstable chemical compounds, such as nitrocellulose or nitroglycerin, which are capable of combustion in the absence of all other material. Because many of these propellants are based largely on a colloid of nitroglycerin and nitrocellulose, they are often referred to as *double base* propellants (this differentiates them from many gun powders which traditionally have been based on one or the other). Most of the accepted solid propellants contain from four to eight different chemicals. In addition to the principal ingredients (fuel and oxidizer), small percentages of additives are used to control the physical and chemical properties of the solid propellant. Additives have been used for the following typical purposes: (1) accelerate or decelerate the burning rate (catalyst); (2) increase chemical stability to avoid deterioration during storage; (3) control various processing properties of propellant during fabrication (curing time, fluidity for casting, wetting agent, etc.); (4) control radiation absorption properties of burning propellant; (5) increase physical strength and decrease elastic deformation; (6) minimize temperature sensitivity. Further information on solid propellant rockets can be found in Section 4.5 of the Reference Bibliography.

2   Desired Properties

In evaluating and comparing solid propellant properties, the following are considered important and desirable. The order in which these desirable characteristics are listed below has no relation to their relative importance. As a comparison with Chapter 6 will indicate, the desired qualities are in many respects similar to those of liquid propellants.

1. *A high release of chemical energy* promotes a high performance and therefore a high value of combustion temperature and specific impulse.
2. *A low molecular weight of the combustion products* is desirable to increase the value of the specific impulse.
3. The solid propellant should be *stable* for a long period of time and *should not deteriorate chemically or physically* during storage.
4. *High density* of the solid propellant permits the use of a small chamber volume and therefore a small chamber weight.
5. The solid propellant should be *unaffected by atmospheric conditions;* for example, it should not be hygroscopic.

6. The propellant *should not be subject to accidental ignition,* that is, its auto-ignition temperature should be relatively high and it should be insensitive to impact. For this reason also the lower combustion pressure limit * should be higher than atmospheric.

7. The propellant should have *high physical strength properties,* particularly its tensile, compressive, and shear strength and its modulus of elasticity and elongation.

8. *A small coefficient of thermal expansion will minimize* the relative motion within the chamber and the thermal stresses within the stored grain.

9. The propellant composition should be *chemically inert during storage and operation* and should not require special materials for chamber or nozzle construction.

10. The propellant should lend itself readily to production and have *desirable fabrication properties,* such as adequate fluidity during casting, or easy control of chemical processes (such as curing) and a minimum of volume change after casting or molding (shrinkage).

11. The propellant's performance properties and fabrication technique should be relatively *insensitive to impurities or small processing variations* to simplify its production and inspection and reduce its cost.

12. The physical properties and combustion characteristics (burning rate), should be predictable and not affected appreciably over a wide range of storage and operating temperatures, ideally from −100 to 180° F. This implies that the *temperature sensitivity is low.*

13. The exhaust gas should be *smokeless* to avoid deposition of smoke particles at operational locations and to avoid detection in military use.

14. The propellant should lend itself readily to bonding to the metal parts, to the application of inhibitors, to *different production techniques,* and should be amenable to the *use of a simple igniter.*

15. The exhaust should be *non-luminous* (to avoid detection in military applications) and *non-toxic.*

---

* Defined on page 325.

16. The method of propellant *preparation should be simple* and should not require a complex chemical plant installation.
17. The solid propellants *conductivity* and *specific heat* should be such as to control heat transfer to the grain.
18. The propellant grain should be *opaque to radiation,* to prevent ignition at locations other than the burning surface.
19. The propellant should *resist erosion.*

3 Basic Chemicals

Oxidizers

The Perchlorates. In the order of decreasing oxidizing potential some of the perchlorates used are:

Sodium perchlorate	$NaClO_4$	52 per cent available oxygen
Potassium perchlorate	$KClO_4$	46 per cent available oxygen
Magnesium perchlorate	$Mg(ClO_4)_2$	34 per cent available oxygen
Ammonium perchlorate	NH_4ClO_4	25.2 per cent available oxygen

All of the perchlorates produce hydrogen chloride (HCl) and other chlorine compounds in their reaction with fuels. These oxidizers produce an exhaust gas which is not only toxic but also highly corrosive to many materials. The hydrochloric acid condenses in a moist atmosphere to form a dangerous fog. With the exception of ammonium perchlorate, all form a dense smoky exhaust because KCl or NaCl are white powders. Ammonium and potassium perchlorate are only slightly soluble in water and therefore can be used for propellants which are exposed to moisture. The other two absorb water readily and therefore are somewhat difficult to use. The perchlorates are usually produced by the electrolysis of chlorides which are naturally available materials. The oxidizing potential of the perchlorates is generally high, and for this reason they are often found in propellants of high specific impulse. The perchlorates are available in the form of small white crystals, and the accurate control of the crystal size influences the fabrication and burning rate.

Inorganic Nitrates. Three nitrates are of interest in solid propellant preparation:

Potassium nitrate	KNO_3	39.5 per cent available oxygen
Sodium nitrate	$NaNO_3$	47 per cent available oxygen
Ammonium nitrate	NH_4NO_3	20 per cent available oxygen

The first two, potassium nitrate and sodium nitrate, produce undesirable smoke in the exhaust because of the solid material formed in the combustion products. The third, ammonium nitrate, has the big advantage of a smokeless, relatively non-toxic exhaust, but its oxidizing potential is low and it is suitable primarily for low performance, low burning rate applications. For gas generator propellants, this has considerable merit. An additional complication is caused by the polymorphic transformations of the crystals with temperature changes, resulting in a change in volume and difficulties in storage and preparation.

The nitrate salts are used in fertilizers and other industrial applications and are relatively cheap and naturally available. Ammonium nitrate can be produced from nitric acid and ammonia.

Organic Nitrates. Some of the organic nitrates most commonly used in propellants are glycerol trinitrate or nitroglycerin, $C_3H_5(ONO_2)_3$, diethyleneglycol dinitrate or DEGN, $(CH_2CH_2-ONO_2)_2O$, and cellulose nitrate or nitrocellulose, $C_6H_7O_2(ONO_2)_3$. The $-ONO_2$ group is characteristic of nitrates. All are basically unstable compounds which are capable of oxidizing their organic material.

Nitroglycerin is a colorless oily liquid, only slightly soluble in water but readily soluble in alcohol and ether. It is rapidly absorbed through the skin, and undue exposure to the material often causes violent headaches. The most significant property of nitroglycerin is violent detonation on slight shock. The molecule contains more than sufficient oxygen to convert the carbon and hydrogen to the corresponding oxides, and gaseous nitrogen is liberated. The generally accepted method of production is the nitration of glycerin using a mixture of nitric and sulphuric acids. Nitroglycerin is somewhat less sensitive in the solid form, and also when absorbed in such materials as diatomaceous earth, sawdust, and charcoal. Commercial dynamites usually contain nitroglycerin absorbed in sawdust, in which form it is sufficiently insensitive to shock to permit handling and shipping with comparative safety. A somewhat similar material is obtained when nitrocellulose is gelatinized with nitroglycerin, the resulting material having satisfactory stability. This is the basis of Ballistite type propellants, or so-called double base propellants.

Commercial nitrocellulose has much the same appearance as ordinary cotton and consists largely of cellulose trinitrate. It is fabricated by the nitration of wood pulp or cotton linters. The degree of nitration influences the properties of nitrocellulose. Highly nitrated material, called guncotton, contains 12.2 to 13.8 per cent nitrogen and thus corresponds closely to pure cellulose trinitrate, the theoretical nitrogen content of which is 14.16 per cent.

Many different compositions of double base propellants have been used successfully. Additives (5 to 30 per cent) are used to aid in the control of physical properties, ease of manufacture, stability during storage, flash suppression, and augmented capacity to prevent ignition by radiation of energy through the translucent grain at locations other than the burning surface. An increase in nitrocellulose content generally increases the physical strength and a high nitroglycerin content tends to increase the performance and burning rate. Tables 9–1 and 10–1 show some typical data on double base propellants.

TABLE 10–1. REPRESENTATIVE COMPOSITIONS OF EXTRUDED AND CAST DOUBLE BASE PROPELLANTS *

Ingredients	Extruded Ballistite (JPN)	Experimental Casting Propellant	Experimental Castable Propellant	German Extrusion World War II
Nitrocellulose	51.5	47.0	59.9	64.7
Nitroglycerin	43.0	37.7	38.7	
Diethyl phthalate	3.25			
Ethyl centralite	1.0	1.0	0.9	
Potassium sulfate	1.25			
Carbon black or graphite	0.2	0.3	0.2	0.1
Candelilla wax	0.02			
Dimethyl phthalate		14.0		
Diethyleneglycol dinitrate				29.3
Phenyl urethanes				4.8
Arcardite				0.1
Barium sulphate and titanium dioxide				0.9
Diphenylamine			0.2	

* Furnished in part by C. E. Bartley, Grand Central Aircraft Company, and in part by U. S. Naval Ordnance Test Station, China Lake, California.

Aromatic Nitro Compounds. Several of the aromatic nitro compounds that have been used in propellants are ammonium picrate, $C_6H_2(NO_2)_3ONH_4$, trinitrotoluene, $CH_3C_6H_2(NO_2)_3$, or

TNT, and dinitrotoluene, $CH_3C_6H_3(NO_2)_2$, or DNT. The nitro compounds contain the $-NO_2$ group, as distinguished from the $-ONO_2$ group in nitrates.

Fuels

Many different organic fuels have been used in solid propellants. They are selected in part for their ability to be oxidized, for adding desirable physical properties to the mixtures, and for their desirable fabrication characteristics. In fabrication many fuels are mixed with a crystalline oxidizer while the fuel is in the liquid state and often at an elevated temperature. Thereafter, the fuel undergoes either a chemical change or a physical change due to temperature drop between the elevated mixing temperature and ambient temperature to harden the grain.

Asphalt–Oil Type Fuels. Asphalt is a bituminous hydrocarbon. It needs to be heated and liquefied to permit it to be mixed with the solid oxidizers. The mixture is then cast into rocket chambers and allowed to cool to a semi-solid state. Because asphalt becomes very brittle and has a tendency to crack at low operating temperatures, it has been necessary to mix oils with the asphalt to improve the physical characteristics at low temperature. However, the maximum operating temperature limits of the propellants are narrow because the material with added oil becomes too soft to withstand deformation in storage or operation at the higher temperatures. Several early United States propellants used asphalt as a fuel together with perchlorate oxidizers.

Plastic Fuels. Various thermosetting plastics have been investigated for rocket propellants, including phenol formaldehyde and phenol-furfural resins. The various components of the plastic are mixed, the oxidizer is added, and the mixture is cast before the plastic sets. With non-thermosetting plastics, such as styrene, a soft non-hardening elastic mixture should be retained.

Rubber Type Fuels. Several types of synthetic rubber and gum-like products can be used for propellant bases. The elastic properties of this material permit simpler design provisions for thermal expansion and contraction of the propellant during storage, and better transfer of pressure loads.

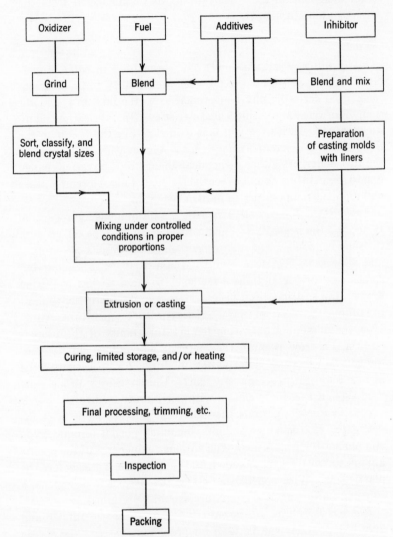

FIGURE 10-1. General processing sequences in the preparation of a fuel-
oxidizer composite type propellant.

4 Manufacture of Some Solid Propellants

The method of fabricating solid propellants is usually different for each basic type, and no general rules can be given for their manufacture. This field involves many complex specialized chemical and physical processes. This section will serve only to illus-

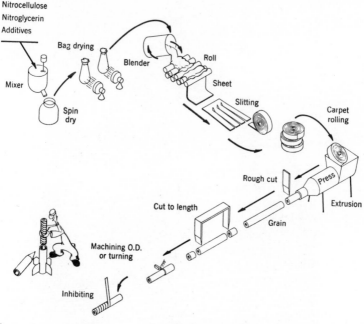

Nitrocellulose
Nitroglycerin
Additives

Bag drying

Blender

Roll

Sheet

Slitting

Carpet rolling

Mixer

Spin dry

Rough cut

Press

Extrusion

Cut to length

Grain

Machining O.D. or turning

Inhibiting

FIGURE 10–2. Diagram for manufacture of double base extruded propellant. (Courtesy U. S. Naval Ordnance Test Station, China Lake, California.)

trate briefly a few of the typical techniques and processes which have been used with certain propellants. Figures 10–1 and 10–2 illustrate typical process sequences, and Figures 10–3 to 10–5 show some typical process equipment.

Fuel–Oxidizer Type Propellants (Composite Propellants)

Propellant formulations which include a crystalline oxidizer in a fuel matrix usually are a liquid mixture at some stage of the fabrication process. They are usually cast and require the following types of processing steps.

Grinding of Oxidizer Crystals. It has been found that the particle size of the crystals has a major effect on the burning rate, the processing properties, and the physical properties of the pro-

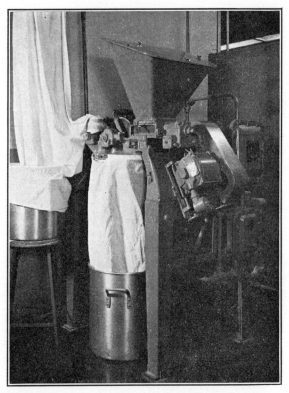

FIGURE 10–3. This grinder is used for grinding small quantities of oxidizer crystals to their desired size. Raw material is fed into hopper on top and products are put into buckets underneath machine. Cloth hoses are used to prevent loss of fine crystals. (Courtesy North American Aviation, Inc.)

pellant. In general, a decrease in particle size results in an increase in burning rate. The effects of crystal size are sometimes so significant that a whole series of propellants can be made with the same composition by merely varying the particle size. This effect is shown in Figure 10–6. The grinding of the crystals to the proper sizes (and also the proper distribution of particle sizes) under controlled atmosphere conditions is a mechanical process which is often difficult to control. A typical experimental grinder is shown in Figure 10–3.

Propellant Mixing. The proper proportions of crystalline oxidizer, fuel, and additives have to be accurately measured and the ingredients mixed thoroughly in a suitable piece of equipment. Some fuels require elevated temperatures (for example, the use

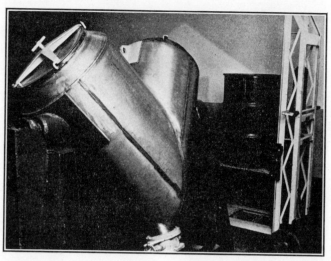

FIGURE 10–4. The mixing and blending of crystals of different sizes and other solid ingredients is accomplished in blenders like this one which is used for experimental batches. The V-shaped tank container is filled through the openings on top of the V and emptied through the valve on the bottom. Blending is accomplished by slow rotation of the unit. (Courtesy North American Aviation, Inc.)

of steam-jacketed mixers) to attain sufficient fluidity to permit mixing. Other fuels (usually consisting of two or more basic ingredients) undergo a chemical change and release heat (for example, certain types of polymerizing plastics) to form the grain. With this last type of fuel, the grains must be cast, extruded, or formed within a prescribed time after mixing. If this chemical reaction is highly exothermic, the mixer may have to include cooling provisions.

Casting of Grain. Many of the propellants which have a crystalline oxidizing agent are cast into the proper grain shape. Some types are pressure molded or extruded, as explained subsequently.

They are cast either directly into the combustion chamber (which has been prepared prior to casting by suitable cleaning processes and often the application of a liner) or into special molds. To form the required port area a metal core or mandrel is inserted into the mold. This core is usually slightly tapered to permit

Figure 10-5. This mixer for small experimental batches has two rotary agitator blades inside a U-shaped container. In this picture the top cover of the mixer has been removed. The hoses on the right permit circulation of steam or hot water; this heats the contents of the mixer to the desired temperature. Hopper on right is used for loading of mixer. Steel enclosure with shatterproof window is used for protection of personnel when mixing particularly hazardous, new experimental formulations. (Courtesy North American Aviation, Inc.)

easy withdrawal after hardening of the propellant. The mandrel is usually coated with some special chemical to prevent the cast propellant from sticking to it. To prevent the formation of air bubbles in the grain during the casting process, a vacuum is sometimes applied. Other propellants are poured under pressure to assure complete filling of the molds. The techniques used in casting propellant vary widely.

Curing. After casting, the propellant is cured. With some fuels, this involves merely a slow and controlled cooling process;

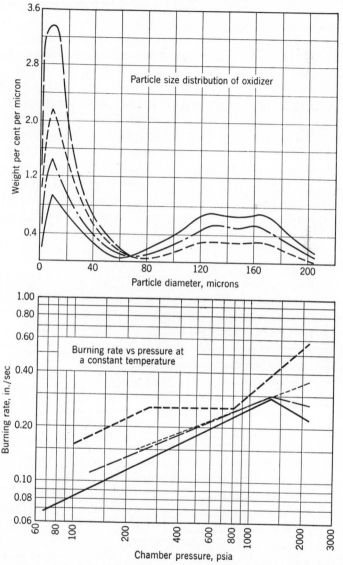

FIGURE 10–6. Effect of oxidizer particle size on the burning rate of a heterogeneous propellant using ammonium perchlorate. (Reproduced from C. E. Bartley and M. M. Mills "Solid Propellant Rockets," Section H, Vol. XII, *Jet Propulsion*, a portion of the series on *High Speed Aerodynamics and Jet Propulsion*, Princeton University Press.)

with others, it involves a chemical reaction in the propellant. The time required for this chemical process depends on the curing temperature—the higher the temperature the faster the curing. Since the curing is often characterized by an exothermic reaction, the center of the propellant grain may be hotter than the outside.

Final Processing. Final processing includes the withdrawal of mandrels, the cutting off of excess propellant in the risers, and the sealing of the chamber. If a mold is used, the grain is removed from the mold and cut to proper size, inhibitors may be applied, and the grain is inserted into the chamber.

The pressure molding process, which has been used successfully with double base propellants and is briefly described later in this section, is also used with some composite propellants, particularly when the mixture is very viscous. Propellants with a high crystalline content fall into this type.

Double Base Type Propellants

A variety of processes has been used with double base propellants, that is, those that have a colloid of nitrocellulose and nitroglycerin as the principal constituent. Ballistite is of this type (see Table 10–1). They are prepared by a solvent or a solventless extrusion process (see Figure 10–2), or sometimes by a casting process. In the solvent process a volatile solvent is mixed with the ingredients to improve the mixing, casting, extrusion, and forming qualities. Resulting grains are dried to remove the solvent. However, the solvent may, by evaporation, cause fissures, shrinkage, and cracks. This process is desirable for propellant grain configuration with thin sections. In the solventless process the blending and mixing are accomplished largely by running the propellant through heated differential rollers or other mechanical shaping devices. The material is then generally extruded through a suitable die at very high pressures (in the order of 5000 to 20,000 pounds per square inch). An extrusion press is shown in Figure 10–7. The extruded grain is generally heated to relieve internal stresses in the material. Although the extrusion process requires costly equipment, it permits the exact control of grain size and shape. In the casting process of double base propellants, nitroglycerin liquid with additives is cast into an evacuated mold which has been preloaded with small pellets of nitrocellulose. Thereafter the mold is heated and the nitrocellulose forms a nearly homogeneous solid with the liquid mixture. This process is relatively non-hazardous and permits the manufacture of very large grains.

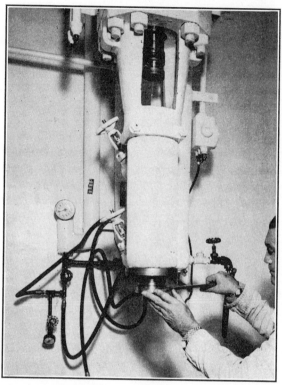

FIGURE 10–7. Insulated 12-in. propellant extrusion press and housing. (Courtesy U. S. Naval Ordnance Test Station, China Lake, California.)

Pressed Powder Charges

Several types of rocket propellants are made by pressing or forming mixtures of loose, small particles into grain shapes. Black powder is such a propellant, consisting of mixtures of several compounds as shown in Table 10–2. Early solid propellant charges and early gunpowder consisted almost entirely of some variety of black powder. It tends to absorb moisture when stored. It is still used in fireworks, signaling rockets, igniter booster

TABLE 10–2. PRESSED POWDERS

	Black Powder	Guanadine Nitrate Type
Composition	KNO$_3$ (57 to 80 per cent) C (Charcoal, ground peach stones, etc., 13 to 29 per cent) Sulphur (ignition aid; 8 to 22 per cent)	Guanadine nitrate Ammonium nitrate Catalysts (e.g., chromates)
Density, lb/ft^3	80–130	90–110
Specific impulse, sec	50–140	130–193
Flame temperature, °F	1500–3500	1900–3200

charges, and life-saving rockets. Manufacture requires mixing the ingredients in the proper proportions and forming them, sometimes under pressure, into the desired grain shape. A binder such as starch, glue, plastic, or oil is added.

Mixtures of ammonium nitrate and guanadine nitrate with appropriate catalysts for decomposition are used for small rockets which propel small model aircraft. Loose powder is compressed under high pressure (perhaps 7000 pounds per square inch) into suitable molds. The finished charge is hard and rock-like in appearance.

Chapter 11

Design of

Solid Propellant Rockets

This chapter describes in general terms some of the problems encountered in solid propellant rocket design.

1 Chamber Pressure Selection

Once a specific propellant has been selected, the designer has some liberty in choosing the chamber pressure, grain geometry, and burning rate to fulfill a desired thrust-time program. The following are some of the general considerations which affect the choice of the chamber pressure.

1. The pressure must be above the lower combustion pressure limit to insure steady smooth burning at all initial grain temperatures.
2. High chamber pressures may be desired in some cases, where the resultant increase in specific impulse is significant. For a given thrust, the higher pressure generally also permits the use of a smaller throat.
3. In general, the overall weight of the rocket unit increases with chamber pressure. This increase also implies heavier supports, more difficult handling, higher heat transfer to the metal parts, and increased costs. These considerations therefore favor the selection of the minimum feasible chamber pressure.
4. The desired burning rate for a specific application also affects the chamber pressure selection, because the burning rate is an exponential function of this pressure.

There is no general rule for the selection of the optimum chamber pressure, particularly since some of the factors (for example, cost, prior experience) are not strictly subject to analysis. Therefore the choice of chamber pressure has to be made on the merits of the specific application.

2   Grain Selection

The grain geometry for a given thrust program and chamber pressure can assume a variety of different configurations. Below are listed some of the factors which need to be considered in selecting the geometry of the solid propellant charge.

1. Many applications present a fundamental geometrical limitation, such as the maximum missile diameter or the maximum overall length.

2. In high performance applications it is important to obtain a high loading density in the chamber and to minimize the void space and the internal channel or port area. Also it is desirable to minimize the residual, ineffective propellant remaining after operation.

3. Often the grain geometry will influence the heating of the walls and, to some extent, of the nozzle. For example, the bonding of an internally burning grain to the chamber wall will materially reduce the heat transfer to the wall and thus permit the use of a thinner and lighter wall.

4. Proper grain design will prevent or control the phenomenon of erosive burning. This erosion is the result of an increased and sometimes erratic rate of burning at those grain areas where high local gas velocities (particularly on the surfaces of internal channels) cause scrubbing and wearing of the exposed surfaces. Further discussion of erosive burning will be found in another section of this chapter.

5. The desired thrust program determines the desired burning area program. As already mentioned in Chapter 9, this burning surface relation with time can be altered to give progressive, regressive, or neutral burning characteristics. A simple rod grain, for example, is highly regressive in its gas evolution, while an internally burning tube grain is very progressive.

Figure 11–1 shows these characteristics for several cylindrical grain configurations in which the ends are inhibited.

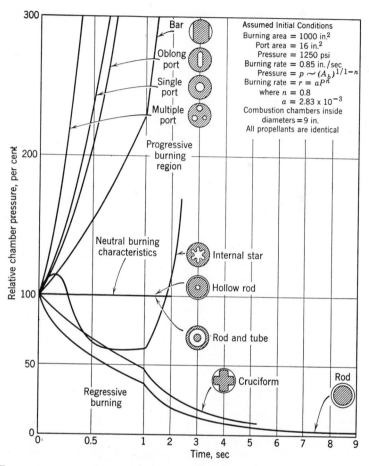

Assumed Initial Conditions
Burning area = 1000 in.²
Port area = 16 in.²
Pressure = 1250 psi
Burning rate = 0.85 in./sec
Pressure = $p \sim (A_b)^{1/1-n}$
Burning rate = $r = aP^n$
where $n = 0.8$
$a = 2.83 \times 10^{-3}$
Combustion chambers inside diameters = 9 in.
All propellants are identical

FIGURE 11–1. Calculated chamber pressure–time histories for several different grain configurations.

By partially inhibiting the exposed surfaces by varying the grain design, by tapering the ends, by perforating the grains, and by employing a combination of several grains in the same chamber, an infinite variety of thrust programs can be achieved.

6. The physical strength characteristics of a given propellant will often limit the grain geometry. This limitation is discussed further in Section 4 of this chapter.

The specifications and limitations of a given application will influence the relative weight that should be attached to the factors mentioned above as they are used in arriving at a selected grain design.

3   Burning Rate and Erosion

Burning progresses in a direction normal to the exposed burning surface and at a rate which is a function of combustion pressure, ambient grain temperature, and the propellant properties. For approximate calculations and for narrow ranges of variables, some simplified formulas such as $r = ap_c{}^n$ (equation 9–1) have been suggested. Another approximate formula which is frequently used is

$$r = a + bp_c \qquad (11\text{–}1)$$

where r is the burning rate, p_c is the chamber pressure, and a and b are constants for a given initial grain temperature.

For design purposes the accuracy given by these simple relations is not usually adequate, and graphical presentation of propellant data or more sophisticated theory must be used. The burning process is a function of the chemical composition, the method of propellant preparation, the initial grain temperature, the burning time, the gas velocity adjacent to the grain, the radiation pattern, and the geometrical shape of the grain. The actual burning process is complex and not well understood. It involves interacting reactions in the solid, liquid, and gaseous phases at high pressures and temperature. A very high temperature gradient usually exists between the solid propellant and the hot gases at the burning surfaces. There are variations in burning rate, caused by grain geometry, minor manufacturing processing differences, and erosion, all with basically the same standard propellant composition and configuration. For these reasons the burning rate is often determined empirically and presented in plots such as Figure 9–4, for specific applications.

In the development of new formulations, a simple apparatus

is used to evaluate the linear burning rate of small propellant rod grains or strands by determining the time intervals between the burning out of wires embedded at predetermined locations in the strand. An apparatus of this type is illustrated schematically in Figure 11–2.

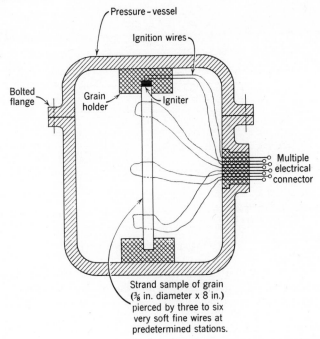

FIGURE 11–2. Schematic of apparatus for measuring linear burning rate.

Erosive burning is the term used to indicate that the burning rate of a solid propellant is affected by the flow of high velocity gases parallel to the burning surface. In a typical grain design with constant port area flow channels, erosion will generally occur inside the channel near the nozzle end where the gas velocity is high. Erosion is characterized by an increase in burning rate and is usually expressed in terms of an erosion coefficient, ϵ.

$$\epsilon = \frac{r}{r_0} \qquad (11\text{–}2)$$

where r is the burning rate with erosion and r_0 is the burning rate of the same propellant without gas flow parallel to its surface. Several investigators have suggested analytical expressions for the approximation of this erosion factor, ϵ. In general it appears to be a function of velocity and has been expressed by the relation (Ref. 3.612)

$$\epsilon = 1 + K \frac{\dot{w}}{\dot{w}^*} \tag{11-3}$$

where K is an erosion burning constant which varies according to Figure 11–3, $\dot{w}$ is the weight flow rate through the channel in

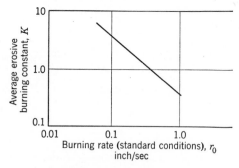

FIGURE 11–3. Typical variation of erosive constant with burning rate. (Reproduced from L. Green, "Erosive Burning of Some Composite Solid Propellants," *Jet Propulsion*, Vol. 24, No. 1, Jan.–Feb. 1954.)

pounds per second, and $\dot{w}^*$ is the weight flow rate which produces a Mach number of 1.0 in the constant area channel. As can be seen from Figure 11–3, the erosion effect is more pronounced in slow-burning propellants.

By permitting erosion to occur under controlled conditions it is possible to decrease the channel cross section and the channel volume and increase the relative amount of propellant in the chamber. The erosion is usually most pronounced at the beginning of burning and diminishes as the flow channels become larger.

4   Forces Acting on the Grain

Dynamic Loads

The dynamic forces acting on a propellant grain have different causes, namely:

1. The grain is pushed toward the nozzle by forces resulting from the *gas pressure difference* between the aft and forward end of those grains where hot gases flow in channels parallel to the chamber axis. A more detailed examination of these gas pressures is given in the next section.
2. The *axial accelerations* of the vehicle also usually cause the grain to be pushed toward the nozzle. This force is not present during static firing.
3. The *friction* of the gas flowing through the port channels causes an additional force in the direction toward the nozzle.
4. Forces are created also by the *impact* of the gases against protrusions or cross perforations.
5. *Side acceleration* caused by maneuvers of the vehicle will tend to put unusual loads on the grain.
6. *Shock loads* or sudden pressurization of the chamber by the igniter gases may require special grain supports.

It is noteworthy that all these categories of forces with the exception of the last two have the same direction and tend to push the grain toward the nozzle. The grain and the grain supports must withstand these forces if the design of the rocket is to be successful.

The support of the grain has been accomplished by different methods: (*a*) The grain is inherently strong enough to withstand the imposed loads and the forces are resisted by the converging section of the nozzle or the closure around the nozzle, (*b*) the grain is reinforced by molding or bonding strong structural members into or onto the grain (for example, case bonding to the chamber wall), and (*c*) the grain is mechanically supported by special fixtures at one or more stations in the rocket.

In methods (*a*) and (*c*) the grain is usually held or supported near the nozzle (see Figure 9–1). The dynamic forces acting on the grain then usually load it in compression as a column. The column strength of the grain is therefore one of its most significant physical properties. From an examination of simple column formulas (Ref. 6.708) it can be seen that the modulus of elasticity is a significant parameter. In many grain designs the column becomes smaller in cross section as the propellant is consumed until it becomes too weak to withstand the compression loading and thus crumbles.

In method (*b*) the strength of the grain and grain support structure usually depends on shear transfer to keep the grain from failing mechanically.

The allowable shear and compression forces vary considerably with the propellant formulation, the rate of loading, manufacturing method, or also with the ambient temperature of the grain. Typical values are given in Table 11–1.

TABLE 11–1.   TYPICAL PHYSICAL PROPERTIES OF A DOUBLE BASE SOLID
ROCKET PROPELLANT SIMILAR TO JPN

Temperature, °F	Compression Stress, psi	Shear Stress, psi
60	1500	1000
100	1050	800
140	700	800

Density	102 lb/cu ft
Coefficient of thermal expansion	8×10^{-5} per °F

Static Loads

The materials used in the preparation of solid propellants usually exhibit a relatively large change in linear dimension or volume with changes in temperature. Thus, uneven changes in the ambient temperature during storage or shipment often cause stresses to be induced in the grain. For example, a simple mechanically supported and unrestrained grain 4 feet long can easily change its length by approximately 1 inch over a temperature range from −65 to +160° F. The stresses introduced by restraining the grain inside the chamber while it undergoes temperature changes must be kept sufficiently low to prevent permanent deformation or cracking of the grain. With some rubber-like propellant formulations, it is possible to absorb this stress internally. Other grain compositions, such as the double base propellants and certain plastic composite propellants, do not readily permit case bonding and therefore must be supported in a flexible manner inside the chamber. The design in these cases is usually such that the propellant is allowed to expand and contract. Sometimes a large spring is used to keep the propellant properly positioned with respect to the nozzle.

In addition to the stress imposed by thermal expansion, the grain must withstand the normal handling shocks and loads imposed upon a typical rocket. In order to prove the ability to withstand rough handling, a rocket model is usually subjected to severe drop tests, vibration tests, or shock tests prior to mass production.

5 Pressure and Velocity Distribution along Length of Rockets with Burning Surfaces Parallel to Rocket Axis

With the aid of Figure 11–4, a simplified explanation is offered here for the changes in the conditions of the gases as they

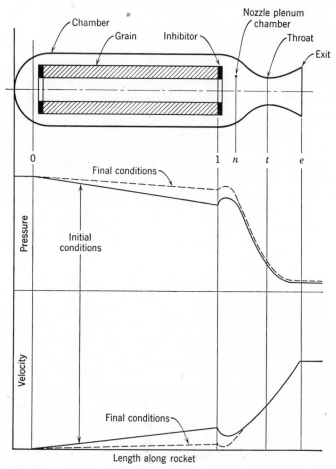

FIGURE 11–4. Pressure and velocity history in solid propellant rocket.

traverse a typical solid propellant rocket. A partial theoretical analysis can be made and it is based on the following simplifying assumptions.

1. The pressure is constant at any one cross section. This implies that the pressure distribution in one port or flow passage is identical with that of the adjacent one.
2. The perfect gas laws apply.
3. There is no friction loss.
4. The thermodynamic processes are adiabatic.
5. The port area, A_p, is constant throughout the length of the grain at any instant. There is no erosive burning.
6. Gas is generated on the exposed surfaces of the port areas only.

The pressure is a maximum at the forward end of the rocket chamber (station 0) and diminishes along the length of the grain. Mass is added at all burning surfaces and this mass is accelerated to a velocity corresponding to the available flow area. The momentum relation indicates that the force due to the pressure difference between any two cross sections acting on the area, A_p, must equal the time rate of change of flow momentum:

$$(p_0 - p)A_p = \dot{m}v$$

or,

$$p_0 - p = \frac{\dot{m}v}{A_p} \tag{11-4}$$

where p_0 is the stagnation pressure or static pressure at station 0; p is the static pressure at any point along the grain; A_p is the port area; $\dot{m}$ is the mass flow rate; and v is the gas velocity at any station. It can be seen that the pressure drop along the grain will increase with increased mass flow or decreased port area. As the port area increases with burning time, the pressure drop becomes less pronounced. This pressure drop will be negligible if the flow velocity in the port channels is small, say less than a Mach number of $\frac{1}{4}$.

After the gases pass through the grain section, they enter a plenum chamber ahead of the nozzle (station n in Figure 11-4) and experience a decrease in velocity, a slight rise in static pressure, and a loss in total pressure.

The relations for this gas expansion depend on the geometry of the specific grain installation and can only be approximated by analysis. The following general conclusions can be drawn for grain designs with burning occurring on exposed port areas:

1. The combustion pressure is not uniform along the length of the chamber. This implies that the burning rate also varies, with the fastest burning rate occurring near the front end. This fact is not readily acknowledged in the simple theory.

2. Because of the pressure losses in the channels and the space upstream of the nozzle, the effective chamber pressure (to be used in the theoretical grain and performance calculations) is lower than the front end stagnation pressure. An exact computation of this effective pressure can be attempted, if the flow losses are known.

3. The pressure and burning rate at any one station will vary with time of burning as the cross-sectional area of the port channels increases.

4. If the pressure losses in the plenum chamber are small relative to the loss in available energy incurred in accelerating the gases in the flow channels, then an approximate value for the specific impulse ratio and the ratio of total pressures across the grain may be obtained from the relations in Section 5 of Chapter 3.

$$\left(\frac{p_0}{p_1}\right)_{static} = 1 + kM_1^2 \qquad (11\text{-}5)$$

$$\left(\frac{p_0}{p_1}\right)_{total} = \frac{1 + kM_1^2}{\left(1 + \dfrac{k-1}{2}M_1^2\right)^{k/(k-1)}} \qquad (11\text{-}6)$$

$$\frac{I_s}{(I_s)_{ideal}} = \sqrt{\frac{1 - \dfrac{\left[(1 + kM_1^2)\dfrac{p_e}{p_0}\right]^{(k-1)/k}}{1 + \dfrac{k-1}{2}M_1^2}}{1 - \left(\dfrac{p_e}{p_0}\right)^{(k-1)/k}}} \qquad (11\text{-}7)$$

where the subscripts are as explained in Figure 11–4; M_1 is the Mach number of the gases at station 1; k is the ratio of specific heats; I_s is the specific impulse for optimum expansion; and $(I_s)_{ideal}$ is the specific impulse of an equivalent rocket which has no internal pressure losses. This correction of the specific impulse is usually small, often below 5 per cent.

6 Grain Volume and Weight Relations

The volume of the chamber has to be sufficiently large to house the required propellant. The volume occupied by the propellant equals

$$V_b = \frac{W_b}{\rho_b} \tag{11-8}$$

$$= \frac{\bar{F}t_b g}{\rho_b c} \tag{11-9}$$

$$= \frac{V_c}{\omega} \tag{11-10}$$

where V_c is the chamber volume; V_b is the volume occupied by propellant; W_b is the weight of solid propellant; ρ_b is the propellant density; ω is the space factor depending on geometrical grain arrangement; $\bar{F}$ is the average thrust; t_b is the effective burning duration of the propellant; and c is the effective exhaust velocity. The space factor can be defined as

$$\omega = \frac{V_b + \text{Void space} + \text{Liner volume}}{V_b} = \frac{V_c}{V_b} \tag{11-11}$$

For restricted burning units, ω has values of approximately 1.03 to 1.25. For unrestricted burning units, the space factor varies from 1.2 to 6.0.

The thrust of a solid propellant unit is equal to the product of the effective exhaust velocity and the mass flow rate. It can also be expressed in terms of the propellant properties:

$$F = A_b r \rho_b I_s \tag{11-12}$$

where r is the propellant burning rate and A_b is the burning area.

The designer is usually given the thrust and duration of the rocket unit. A standard propellant, whose experimental properties are available, is selected. Experimental propellant data are usually presented in the form of three curves (Figure 11–5) which show:

1. Specific impulse or exhaust velocity as a function of chamber pressure.

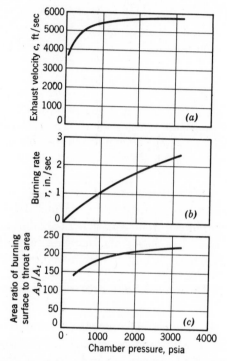

FIGURE 11–5. Typical characteristic curves at constant initial temperature of 70° F, a nozzle area ratio of 10.0, and sea level conditions for an asphalt–potassium perchlorate type propellant.

2. Burning rate as a function of chamber pressure. Equations 9–1 and 11–1 are often too simplified to be of value to the designer.

3. Area ratio as a function of chamber pressure. Although this relation is presented by equation 9–5, deviations from the perfect gas laws and internal chamber volume effects necessitate accurate plots.

The chamber pressure is selected in accordance with some of the considerations listed at the beginning of this chapter. The specific impulse is determined from curve (a) of Figure 11–5. The propellant weight can then be found.

$$W_b = \frac{Ft_b}{I_s} \tag{11–13}$$

The length of the restricted end-burning propellant charge is found from the burning rate, which is determined from curve (b) of Figure 11–5.

$$L_b = rt_b \tag{11–14}$$

L_b is the length of the restricted charge, t_b is the burning time, and r is the propellant burning rate. The cross-sectional area, A_b, of the restricted charge is found from the volume and density, ρ_b, of the propellant grain stick.

$$L_b A_b \rho_b = W_b \tag{11–15}$$

The throat area is found from curve (c) and A_b. The chamber volume is determined from equation 11–11 for a given space factor. For more complex grain shapes a more involved geometrical relation must be used to determine the grain dimensions.

7   Hardware Design for Solid Propellant Rockets

Chamber

The chamber of the solid propellant rocket contains all the grain and has to withstand pressure, starting surges, and often severe heating. The exact pressure to which a chamber is subjected is often difficult to determine, because some grains (and some igniter designs) cause momentary high pressure surges. A typical and somewhat arbitrary set of pressure design factors is as follows:

Nominal steady state operating pressure	100 per cent
Pressure at maximum specified grain operating temperature	120 per cent
Design surge pressure	150 per cent
Hydrostatic proof pressure	165 per cent
Design yield pressure	185 per cent
Design burst pressure	205 per cent

These factors depend upon past experience, application requirements, expected variations between production grain performance, and quality control of manufactured chambers.

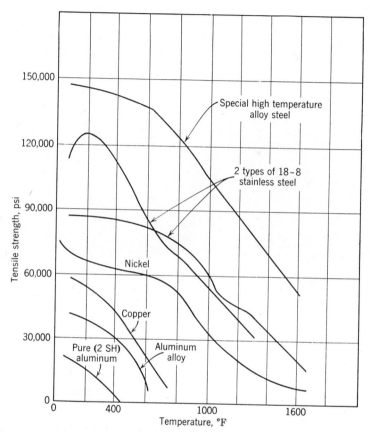

FIGURE 11-6. Typical variation of tensile strength with temperature. (For exact values many tests of specific specimens with carefully controlled heat treatment and composition are required.)

The temperature of the wall, which carries the pressure load, determines the physical properties of the stress-carrying members and therefore largely the design and weight of the chamber. As the wall material becomes hotter, its ability to carry load diminishes. Therefore, it is good design practice to limit the heating of rocket chamber walls because this will tend to reduce the required wall thickness. Various types of insulation (including case bonding of some types of propellants) have proved successful.

The variation of the tensile strength of several metals with temperature is shown in Figure 11–6. These data are based on tests in which the metal was exposed for a relatively long time (say 15 minutes) to a high temperature environment. With short time exposure (say less than 5 seconds) such as exists in rockets, these values have been found to be conservative. High strength heat-

FIGURE 11–7. Inspection of alignment, concentricities, and dimensions of chamber and nozzle of Nike rocket booster, performed before and after proof testing. (Photo Redstone Arsenal, U. S. Army.)

treated steels have been used for light weight units. Special manufacturing processes for forming the chamber cases have been developed.

The fast heating of the inner wall surface produces a temperature gradient and, therefore, thermal stresses across the wall. The theory of transient heat transfer has been treated by a number of authors, and by means of a relaxation method, a reasonable approximation of the temperature-time history at any location may be obtained. The subject of heat transfer is discussed in Chapter 5.

The chamber design must also provide for attachment of nozzle or nozzles, one or more support points for mounting, safety plugs, handling hooks, and provisions for loading the grain.

Alignment, concentricities, and center of gravity location have to be held to close tolerances, particularly in some missile applications. See Figure 11–7.

Nozzles

The nozzles of solid propellant rocket units, like the chambers, are usually uncooled, that is, no forced convection cooling can be readily employed. The nozzle section of the rocket is subjected to severe conditions (it is usually not possible to protect the inner nozzle surface with a propellant film or insulation which lasts

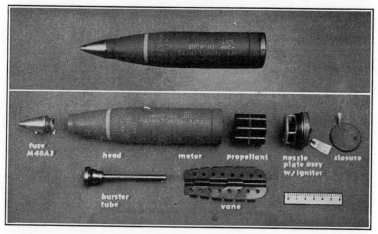

FIGURE 11–8. Spin-stabilized infantry 115-mm smoke rocket T209E1. Seven individual grains are held by a perforated grain holder at a short distance away from a nozzle plate. A slight inclination of the individual nozzles within the nozzle plate induces the rotation of the rocket. (Photo Redstone Arsenal, U. S. Army.)

more than perhaps 1 or 2 seconds) because of the relatively high heat transfer rates and because of the mechanical erosion effects of the hot, high velocity gases which contain entrained solid matter.

Metal nozzles with protective coatings (for example, chrome plate) have been used successfully for short durations. Extra metal is usually added to act as a heat sink. Ceramic nozzles or graphite nozzle inserts have been successful for longer periods (see Figure 9–1 and Section 4 of Chapter 5). The erosion and wear of the nozzle throat have to be held to a negligibly small value to control the variation in performance over the burning time. In some solid propellant rockets multiple nozzles (several nozzles in parallel) are used. These are built into a nozzle plate as shown in Figure 11–8.

Accurate alignment of the nozzle axis with the center of gravity of the flying vehicle (particularly in unguided vehicles) is very important in order to minimize flight errors. Therefore, unusually close tolerances are often specified on those dimensions which control the alignment of the nozzle axis.

To prevent the entry of moisture into the chamber and to aid ignition, a closure across the nozzle is usually provided.

Igniters

The igniters used for solid propellant rocket units are almost exclusively of the pyrotechnic type. In some cases, the igniter is put into the forward end of the chamber so that the ignition gases will sweep past the complete propellant charge before reaching the nozzle. The igniters are often held within the propellant charge, and electric wires are connected to it through the nozzle. Where wire and igniter fragments, which are ejected in starting, may cause damage, the igniter is built into the chamber wall and the wires are sometimes introduced through a pressure tight seal. Some designs of igniters built into the nozzle have been satisfactory.

A pyrotechnic igniter is shown in Figure 11–9 and usually contains an electrically heated wire, which is surrounded by a small amount of primer (usually less than one gram). The primer propellant is a substance which is sensitive to temperature and will ignite readily and burn when heated. The main igniter charge is immediately adjacent to the primer. It produces a hot flame which ignites the rocket grain. Igniter cases are usually sealed to prevent absorption of moisture and to control the ignition at altitude. Some igniter cases are made of a plastic so that they will burn and therefore will not form an obstruction to the gas flow. The igniters, like the propellant charge, must be resistant to moisture and capable of storage and operation over a wide range of operating environment.

Some of the principal design considerations in igniters are the type, grain size, formulation, and moisture content of the igniter propellants, the construction and fastening of the igniter case, the location of the igniter with respect to the grain, the surface condition of the main charge, the size, direction, shape, and temperature of the ignition flame, the nozzle closure rupture pressure, the amount of hot solid particles in the igniter gases, the time delay between electrical signal and first pressure rise, the amount of debris ejected through the nozzle at the start, the electrical energy, the time-pressure relationship between igniter pressure and the operating pressure of the rocket. If the igniter gases raise the chamber pressure too fast and too high, then the nozzle closure (if

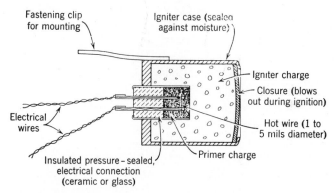

FIGURE 11-9. Schematic drawing of typical pyrotechnic igniter.

there is one) will blow out, or in some cases the shock will fracture the main grain. If the igniter pressure is too low, then ignition of the rocket's charge may not take place. With these many variables, many of which are closely interrelated, it has not been possible to postulate a good ignition theory, and an empirical approach has generally been valid.

Accessories

Many rocket units incorporate a safety diaphragm which permits gases to escape when the chamber pressure becomes excessively high. The diaphragm usually has to be insulated from the chamber, so that the predetermined bursting pressure of the diaphragm will not change with heating by the hot gases. A deflector cap is usually built downstream of the diaphragm. This cap will direct the gases in several directions so as to give a very small thrust when the gases pass through the ruptured diaphragm.

A bursting diaphragm together with an electrically operated pyrotechnic blow-off charge can be used for stopping the operation of a solid propellant rocket. In this case either the extra nozzle area opened by the diaphragm may lower the chamber pressure sufficiently to prevent continuous active high thrust combustion or the diaphragm may be so located as to nullify the thrust produced by the regular exhaust nozzle (for example, flow of gas in opposite direction).

Other accessories include handling hooks, means for loading and/or replacing the propellant (for example, flanges), brackets for upright storage, brackets for mounting the rocket in vehicles, moisture seals, protective dust caps, provisions for mounting the grain in the chamber, and inspection ports. Particularly in large heavy rockets, the handling provisions must prevent accidental local overstressing of the chamber due to dents or drops.

8 Design Calculations

No general rule can be given for the design of solid propellants. In addition to the principles described in the three chapters on solid propellants—the general principles of thermodynamics, thermochemistry, and heat transfer (Chapters 3, 4, and 5)—the fundamentals of organic chemistry, stress analysis, applied mechanics, and metallurgy are used. The following example is intended to show in a very simplified form a few of the design principles. Each specific application, each propellant category, requires a slightly different design approach; furthermore a good part of the fundamental design information is based on prior experience, manufacturer's preferences, and available experimental data.

Example 11–1. Make a preliminary determination of the design parameters of a solid rocket using a composite propellant. The following data are given:

Specific impulse	I_s = 200 sec at sea level and 1000 psi
Burning rate	r = 0.8 in./sec at 1000 psi and 60° F
Specific weight	ρ_b = 0.06 lb/in.^{3}
Specific heat ratio	k = 1.25
Chamber pressure	p_c = 1000 psi
Desired average thrust	F = 20,000 lb
Maximum vehicle diameter	D = 16 in.
Desired duration	t_p = 1.8 sec

Grain shape: two concentric hollow tubes, each similar to the one shown in Figure 11-4, with inhibited ends (assume neutral burning).

Solution. (a) *Grain configuration:* The desired total impulse is (equations 9-9 and 9-10):

$$I_t = Ft_b = I_s W_u = 20,000 \times 1.8 = 36,000 \text{ lb-sec}$$

The effective propellant weight is

$$W_u = \frac{I_t}{I_s} = \frac{36,000}{200} = 180 \text{ lb}$$

The required burning surface to produce 20,000 lb of thrust is (equations 1-8 and 11-12):

$$F = \dot{w}I_s = \rho_b A_b r I_s$$

$$A_b = \frac{F}{\rho_b r I_s} = \frac{20,000}{0.06 \times 0.8 \times 200} = 2080 \text{ in.}^2$$

The web thickness is $b = 2rt_b = 2 \times 0.8 \times 1.8 = 2.88$ in. The actual web thickness has to be somewhat larger to allow for residual propellants which are ineffective. This is arbitrarily chosen to be 2 per cent, making the web thickness equal to $1.02 \times 2.88 = 2.94$ in.

The maximum diameter of the grain is determined by the given maximum outside diameter of 16 in., by the thickness of the chamber wall, and by allowance for an annular passage space or port area sufficiently large to avoid erosion. The wall thickness of the cylindrical shell is determined by the conventional relation

$$t_w = \frac{p_c \times \text{radius}}{\text{stress}}$$

The value for the applied pressure p_c depends on the safety factor desired for the particular application, and the value of the stress depends on the material and the heating of the wall. By using a safety factor of 205 per cent of the rated operating pressure (see Section 7) and a maximum tensile strength of 130,000 psi (see Figure 11-6) for heat-treated alloy steel at slightly elevated temperature, the wall thickness can be estimated for a mean diameter of 15.87 in. (one-eighth less than outside diameter).

$$t_w = \frac{2.05 \times 1000 \times 15.87}{130,000 \times 2}$$

$$= 0.125 \text{ in.}$$

The port area on the outside of the grain has to be sufficiently large to avoid high velocity scrubbing (and to limit erosion); arbitrarily the limiting velocity is taken here to be below 700 ft/sec. By using equations 3-3, 3-2, and 11-12 and solving for the port Area A_p,

$$\dot{w} = \rho_b A_b I$$

$$V = RT/p$$

$$A_p = \frac{V\dot{w}}{v} = \frac{\dot{w}RT}{pv} = \frac{\rho_b r A_b RT}{pv}$$

$$= \frac{0.06 \times 0.8 \times 2080 \times 52 \times 5000}{1000 \times 700}$$

$$= 36.5 \text{ in.}^2$$

This total port area has to be distributed into the several annular port areas between individual grains. A set of dimensions can be determined by geometrical relations and a typical set of values might be:

	Thickness, in.	Inside Diameter, in.	Outside Diameter, in.	Cross-sectional Area, in.^{2}
Steel wall	0.125	15.75	16.00	
Outer port annulus	0.38	14.99	15.75	18
Outer grain tube	2.94	9.11	14.99	111.5
Center port annulus	0.87	7.38	9.11	23
Inner grain tube	2.94	1.50	7.38	40.7
Inner port hole			1.50	1.8

The total void area is $18 + 23 + 1.8 = 42.8$ in.^{2}, which is more than the minimum required to avoid excessive erosion. The individual port annuli should be designed so that their cross-sectional areas are proportional to the respective exposed burning areas, i.e., to the exposed circumferences of the grain tubes feeding into the individual ports. The total cross-sectional area of propellant is $111.5 + 40.7 = 152.2$ in.^{2} The length of required grain can then be found (allowing for 2 per cent excess).

$$L_b = \frac{V}{A} = \frac{(W_u/\rho_b) \times 1.02}{A} = \frac{180 \times 1.02}{0.06 \times 152.2}$$

$$= 20.0 \text{ in.}$$

Allowing 0.1 in. on each grain end for inhibitors, the overall grain length will be 20.2 in.

The nozzle throat area A_t can be estimated from equation 3–21:

$$A_t = \frac{F}{C_F p_c} = \frac{20,000}{1.4 \times 1000} = 14.3 \text{ in.}^2$$

The area ratio A_b/A_t is therefore $2080/14.3 = 146$. This value can be compared with experimental information.

(b) *Hardware:* Detail estimates of hardware weights will depend on the selection of proper materials, prior experience with similar hardware, heating of the metal parts by the gases, thermal expansion, and other factors. The example here is very much simplified to show that hardware weights are estimated by analyzing the weight of the individual components. A more sophisticated analysis based on some experimental data would probably permit a much more accurate evaluation.

The weight of the cylindrical portion of the outer wall will be

$$t_w \pi D L_b \rho = 0.125 \times \pi \times 15.87 \times 20.2 \times 0.29$$

$$= 36.2 \text{ lb}$$

The two ends of the chamber will probably be elliptical or spherical, and their weight can be estimated by suitable formulas derived for each specific configuration. Detail stress considerations of special tank ends are outside the scope of this text, and therefore the weight for the chamber ends will be assumed to be 30.5 lb.

The nozzle weight can be estimated from a drawing or a sketch, after the basic nozzle dimensions are known. These dimensions can be determined from the relations given in Chapter 3. The results are

$$C_F = 1.40$$

$$D_t = 4.28 \text{ in.}$$

$$D_e = 13.5 \text{ in.}$$

For a 15° half angle on the nozzle divergence, the total nozzle length will be approximately 18 to 19 in., and a layout of the nozzle (with ceramic insert) is assumed to give a nozzle weight of 35 lb. The flanges for opening the chamber and inserting the grain will weigh about 11 lb; the grain supports, safety diaphragms, grain expansion provisions, bolts, and mounting lugs will weigh an additional 17 lb. The total hardware weight is therefore

$$36.2 + 30.5 + 35 + 11 + 17 = 129.7 \text{ lb}$$

Allowing for ineffective propellant (2 per cent) and for inhibitors (2 lb), the impulse-to-weight ratio of this rocket can thus be estimated as

$$\frac{I_t}{W_e + W_u + W_{\text{ineffective}}} = \frac{36,000}{129.7 + 180 + (0.02 \times 180 + 2)} = 114$$

Comparison with Table 9-2 shows this to be an average design. A careful design, based on test information and a development program, would probably permit a reduction in hardware weights.

(c) *Volume relation:*

Total volume occupied by grain	$20.5 \times 148.5 =$	3050 in.^{3}
Port passage volume	$20.5 \times 45.6 =$	940 in.^{3}
Void volume at chamber ends		840 in.^{3}
Total Volume		4830 in.
Volume of effective propellant	$3050(1/1.02)(20/20.2) =$	2950 in.^{3}
Space factor	$\omega = 4830/2950 =$	1.64

There is room in both chamber ends for additional propellant, which would improve the volumetric usage and thus the performance of the rocket.

Problems

1. Determine the differential growth of a 24-in.-long grain with a linear thermal coefficient of expansion of 7.5×10^{-5} per °F for temperature limits of -40 and 140° F.

Answer: 0.32 in.

2. The following data is given for an internally burning solid propellant grain:

Length	40 in.
Port area	27 in.^{2}
Propellant weight	240 lb
Pressure at front end of chamber	1608 psi
Pressure at nozzle end of chamber	1412 psi
Propellant density	0.60 lb/in.^{3}
Vehicle acceleration	21.2 g

Determine the initial forces on the propellant supports due to pressure differential and vehicle acceleration.

Answer: 19,600 lb, 5090 lb.

3. For a maximum port gas velocity corresponding to a Mach number of 0.85, a front end chamber pressure of 1800 psia, and a specific heat ratio of 1.25, compute the static and total pressure at the exit of the port channel and the per cent loss in specific impulse due to the unavailability of energy in accelerating gases through the ports.

4. A solid propellant unit with an end-burning grain has the following nominal sea level characteristics:

Nominal thrust	1100 lb
Nominal duration	14 sec
Propellant data	Use Figure 11–5
Nozzle area ratio	10.0
Chamber pressure	2000 psia
Propellant density	0.063 lb/in.^{3}
Impulse weight ratio	96
Temperature sensitivity	0.01
Operating temperature	60° F

Determine grain geometry, propellant weight, hardware weight, and specific impulse.

5. For the rocket in problem 4 determine the approximate thrust and duration at $-20°$ F and 130° F.

Symbols

A surface or cross section area, ft^2

A_p port or flow channel cross section, ft^2

a burning rate constant (not dimensionless)

b constant

c effective nozzle exhaust velocity, ft/sec

F thrust, lb

g acceleration of gravity, ft/sec^2

I_s specific impulse, sec

I_t total impulse, lb-sec

K erosion constant

k specific heat ratio

L_b length of grain, ft

M Mach number

$\dot{m}$ mass flow rate, slugs/sec

p pressure, lb/ft^2

R gas constant ft-lb/$^\circ R$ lb

r burning rate, ft/sec or in./sec

t time, sec

t_b burning time, sec

t_w wall thickness, in.

V volume, ft^3

v flow velocity, ft/sec

W weight, lb

$\dot{w}$ weight flow rate, lb/sec

$\dot{w}^*$ weight flow rate at flow velocity of $M = 1.0$, lb/sec

Greek Letters

ϵ erosion coefficient

ρ density, lb/ft^3

ω space factor

Subscripts

b solid propellant condition

c chamber condition

e nozzle exit condition

t throat condition

0 front end or ideal initial condition

1 conditions at port exit

Chapter 12

Flight Performance

This chapter deals with the performance of rocket-powered vehicles such as airplanes, missiles, space ships, projectiles, and gliders.

1 Forces Acting on Vehicle

The external forces commonly acting on flying missiles are thrust, aerodynamic forces, and gravitational attraction. Other forces, such as centrifugal force and Coriolis force, are small and can generally be neglected for simple calculations.

Thrust

The thrust is the force produced by the power plant, such as a propeller or a rocket. It usually acts in the direction of the axis of the power plant, that is, along the propeller shaft axis or the rocket nozzle axis.

The thrust force of a rocket has been expressed by equation 1–4 as a function of the effective exhaust velocity and the propellant flow rate $F = \dot{w}c/g$. In most rockets the mass rate * of propellant consumption is constant, and the mass flow rate may therefore be expressed in terms of the initial mass of propellants in the missile m_p and the burning time of the propellants t_p by neglecting starting and stopping transients.

$$\frac{w}{g} = \frac{m_p}{t_p} \tag{12–1}$$

The thrust is therefore

$$F = \frac{m_p}{t_p} c \tag{12–2}$$

* See footnote on page 20.

The instantaneous mass of the vehicle m can be expressed as a function of the initial mass of the full vehicle m_0 and the instantaneous time t.

$$m = m_0 - \frac{m_p}{t_p} t$$

$$= m_0 \left(1 - \frac{m_p}{m_0} \frac{t}{t_p} \right)$$

$$= m_0 \left(1 - \zeta \frac{t}{t_p} \right)$$

$$= m_0 \left(1 - \frac{\lambda - 1}{\lambda} \frac{t}{t_p} \right) \qquad (12\text{--}3)$$

Equation 12–3 expresses the vehicle mass in a form useful for simplified trajectory calculations. The mass ratios ζ and λ are defined as follows:

$$\zeta = \frac{m_p}{m_0} = \frac{\text{Effective propellant mass}}{\text{Initial vehicle mass}} = \frac{W_0 - W_e}{W_0} \qquad (12\text{--}4a)$$

$$\lambda = \frac{m_0}{m_0 - m_p} = \frac{\text{Initial vehicle mass}}{\text{Final vehicle mass}} = \frac{W_0}{W_e} \qquad (12\text{--}4b)$$

Here W_0 and W_e are the initial take-off weight and the empty or final weight. The coefficients are related by the equations

$$\zeta = \frac{\lambda - 1}{\lambda} = 1 - 1/\lambda \qquad (12\text{--}4c)$$

Aerodynamic Forces

The *drag* is the aerodynamic force in a direction opposite to the flight path due to the resistance of the body to motion in a fluid. The *lift* is the aerodynamic force acting in a direction normal to the flight path.

The lift L and drag D are expressed as functions of the flight speed v, the mass density of the fluid in which the vehicle moves ρ, and a typical surface area A.

$$L = C_L \tfrac{1}{2} \rho A v^2 \qquad (12\text{--}5a)$$

$$D = C_D \tfrac{1}{2} \rho A v^2 \qquad (12\text{--}5b)$$

where C_L and C_D are lift and drag coefficients, respectively. For airplanes and winged missiles the area A is understood to mean the wing area. For wingless missiles it is the maximum cross-sectional area normal to the missile axis. The lift and drag coefficients are primarily functions of flight Mach number and the angle of attack. For low flight speeds the effect of Mach number may be neglected, and the drag and lift coefficients will be functions of angle of attack only as shown for a typical subsonic airfoil in

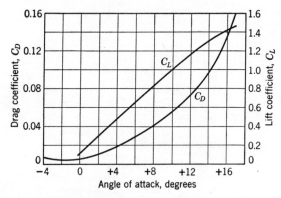

FIGURE 12-1. Variation of lift and drag coefficients with angle of attack for a typical subsonic airfoil.

Figure 12-1. The variation of the drag and lift coefficients for a typical supersonic missile is shown in Figures 12-2 and 12-3. The values of these coefficients reach a maximum near a Mach number of unity.

The aerodynamic forces acting on a flying vehicle are dependent on the speed of the vehicle, its size and shape, and on the density of the atmosphere at the flight altitude. The properties of the atmosphere are listed in Table 3-4. References to general data on flight theory and aerodynamics can be found in Section 8.1 and 8.2 of the Reference Bibliography. References for data on the atmosphere and space can be found in Section 8.5.

Gravity

Gravitational attraction is exerted upon a flying vehicle by all planets, stars, the moon, and the sun. It pulls the vehicle in the direction of the center of mass of the attracting body. Within

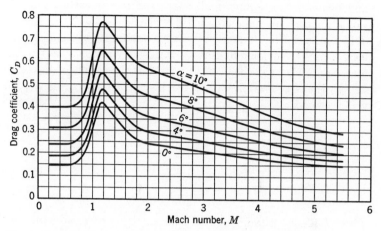

FIGURE 12–2. Variation of drag coefficient with Mach number of V-2 rocket missile based on body cross-sectional area with jet off.

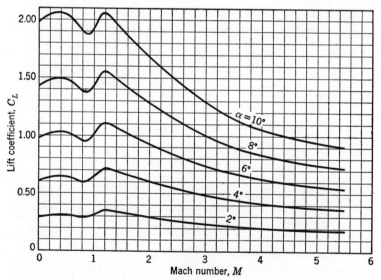

FIGURE 12–3. Variation of lift coefficient with Mach number of V-2 rocket missile based on body cross-sectional area.

the immediate vicinity of the earth the attraction of other planets and bodies is negligibly small compared to the earth's gravitational force. This force is called the *weight*.

If the variation of gravity with geographical latitude is neglected, the acceleration of gravity varies only as the square of the distance from the earth's center. If R_0 is the radius of the earth and g_0 the acceleration on the earth's surface at radius R_0, the gravitational attraction g will be

$$g = g_0 \left(\frac{R_0}{R}\right)^2$$

$$= g_0 \left(\frac{R_0}{R_0 + h}\right)^2 \tag{12-6}$$

where h is the altitude. At the equator the earth's radius is 3963 miles with $g_0 \sim 32.2$ feet per second.

2 Basic Relations of Motion

For a vehicle which flies within the proximity of the earth the gravitational attraction of all other heavenly bodies may be

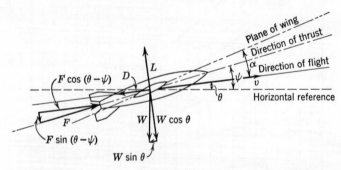

FIGURE 12-4. Free body force diagram for flying vehicle.

neglected. Let it be assumed that the vehicle is moving in rectilinear equilibrium flight and that all control forces, lateral forces, and moments which tend to turn the vehicle are zero. The trajectory is two-dimensional and is contained in a fixed plane.*

* A three-dimensional analysis of the motion of rocket projectiles and the deviations from their flight paths is given in reference 8.102.

The vehicle has wings which are inclined to the flight path at an angle of attack α and which give a lift in a direction normal to the flight path. The direction of flight does not coincide with the direction of thrust. Figure 12–4 shows these conditions schematically.

Let m be the instantaneous mass of the rocket-propelled vehicle, dv/dt the acceleration in the direction of flight, F the thrust of the propulsion unit, L the aerodynamic lift force, D the aerodynamic drag force, g the acceleration of gravity at any altitude, θ the angle of the flight path with the horizontal, and ψ the angle of the direction of thrust with the horizontal.

In the direction of the flight path the product of the mass and the acceleration has to equal the sum of all forces:

$$m \frac{dv}{dt} = F \cos (\theta - \psi) - D - mg \sin \theta \qquad (12\text{–}7)$$

The acceleration perpendicular to the flight path is $v^2/\mathcal{R} = v \, (d\theta/dt)$, where $\mathcal{R}$ is the instantaneous radius of the flight path. The equation of motion in a direction normal to the flight velocity is

$$mv \frac{d\theta}{dt} = F \sin (\theta - \psi) + L - mg \cos \theta \qquad (12\text{–}8)$$

By substituting from equations 12–5a and 12–5b, these two basic equations can be solved for the accelerations as

$$\frac{dv}{dt} = \frac{F}{m} \cos (\theta - \psi) - \frac{C_D}{2m} \rho v^2 A - g \sin \theta \qquad (12\text{–}9)$$

$$v \frac{d\theta}{dt} = \frac{F}{m} \sin (\theta - \psi) + \frac{C_L}{2m} \rho v^2 A - g \cos \theta \qquad (12\text{–}10)$$

Since several other quantities, such as control forces and stability considerations, enter into the analysis, and since the lift coefficient, drag coefficient, altitude, flight angle, and burning time depend on a number of independent variables, which are usually different for each vehicle, no general solution can be given. An arbitrary division of the trajectory into small elements and a step-by-step solution are usually indicated. Equations 12–9 and 12–10 can be simplified for various special applications, as shown in subsequent sections.

If the thrust at a given altitude and the propellant consumption are assumed constant, the instantaneous mass of the vehicle is only a function of time as expressed in equation 12–3. In a two-dimensional analysis, the basic equations of motion then reduce to

$$\frac{1}{g}\frac{dv}{dt} = \left[\frac{I_s \dfrac{\zeta}{t_p}\cos(\theta - \psi) - C_D \dfrac{1}{2}\rho v^2 \dfrac{A g_0}{W_0 g}}{1 - \dfrac{\zeta t}{t_p}} - \sin\theta\right] \quad (12\text{--}11)$$

$$\frac{v}{g}\frac{d\theta}{dt} = \left[\frac{I_s \dfrac{\zeta}{t_p}\sin(\theta - \psi) + C_L \dfrac{1}{2}\rho v^2 \dfrac{A g_0}{W_0 g}}{1 - \dfrac{\zeta t}{t_p}} - \cos\theta\right] \quad (12\text{--}12)$$

where I_s is the specific impulse, ζ is the mass ratio of the initial propellant mass to the filled vehicle mass, and W_0/A is the so-called loading density, which is the initial weight of the full vehicle divided by the maximum cross-sectional area.

If the direction of thrust coincides with the flight direction, $\psi = \theta$, $\cos(\theta - \psi) = 1$, $\sin(\theta - \psi) = 0$, and the specific impulse will not enter into equation 12–12.

$$\frac{1}{g}\frac{dv}{dt} = \left[\frac{I_s \dfrac{\zeta}{t_p} - C_D \dfrac{1}{2}\rho v^2 \dfrac{A g_0}{W_0 g}}{1 - \dfrac{\zeta t}{t_p}} - \sin\theta\right] \quad (12\text{--}13)$$

$$\frac{v}{g}\frac{d\theta}{dt} = \left[\frac{C_L \dfrac{1}{2}\rho v^2 \dfrac{A g_0}{W_0 g}}{1 - \dfrac{\zeta t}{t_p}} - \cos\theta\right] \quad (12\text{--}14)$$

The significance of each term in these equations is discussed in the subsequent section. The basic equations of motion for a trajectory with constant acceleration are given in reference 8.103. They differ from the equations above, which stipulate constant propellant flow.

3 Simplified Vertical Trajectory

The velocity and altitude reached by a vertically ascending rocket-powered vehicle can be found from the basic equation of motion. It is assumed that the earth is stationary, the direction of thrust coincides with the direction of flight, and the side forces are zero. The equation of motion can then be written from equation 12–13 for a vertical trajectory:

$$\frac{dv}{dt} = \frac{\dfrac{c\zeta}{t_p}}{1 - \dfrac{\zeta t}{t_p}} - g - \frac{C_D \dfrac{1}{2} \rho v^2 \dfrac{A}{W_0} g_0}{1 - \dfrac{\zeta t}{t_p}} \qquad (12\text{--}15)$$

The velocity at the end of burning can be found by integrating between the limits of $t = 0$ and $t = t_p$ when $v = v_0$ and $v = v_p$. The first two terms can readily be integrated. The last term is of significance only if the vehicle spends a considerable portion of its time within the atmosphere. It can be integrated graphically or by numerical methods, and its value can be designated as $B_1 C_D \dfrac{A}{W_0}$ such that

$$B_1 = g_0 \int_0^{t_p} \frac{\frac{1}{2}\rho v^2}{1 - \dfrac{\zeta t}{t_p}} \, dt \qquad (12\text{--}16)$$

The cut-off velocity or velocity at the end of burning v_p is then

$$v_p = -\bar{c} \ln (1 - \zeta) - \bar{g} t_p - \frac{B_1 C_D A}{W_0} + v_0 \qquad (12\text{--}17)$$

where v_0 is the initial velocity, such as may be given by a booster, $\bar{g}$ is an average gravitational attraction evaluated with respect to time from equation 12–6, and $\bar{c}$ is a time average of the effective exhaust velocity. If aerodynamic forces outside the earth's atmosphere are neglected and no booster or means for attaining an initial velocity ($v_0 = 0$) is assumed, the velocity at the end of burning reached in a vertical trajectory will be

$$v_p = -\bar{c} \ln (1 - \zeta) - \bar{g}t_p$$
$$= \bar{c} \ln \lambda - \bar{g}t_p \qquad (12\text{-}18)$$

Vehicle velocities in a non-vertical trajectory can be larger than the value indicated by the equation above, because the negative last term is multiplied by the sine of the angle of the trajectory with the horizontal.

The first term, usually the largest, is directly proportional to the exhaust velocity and very sensitive to changes in the mass ratio, because of the logarithmic relation. In fact, the vehicle velocity will become infinite as $\zeta \rightarrow 1.0$, that is, as the vehicle weight is almost entirely composed of propellant, irrespective of the magnitude of the effective exhaust velocity.

The second term is always negative, but its magnitude is small if the burning time t_p is very short or if the flight takes place at very high altitudes where $\bar{g}$ is comparatively small.

If the second term is also neglected, the velocity at the end of burning can be expressed as

$$v_p = -\bar{c} \ln (1 - \zeta)$$

$$= \bar{c} \ln \frac{m_0}{m_0 - m_p} \qquad (12\text{-}19)$$

$$= \bar{c} \ln \lambda$$

This is the maximum vehicle velocity that can be obtained in a gravitationless vacuum. The relation and the effect of variations in $\bar{c}$, λ, and ζ are shown in Figure 12–5 for various mass ratios and exhaust velocities.

For high mass ratios and for very high exhaust velocities, the vehicle velocity in a vacuum without gravity will approach infinity in the equation above. Ackeret has shown that as the velocities approach the velocity of light (3×10^9 centimeters per second) the theory of rockets as presented in this section is no longer applicable but is determined from relativistic mechanics (Ref. 8.104). The vehicle velocity cannot exceed the speed of light, and the expression for a vehicle velocity within a gravita-

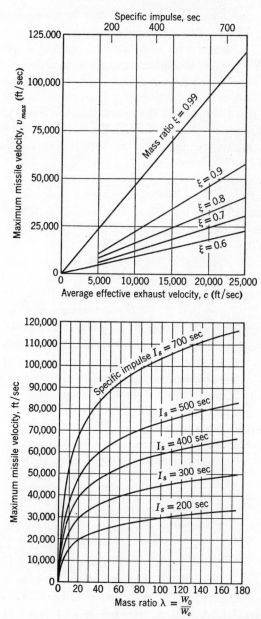

FIGURE 12-5. Maximum missile velocity in gravitationless, drag-free space for different mass ratios and specific impulses (plot of equation 12-19).

tionless vacuum given above is valid only if the exhaust velocities are low compared to the speed of light. The equation above holds for all mass ratios up to an exhaust velocity of 100 million feet per second, which is approximately one-tenth the velocity of light. For higher exhaust velocities deviations can be neglected only at low mass ratios, for the mass ratio has no meaning when the vehicle speed approaches the speed of light. Since these high exhaust velocities are impossible to attain with present available means, the relativistic theory of rockets is today of academic interest only.

From equation 12–19 it can be seen that the *effect of mass ratio on the missile velocity* is a major one. By increasing this ratio from 0.80 to 0.90, the interplanetary maximum missile velocity in a gravitationless vacuum is increased by 43 per cent. A mass ratio of 0.80 would indicate that only 20 per cent of the total vehicle weight is available for structure, skin, payload, propulsion system, radios, guidance system, aerodynamic lifting surfaces, etc.; the remaining 80 per cent is propellant. It requires extremely careful design to exceed a mass ratio of 0.80; mass ratios approaching 0.90 appear to be the probable practical limit for single stage vehicles. This marked influence of mass ratio on the velocity at power cut-off, and therefore also the range, not only is true of interplanetary space ships in a vacuum but applies to almost all types of rocket-powered vehicles. This is the reason why such importance is placed upon saving weight on every component comprising the missile.

The *height at the end of burning* can be found by integrating equation 12–15 twice and evaluating the integral between $t = 0$ and $t = t_p$.

$$h_p = \bar{c} t_p \left[1 + \frac{1 - \zeta}{\zeta} \ln (1 - \zeta) \right] - \frac{1}{2} \bar{g} t_p{}^2 + v_0 t_p + h_0$$
$$- \frac{B_2 C_D A}{W_0} \quad (12\text{–}20)$$

where h_0 is the initial launching height and B_2 is the integral of B_1, given by equation 12–16, with respect to time. The last term gives the drag effect. The kinetic energy at the end of powered vertical flight is converted into potential energy, and the vehicle will rise an additional height equal to $v_p{}^2/2g$. The *maximum vertical trajectory height* is, therefore,

$$h_{max} = h_p + \frac{v_p{}^2}{2\bar{\bar{g}}}$$

$$= \frac{1}{2\bar{\bar{g}}} c^2 [\ln (1 - \zeta)]^2 + \bar{c} t_p \left[1 + \frac{1 - \zeta}{\zeta} \ln (1 - \zeta) + \frac{\bar{g}}{\bar{\bar{g}}} \ln (1 - \zeta) \right]$$

$$+ \frac{v_0{}^2}{2\bar{\bar{g}}} + h_0 + v_0 \left[-t_p \left(\frac{\bar{g}}{\bar{\bar{g}}} - 1 \right) - \frac{\bar{c}}{\bar{\bar{g}}} \ln (1 - \zeta) \right]$$

$$+ \frac{1}{2} \bar{g} t_p{}^2 \left(\frac{\bar{g}}{\bar{\bar{g}}} - 1 \right) - C_D \frac{A}{W_0} \left[B_2 + \frac{v_0 B_1}{\bar{\bar{g}}} \right.$$

$$\left. - B_1 t_p \frac{\bar{g}}{\bar{\bar{g}}} - \frac{\bar{c} B_1}{\bar{\bar{g}}} \ln (1 - \zeta) - \frac{B_1{}^2}{2\bar{\bar{g}}} C_D \frac{A}{W_0} \right] \qquad (12\text{--}21)$$

In this equation $\bar{g}$ represents the time average of the gravitational acceleration between the launching altitude h_0 and the altitude at cut-off h_p, and $\bar{\bar{g}}$ represents the average value of g between the cut-off altitude h_p and the maximum altitude h_{max}. For accurate calculations a numerical integration is recommended. For trajectories near the earth's surface $\bar{g} = \bar{\bar{g}} = g_0$.

The first term is again a function of the effective exhaust velocity and the mass ratio, but it is much more sensitive than the first term of the velocity relation, equation 12–17, because it is squared. An increase in exhaust velocity or a decrease in the empty weight of the vehicle will increase the maximum vertical trajectory height appreciably. The second term is always negative and proportional to the burning time. A short burning time reduces the magnitude of the second term of the equation but requires a high thrust, which gives the vehicle high velocities and high drag near the earth's surface. For these reasons there is usually an optimum thrust and an optimum burning time at which the zenith height of the vertical trajectory is a maximum. The third, fourth, and fifth terms are corrections for launching with an initial velocity or from an elevated launching station. The sixth term determines the gain in vertical height due to decreased gravitational attraction at high altitude. For trajectories below 100 miles this term can be neglected.

The last term defines the drag and is negative in sign. With improved aerodynamic design, the drag coefficient and the drag force become smaller. The loading density W_0/A is proportional to the length and the average density of a missile. Compact design and longer missiles have therefore a reduced drag. In a vacuum ($\rho = 0, C_D = 0$), the drag term becomes zero.

Results of the maximum zenith altitude calculated for vertical ascent by this theory are usually not more than 20 per cent above the values obtained from vertical launching tests. The discrepancies are believed to be due to inefficient utilization of propellants during starting and cut-off transients, an increased drag due to small oscillations and yawing of the missile, a deviation from the vertical, and other reasons.

If the initial velocity v_0 and the height of launching are assumed to be zero and if drag can be neglected, the maximum height of a simplified vertical trajectory will be

$$
\begin{aligned}
h_{max} = \bar{c}^2 [\ln (1 - \zeta)]^2 \\
+ \bar{c} t_p \left[1 + \frac{1 - \zeta}{\zeta} \ln (1 - \zeta) + \frac{\bar{g}}{\bar{\bar{g}}} \ln (1 - \zeta) \right] \\
+ \frac{1}{2} \bar{g} t_p{}^2 \left(\frac{\bar{g}}{\bar{\bar{g}}} - 1 \right) \quad (12\text{--}22)
\end{aligned}
$$

The relative effects of exhaust velocity $\bar{c}$, mass ratio ζ, burning time t_p, and the loading density W_0/A are shown in Figures 12–6 and 12–7 for calculated vertical trajectories.

A general analysis of the trajectory range does not reduce to simple mathematical terms and needs to be studied separately for each type of rocket vehicle. In general, the range increases with an increase in specific impulse, a decrease in the mass ratio, an increase in the C_L/C_D ratio, a decrease in the drag coefficient by an improved aerodynamic configuration, and by shifting a large part of the trajectory of larger vehicles to high altitudes. A high vehicle speed ($v \rightarrow c$), particularly at high altitudes, will increase the range because the rocket's energy will be used more efficiently. See equation 1–6. Simplified cases of horizontal trajectory range computations are given in references 8.102 and 8.103.

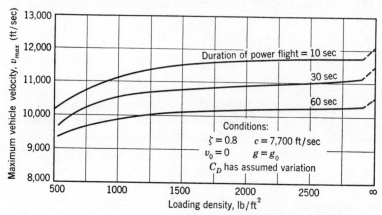

FIGURE 12–6. Maximum vehicle velocity as a function of loading density. (Reproduced from F. J. Malina and M. Summerfield, "The Problem of Escape from the Earth," *Journal of Aeronautical Sciences,* Vol. 14, No. 8, August 1947.)

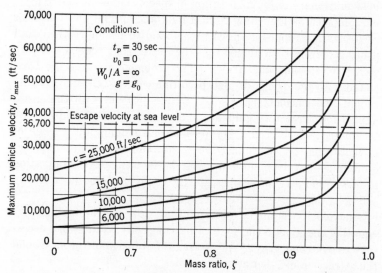

FIGURE 12–7. Velocity at end of burning as a function of mass ratio. (Reproduced from F. J. Malina and M. Summerfield, "The Problem of Escape from the Earth," *Journal of Aeronautical Sciences,* Vol. 14, No. 8, August 1947.)

The net acceleration for vertical take-off at sea level is

$$a = \frac{F_0 g}{W_0} - g_0$$

$$\frac{a}{g_0} = \frac{F_0}{W_0} - 1 \tag{12-23}$$

where a/g is the initial take-off acceleration in multiples of the sea level gravitational acceleration g_0, and F_0/W_0 is the thrust to weight ratio at take-off. For large surface-to-surface missiles this initial thrust to initial weight ratio has values between 1.2 and 2.2; for small missiles (air-to-air, air-to-surface, and surface-to-air types) this ratio is usually larger, sometimes even as high as 50 or 100.

4   Space Travel

The rocket offers a possible means for escaping the earth, for interplanetary travel, for escaping our solar system, and for creating a stationary or moving station in space. Other means of locomotion, such as launching from a long and special gun barrel or electrostatic propulsion, have been found to be impractical, and it has generally been agreed that the rocket is at present the only means for solving space travel. The problems involved are associated with the design of high performance rocket engines, lightweight and efficient space ships, communication with the earth, navigation, trajectory guidance and control, take-off and landing techniques, survival in a gravitationless vacuum, and evasion of meteoric matter. Although these and many other problems require much development and research, the basic physical question as to whether a vehicle can escape the earth has been theoretically solved.

The velocity required to escape from the earth can be found by equating the kinetic energy of a moving body to the work necessary to overcome gravity, neglecting the rotation of the earth and the attraction of other celestial bodies.

$$\frac{mv^2}{2} = m \int g \, dR$$

By substituting for g from equation 12-6 and by neglecting air friction, the following relation for the escape velocity is obtained:

$$v_e = R_0 \sqrt{\frac{2g}{R_0 + h}} \qquad (12\text{--}24)$$

where v_e is the escape velocity, R_0 is the radius of the earth, g_0 is the acceleration of gravity at sea level, and h is the altitude.

The velocity of escape at the earth's surface is 36,700 feet per second and does not vary appreciably within the earth's atmos-

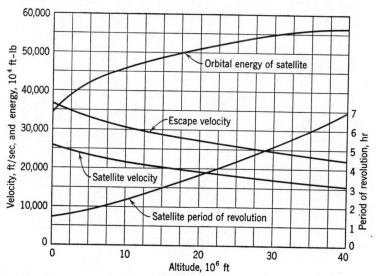

FIGURE 12–8. Orbital energy, orbital velocity, period of revolution, and escape velocity of a satellite vehicle as functions of altitude. A circular satellite orbit is assumed.

phere as shown by Figure 12–8. It is physically impossible to send vehicles at this high velocity through the atmosphere because they will burn up at the excessively high skin temperature. A practical interplanetary space ship will have to traverse the earth's atmosphere at relatively low velocity and accelerate to the escape velocity beyond the atmosphere. In order to use rocket propulsion effectively in space, very high nozzle area ratios (above 20) and vector thrust control are desirable.

Three different types of *space ships* will be considered, namely satellites, interplanetary travel, and the escape from the solar system; the basic requirements of each will be listed.

A rocket space ship which becomes a *satellite* of the earth, and which will revolve around the earth in a fashion similar to the moon, could remain in an orbit outside the earth's atmosphere for an indefinite time without addition of further energy. The use of these satellites as reconnaissance patrol, as weather and cloud observation platforms, and as short wave radio stations has been suggested. The altitude of the orbit has to be above the earth's atmosphere to prevent the expenditure of energy in the form of drag, which would pull the missile closer to the earth.

For a circular trajectory the velocity of a satellite has to be sufficiently high so that its centrifugal force will balance the earth's gravitational attraction.

$$m \frac{v_s^2}{R} = mg$$

The satellite velocity v_s is found by using equation 12–6

$$v_s = R_0 \sqrt{\frac{g_0}{R_0 + h}} \qquad (12\text{–}25)$$

which is smaller than the escape velocity by a factor of $\sqrt{2}$. The period in seconds of one revolution for a circular orbit relative to a stationary earth is

$$\tau = \frac{2\pi(R_0 + h)}{v_s}$$

$$= \frac{2\pi}{R_0 \sqrt{g_0}} (R_0 + h)^{3/2} \qquad (12\text{–}26)$$

The energy necessary to bring a unit of mass into a satellite orbit consists of its kinetic and potential energy, namely,

$$E = \tfrac{1}{2} v_s^2 + \int_{R_0}^{R} g \, dR$$

$$= \frac{1}{2} R_0^2 \frac{g_0}{R_0 + h} + \int_{R_0}^{R} g_0 \frac{R_0^2}{R^2} \, dR$$

$$= \frac{1}{2} R_0 g_0 \left(\frac{R_0 + 2h}{R_0 + h} \right) \qquad (12\text{–}27)$$

The escape velocity, satellite velocity, satellite period, and satellite orbital energy are shown as functions of altitude in Figure 12–8.

A satellite circulating round the earth at an altitude of 300 miles would have a velocity of 24,200 feet per second, would circle a stationary earth in 1.63 hours, and would require an energy of 4.64×10^5 Btu to place one slug of space ship mass into its orbit.

The case of the circular orbit described above is a special case of the more general elliptic orbit; here the earth (or any other heavenly body around which another body is moving) is located at one of the focal points of this ellipse. The equations of motion may be derived from Keppler's laws and the elliptical orbit can be described as follows, when expressed in polar coordinates

$$v = [\mu(2/R - 1/a)]^{1/2} \qquad (12\text{--}28)$$

where v is the velocity of the body in the elliptical orbit, R is the instantaneous radius around the attracting body, a is the semi-

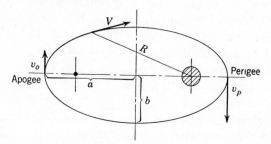

FIGURE 12–9. Elliptical orbit.

major axis of the ellipse, and μ is a constant for any gravitational field equal to $g_0 R_0$. These symbols are defined further in Figure 12–9. From this equation it can be seen that the velocity will be a maximum when the orbit comes closest to its attracting focal center (namely when the moving body is at its *perigee* position) and that its velocity is a minimum at its *apogee*. By substituting for R in equation 12–28 and by defining e as the eccentricity of the ellipse, the velocities at the apogee v_a and the velocity at the perigee v_b can be expressed as

$$v_a = \sqrt{\frac{\mu}{a}\frac{1-e}{1+e}} \qquad (12\text{–}29)$$

$$v_b = \sqrt{\frac{\mu}{a}\frac{1+e}{1-e}} \qquad (12\text{–}30)$$

Another property of an elliptical orbit is that the product of velocity and instantaneous radius remains constant, namely $v_a R_a = v_b R_b$.

The exact path that a satellite will take depends on the velocity (magnitude and vector orientation) with which it is started into its orbit. The actual differences between the magnitudes of the velocities for different orbits around the earth are relatively very small; and small rockets are used for making fine adjustments to the vehicle velocity in order to obtain the desired flight path.

The second case is the *interplanetary space ship* which is capable of transferring a payload between planets. Venus, Mars, and the moon have been mentioned as possible destinations. The space ships have to overcome the gravitational attraction of the earth and have to be capable of expending energy against the gravitational pull of the sun and other planets. The problems of navigation, communication, guidance, take-off, and landing need further investigation.

The energy necessary to escape from earth can be calculated as $\frac{1}{2}mv_e{}^2$ from equation 12–24. It is 8.74×10^5 Btu per slug of mass, which is more than that required for a satellite (Ref. 8.105).

The gravitational attraction of various heavenly bodies and their respective escape velocities depend on their masses and diameters as listed in Table 12–1. The velocity which a vehicle has to attain in order to travel to different heavenly bodies is a function of the velocity needed to escape from the earth, also of the "braking" necessary to accomplish a landing and other factors. For example, for an earth to moon and return journey it is necessary to overcome the pull of the earth's gravity (escape velocity = 36,700 ft/sec), to apply reverse thrust in landing on the moon and thus counteract the moon's attraction (moon's escape velocity = 7700 ft/sec), to escape from the moon (7700 ft/sec), and to apply rocket braking or aerodynamic drag braking for a

TABLE 12-1. CHARACTERISTIC DATA FOR SEVERAL HEAVENLY BODIES *

Name	Mean Radius of Orbit, million miles	Period of Revolution	Mean Diameter, miles	Relative Mass (Earth = 1.0)	Specific Gravity	Acceleration of Gravity at Surface, ft/sec^2	Escape Velocity at Surface, ft/sec
Sun	—	—	864,100	331,950	1.41	897.07	2,023,000
Moon	0.23886	27.3 days	2,160	0.012	3.33	5.190	7,693
Mercury	35.96	87.97 days	3,100	0.05	5.46	10.449	13,109
Venus	67.20	224.70 days	7,600	0.81	5.06	28.297	33,697
Earth	92.90	365.256 days	7,919.6	1.00	5.52	32.172	36,677
Mars	141.6	686.98 days	4,140	0.11	4.12	12.95	16,825
Jupiter	483.3	11.86 years	86,800	318.4	1.35	85.27	197,700
Saturn	886.2	29.46 years	71,500	95.3	0.71	37.62	119,200
Uranus	1783	84.01 years	29,400	14.5	1.56	33.85	72,490
Neptune	2794	164.8 years	27,000	17.2	2.47	47.61	82,380
Pluto	3670	247.7 years	~3,600	?	—	—	—

* Data taken in part from W. E. Forsythe, *Smithsonian Physical Tables*, Smithsonian Institution, Washington, D. C., 1954, and in part from *The American Ephemeris and Nautical Almanac*, U. S. Government Printing Office, Washington, D. C., 1953.

landing on earth. Assuming that no rocket energy has to be expended in the landing on the earth, then this mission requires a total velocity of 36,700 + 7700 + 7700 = 52,100 ft/sec; this will require a multiple stage vehicle. Actually drag losses in the atmosphere, gravity corrections, and navigational corrections would increase this value to perhaps 63,000 ft/sec. From Figure 12–5 it can be seen that this vehicle velocity requires very high mass ratios (that is, multiple stage missiles), and very high effective rocket nozzle exhaust velocities. If a reversed rocket thrust is applied and no drag braking is used, then this vehicle velocity would be approximately 105,000 ft/sec.

Typical vehicle velocities required for various interplanetary missions have been estimated (Ref. 8.305) as shown in Table 12–2. By starting interplanetary journeys from a space satellite

TABLE 12–2.   MAXIMUM VEHICLE VELOCITIES FOR TYPICAL
INTERPLANETARY MISSIONS

Mission	Ideal Velocity,* ft/sec	Approximate Actual Velocity, ft/sec
Satellite orbit around earth (no return)	26,000 to 35,000	30,000 to 41,000
Escape from earth (no return)	36,700	42,500
Escape from moon	7,700	9,200
Earth to moon (landing on moon, no return)	44,200	53,000
Earth to Mars (no return)	57,500	66,000
Earth to Venus (no return)	73,000	85,000
Earth around moon and return to earth †	74,000	83,000
Earth to moon, landing on moon and return to earth †	88,000	105,000
Earth to Mars, landing on Mars, and return to earth †	112,000	130,000

* Neglects air resistance, navigational corrections, and gravitational losses.
† Assumes no savings by air braking within atmospheres.

station a considerable saving in this vehicle velocity can be achieved, namely the velocity necessary to achieve the satellite orbit.

The time required for some of these space journeys depends on the trajectory. By taking full advantage of the gravitational pull of the target planet, it is possible to arrive at a trajectory ellipse which requires the minimum expenditure of energy and therefore the minimum vehicle velocity. On this basis Clarke estimates (Ref. 8.305) 116 hours to go to the moon, approximately 259 days to go to Mars, 146 days to travel to Venus, and 2 years and 9 months for a journey to Jupiter. If higher velocities are used (which would require bigger vehicles with more stages), then this transit time can be reduced considerably.

As a final case, the *escape from the earth and the solar system* is considered. It will take 70.4×10^5 Btu per slug mass of space ship to escape the solar system (Ref. 8.105). Since this energy is approximately eight times as much energy as is required for escape from the earth, this escape may become feasible with more efficient propulsion systems, such as with nuclear energy rockets.

References to further study on space travel can be found in Sections 7.8, 8.3, and 8.4 of the Reference Bibliography.

5 Vehicle Types

This section gives a brief description of several vehicles which use rockets for propulsion. It expands the discussion given in Section 2 of Chapter 1. References for further study can be found in Sections 7.1–7.7 of the Reference Bibliography.

Rocket Projectiles

Short range uncontrolled single step missiles, such as are shown in Figures 1–7 and 1–8, which carry a military warhead are called rocket projectiles. Their general equations of motion are derived in Section 2 and a detailed analysis is given in reference 8.102.

Since rocket projectiles are essentially unguided missiles, the accuracy of hitting a target will depend on the initial aiming and the dispersion induced by uneven drag, wind forces, oscillations, and misalignment of jet, body, and fins. Deviations from the intended trajectory are amplified if the projectile is moving at a low initial velocity, because the aerodynamic stability of a projectile with fins is small at low flight speeds. When projectiles are launched from aircraft at a relatively high initial velocity or when projectiles are given stability by spinning them on their axis, their accuracy of reaching a target is increased two- to ten-fold, compared to a simple fin stabilized rocket launched from rest.

In *air-launched rockets* the time of flight to a given target, usually called the time to target t_t, is an important flight performance parameter. With the aid of Figure 12–10 it can be derived in a simplified form by considering the distance traversed by the rocket (called here the range S) to be the integrated area underneath the velocity curve. This simplification assumes no drag, no gravity effect, nearly horizontal flight, a relatively small

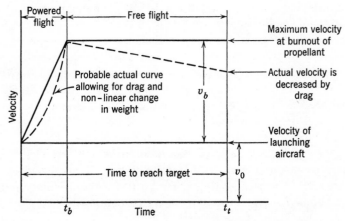

FIGURE 12–10. Typical trajectory for an unguided air-launched rocket projectile.

distance traverse during powered flight compared to the total range, and a linear increase in velocity during powered flight.

$$t_t = \frac{S + \frac{1}{2}v_p t_p}{v_0 + v_p} \qquad (12\text{–}31)$$

where t_t is the time to target in seconds, S is the range in feet, v_p is the velocity increase of the rocket during powered flight up to the time of burnout in feet per second, t_p is the time of rocket burning in seconds, and v_0 is the initial velocity of the launching aircraft in feet per second. For more accurate values the velocity increase v_p can be given by equation 12–17. A more refined approximation to this formula is given in problem 12–5. More accurate values can only be obtained through a detailed step-by-step trajectory analysis which considers the effects of drag and gravity. This parameter of time to target is used in comparing one rocket projectile with another, since flight errors and the probability of hitting a given target are usually a function of the time to target. In general, a short value of t_t is desirable for most applications. In one air-to-air combat situation the effectiveness of the rocket projectile varied approximately inversely as the cube of the time to target.

Guided Missiles

The application and types of guided missiles have been discussed in the first chapter. Their accuracy is high compared to that of rocket projectiles, because their flight path is controlled and deviations from the intended trajectory can be corrected. A large number of different types of guided missiles have been and are being developed. The problems, principles, and mechanisms for controlling and guiding a high speed, rocket-propelled vehicle are beyond the scope of this book. Figures 1–9, 2–11, 2–12, 13–6, and 13–15 show typical guided missiles.

A simple rocket-propelled missile without booster is limited in range or altitude by the requirements of mechanical design for high mass ratios and by the relatively low energy content of existing rocket propellants. Calculations will show that altitudes above 250 miles and ranges over 300 miles can generally be attained only with single step missiles having small payloads or with multiple step missiles. Longer ranges may be possible with winged missiles. The design of a satellite missile or an escape vehicle with single step rocket units is inefficient because the bulk of the empty mass of the missile has to be continually accelerated, even after it is no longer useful.

It was shown in Chapter 4 that exhaust velocities exceeding 10,000 feet per second are attainable only from a few propellant combinations. In order to achieve a vehicle velocity of 25,000 feet per second with a 100-second burning time, the mass ratio of such a missile would have to be over 0.91, which is a physical improbability.

The use of a dense propellant permits a higher mass ratio ζ for a given missile, thereby increasing the range. For a given range, the high density propellants permit a smaller missile construction, giving less drag. The effect of the average propellant bulk density on the range can be computed for any given missile and presented in a form similar to Figure 12–11.

Multiple step rocket missiles permit a higher vehicle velocity and give an improved performance for long ranges or high velocities. Figure 2–2 shows a proposed two-step missile and Figure 2–13 shows a booster-missile combination. As the propellant is consumed in each step, it is dropped from the missile and the operation of the propulsion system of the next step is started. The last step, which usually is the smallest, carries the useful load. A simple two-step rocket consists of a missile with a booster rocket, which is dropped when it is no longer useful in adding energy to the payload, namely, when its propellant is exhausted.

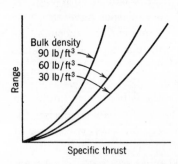

FIGURE 12–11. Effect of specific impulse and propellant bulk density on missile range.

The problem of separating the empty mass of an expended step from the useful remainder of the missile and the problem of initiating the successful and immediate combustion in the next step are not present in single stage units. Since the number of individual components (chambers, valves, thrust controls, igniters, aerodynamic controls, and so forth) is directly proportional to the number of steps, the design and operational difficulties become more numerous as steps are added.

The general theory of multiple step rockets is derived in references 8.101 and 8.105. Assuming that the cut-off of an expended step is simultaneous with the starting of the next step, the velocity at the cut-off of the last step can be determined as

$$v_p = -nc \ln \left[\sigma(1 - \gamma) + \gamma \right] - g t_p \qquad (12\text{--}32)$$

where v_p is the vehicle velocity at the final power cut-off, n is the number of steps, c is the average effective exhaust velocity, σ is a structural factor defined as the ratio of the empty weight to the filled weight of any step, γ is a payload ratio defined as the ratio of the weight of the carried load (other step missiles plus payload) to the weight of the missile step under consideration, g is the acceleration of gravity, and t_p is the total burning time of the propellants from the starting of the first step to the cut-off of the last step.

If drag is neglected, it can be shown (Ref. 8.101) that a constant value of γ for all the steps gives an optimum missile configuration. The assumption of a constant structural factor σ introduces only small errors.

As the number of steps is increased, the initial take-off weight can be decreased; but the gain in a smaller initial weight becomes less apparent when the total number of steps is large. Actually, the number of steps should not be chosen too large, because the physical mechanisms become very complex and large. The most economical number of steps is usually between 2 and 10.

The payload of a multiple step rocket is essentially proportional to the take-off weight, even though the payload is only a very small portion of the initial weight. If a payload of 50 pounds requires a 6000-pound multiple step rocket, a 500-pound payload would require a 60,000-pound rocket unit.

Rocket Airplanes

The high propellant consumption (see Figure 12–12) and the required high mass ratios of propellant mass to the filled airplane mass limit the value of rocket propulsion for aircraft. (See Sections 7.6 and 8.1 of the Reference Bibliography.) The hazard in handling and storing rocket propellants, the loud noise, and the necessity for special airfield installations restrict their use as commercial power plants. Only for special research and high speed military planes has the rocket found application.

The rocket plane, however, is the only known man-carrying prime mover, capable of reaching extreme altitudes and of flying at very high speeds, and as such is distinguished from other types of propulsion units, such as engine-driven propellers, turbojets, or ramjets. A comparison of these airplane power plants for a single seat, pursuit type airplane (Ref. 7.601) showed that, even though the dry weight of a rocket propulsion system is approximately one-twentieth or less the weight of a conventional piston engine-propeller combination, the high propellant consumption of rockets makes a rocket-driven plane practical only for very short durations. The dry weight of the engine installation depends on the design altitude. Figure 12–13 shows that the rocket is the only aircraft power plant, the dry weight per unit thrust of which does not increase with altitude.

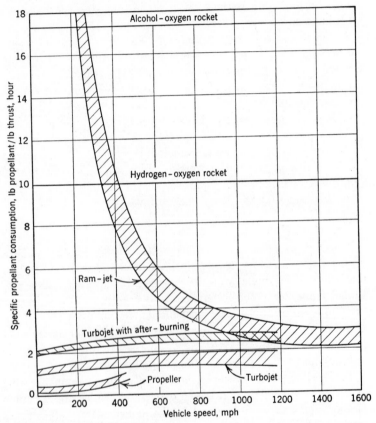

FIGURE 12–12. Propellant or fuel consumptions versus flight speed for different propulsion systems.

In rocket planes a high rate of climb, a long range, and a fast acceleration can be obtained most economically at high thrusts and high speeds because the propulsive efficiency increases with speed up to the point where the flight speed equals the exhaust velocity. The change of thrust with altitude is small for rockets if compared to other propulsion systems (see Figure 12–14). An analysis of the flight performance of a subsonic rocket airplane indicates that the maximum speed and the rate of climb increase phenomenally with altitude (Ref. 7.602).

Because of the very high fuel consumption, rocket aircraft are limited in their flight duration and range. The experimental

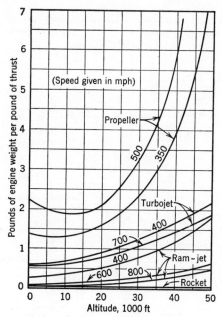

FIGURE 12–13. Power plant dry weight per pound of maximum available thrust as a function of altitude. (Reproduced from B. Hamlin and F. Spencerley, "Comparison of Propeller and Reaction Propelled Airplane Performances," *Journal of the Aeronautical Sciences*, Vol. 13, No. 8, 1946.)

rocket plane shown in Figure 1–5 had a powered flight duration of only 5 minutes at full thrust. The German Me 163 fighter was able to operate somewhat over 3 minutes at full power and over 12 minutes at reduced power; however, it was able to climb to 40,000 feet in less than 3 minutes. By gliding between power bursts the Me 163 was able to stay in the air over 30 minutes. The maximum range of rocket aircraft is also limited, unless a multiple stage aircraft is used in which the first stage is dropped, for it serves only to reach altitude. The maximum attainable range of a small fighter aircraft is shown in Figure 12–15.

Rocket-Assisted Take-off

By applying a short duration burst of rocket power, it is possible to reduce the required take-off ground distance and/or to increase the payload of airplanes at take-off. (See Section 7.4 of the Reference Bibliography.) Both liquid propellant and solid

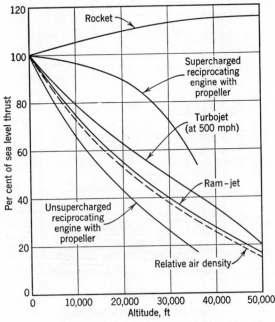

FIGURE 12–14. Typical variation of thrust with altitude for different propulsion systems.

propellant rocket propulsion systems are used. Figures 1–12, 1–13, 9–1, 9–3, and 9–6 show typical solid propellant assisted take-off units. Liquid propellant assisted take-off units (see Figures 1–6 and 2–10) are capable of durations of 25 to 60 seconds. Solid propellant rockets have been more commonly used as assisted take-off units, primarily because of the simplicity of installation and servicing.

Assisted take-off units have been used on carrier aircraft and also on flying boats, where they make take-off in rough weather possible. Figure 12–16 illustrates that the margin in forward thrust over the drag and water resistance can be increased by a large factor by using an assisted take-off unit. This margin is the force available for accelerating the aircraft or flying boat.

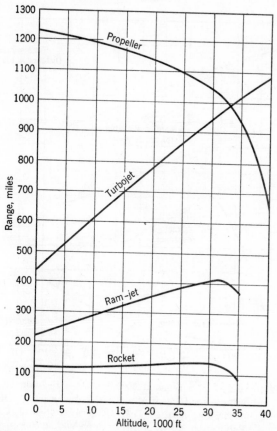

FIGURE 12-15. Maximum range of small fighter plane, including climb. (Reproduced from B. Hamlin and F. Spencerley, "Comparison of Propeller and Reaction Propelled Airplane Performances," *Journal of the Aeronautical Sciences*, Vol. 13, No. 8, 1946.)

The use of rockets for assisted take-off is at present one of the main commercial applications of rocket power plants. It is, for instance, possible to decrease the required take-off distance for a DC-3 transport plane by 29 per cent at a sea level airport and 34 per cent at an airport with an altitude of 6000 feet when using

1000 pounds of rocket assistance for 14 seconds. These rocket units can be installed either as a permanent part of the airplane or as a detachable unit, which can be dropped after use. Many

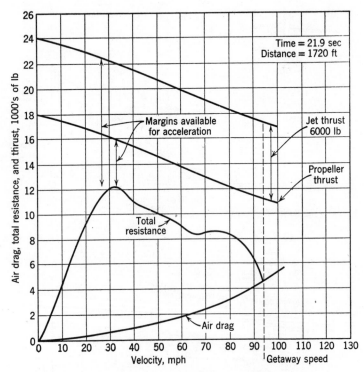

FIGURE 12–16. Effect of a constant 6000-lb jet assisted take-off thrust on the time and distance for take-off of a 60,000-lb flying boat. (Reproduced from C. M. Bolster, *The Assisted Take-off of Aircraft*, J. J. Cabot Fund Publication No. 9, Norwich University, 1950.)

of these droppable units have parachutes so that they can be salvaged, serviced, and used over again.

6 Aerodynamic Effect of Jets

The effect of rocket exhaust jets on the aerodynamic characteristic of missiles is to decrease the drag at supersonic missile speeds and to increase it at subsonic speeds.

On *subsonic* vehicles, a supersonic rocket jet acts very much like an ejector and sucks adjacent air into its path. This has a considerable effect on vehicles such as missiles, projectiles, and certain airplanes in which the rocket is located on a tapering aft end. The ejector action of the flame will accelerate the adjacent air, thereby increasing the skin friction locally and reducing the pressure on the vehicle body near the nozzle location. These effects tend to increase the drag but are partially counteracted by thrust augmentation effect of the moving air and the lowered atmospheric pressure at the nozzle, causing an increase in pressure thrust.

At *supersonic* speeds, there is a turbulent wake area with a low local pressure at the aft end of projectiles. With the action of a rocket jet, the void space is filled with rocket gases and the pressure on the aft portion of the body is increased. This decreases the drag or, in other words, increases the thrust. In addition, a shock wave is formed under certain conditions at the boundary of the jet and the air stream, which also tends to contribute to a decrease in drag by influencing the adjacent boundary layer. A rocket jet on the aft end of a flying streamlined body is therefore desirable for supersonic speeds.

7 Flight Stability

Aerodynamic stability of vehicles is a prerequisite to flight. This stability can be built in by proper design so that the flying article will be inherently stable or stability can be obtained by appropriate controls, such as the aerodynamic control surfaces on an airplane or jet vanes immersed in the exhaust gas of a rocket on a guided missile.

Flight stability exists when the overturning moments (for example, those due to a wind gust or misalignment of wings) are smaller than the stabilizing moments induced by controls or by tail surfaces. When the destabilizing moments exceed the stabilizing moments about the center of gravity, then the vehicle will turn or tumble. In unguided vehicles, such as rocket projectiles, stability of flight in a rectilinear motion is achieved by giving a large stability margin to the vehicle. This is accomplished by tail fins and by locating the center of gravity ahead of the center of aerodynamic pressure. Here the stabilizing moments are very large, even for a very small deflection of the vehicle axis from the line of flight, that is, a small angle of attack. In a controlled missile a nearly neutral inherent stability is desired, so that the control forces that have to be applied are small, thus requiring small control surfaces with little actuating mechanism and structural weight. Neutral stability is achieved by locating aerodynamic surfaces and weight distribution of the components within the vehicle in such a manner that the center of gravity and the center of aerodynamic pressure coincide.

Since the aerodynamic moments change with Mach number, the center of pressure does not stay fixed during accelerating flight but shifts usually along the vehicle axis. The center of gravity also changes its position as propellant is consumed and the vehicle weight decreases. Thus it is usually very difficult to achieve neutral missile stability at all altitudes, speeds, and flight conditions.

Stability considerations affect rocket design in several ways. It is possible to exercise some control over the travel of the center of gravity, by judicious design. In liquid propellant rockets, special design provisions, special tank shapes, and careful selection of tank location in the missile afford this possibility. The designer generally has less freedom in controlling the travel of the center of gravity of solid propellant rockets.

The rocket has been used satisfactorily to obtain control moments in at least three ways. Jet vanes can be inserted into the rocket exhaust gas of the rocket nozzle. The deflection of these vanes in this high velocity stream will produce the desired control forces. Another method is to mount the rocket thrust chamber on a set of gimbals or trunions (essentially a universal joint) to permit deflection of the thrust vector and thus create moments about the vehicle's center of gravity. Yet another way is to use the exhaust gas from the turbopump in directionally swiveled nozzles to obtain attitude control forces.

Problems

1. For a vehicle in gravitationless space determine the mass ratio necessary to boost the vehicle velocity by 2000 ft/sec when the effective exhaust velocity is 7200 ft/sec.
   Answer: 0.243.

2. What is the mass ratio m_p/m_0 for a vehicle which weighs one-fifth its original take-off weight at the time of the completion of rocket operation.
Answer: 0.80.

3. Determine the burnout velocity and burnout altitude for a dragless projectile with the following parameters for a simplified vertical trajectory.

$$\bar{c} = 7250 \text{ ft/sec}$$

$$m_p/m_0 = 0.57$$

$$t_p = 5.0 \text{ sec}$$

$$v_0 = h_0 = 0$$

Answers: $v_p = 5850$ ft/sec; $h_p = 112{,}000$ ft.

4. If this projectile had a drag coefficient essentially similar to the 6 degree curve in Figure 12–2, redetermine the answers of problem 3 and the approximate percentage errors in v_p and h_p. Use a step-by-step method.

5. Derive an equation for the time to target t_t over a range S of a horizontal flight of an air-launched rocket assuming that the flight velocity increase during rocket operation is a function of the specific impulse I_s, the time of burning t_p, the empty weight at burnout W_e, and the initial loaded weight W_0 of the rocket. Assume a constant propellant weight flow and an aircraft launching velocity v_0. In this problem there is no limitation on the duration of powered flight, if compared to equation 12–31.
Answer:

$$t_t = \frac{S}{I_s g \ln (W_0/W_e) + v_0} \left[1 + \frac{W_0}{W_0 - W_e} \left(\ln \frac{W_0}{W_e} - 1 \right) \right]$$

6. For a satellite cruising in a circular orbit altitude of 500 miles, determine the period of revolution, the flight speed, and the energy expended to bring a unit mass into this orbit.

7. A large ballistic rocket vehicle has the following characteristics:

Propellant mass flow rate	12 slugs/sec
Nozzle exit velocity	7100 ft/sec
Nozzle exit pressure	5 psia (assume no separation)
Atmospheric pressure	14.7 psia (sea level)
Take-off weight	12.0 tons
Burning time	50 sec
Nozzle exit area	400 in.^{2}

Determine (*a*) the sea level thrust, (*b*) the sea level effective exhaust velocity, (*c*) initial thrust to weight ratio, (*d*) the initial acceleration, and (*e*) the mass ratio.
Answers: 81,320 lb, 6775 ft/sec, 3.38, 2.38.

8. In the problem above compute the altitude and missile velocity at the time of power plant cut-off, neglecting the drag of the atmosphere and assuming a simple vertical trajectory.

Symbols

A	area, ft^2
a	major axis of ellipse, ft
B_1, B_2	numerical values of drag integrals
C_L	lift coefficient
C_D	drag coefficient
c	effective exhaust velocity, ft/sec
$\bar{c}$	average effective exhaust velocity, ft/sec
D	drag force, lb
d	total derivative
E	energy, ft-lb
e	eccentricity of ellipse
F	thrust force, lb
F_0	initial thrust force, lb
g	gravitational acceleration, ft/sec^2
g_0	gravitational acceleration at sea level, ft/sec^2
$\bar{g}, \bar{\bar{g}}$	average gravitational attraction, ft/sec^2
h	altitude, ft
h_p	altitude of rocket power cut-off, ft
I_s	specific impulse, sec
m	instantaneous mass, lb-sec^2/ft
m_p	propellant mass, lb-sec^2/ft
m_0	initial launching mass, lb-sec^2/ft
R	instantaneous radius from vehicle to center of earth, ft
R_0	earth radius, ft
$\mathcal{R}$	instantaneous radius of curvature
S	range, ft
t	time, sec
t_p	time from launching to power cut-off, sec
t_t	time to target, sec
v	velocity, ft/sec
v_a	orbital velocity at apogee
v_b	orbital velocity at perigee
v_0	launching velocity, ft/sec
W	weight, lb
W_0	initial total launching weight, lb
W_e	empty or final weight at cut-off of rocket power, lb
$\dot{w}$	propellant flow rate, lb/sec

Greek Letters

α	angle of attack
γ	payload ratio of step rockets
θ	angle between flight direction and horizontal
ζ	mass ratio ($\zeta = m_p/m_0$)
λ	vehicle mass ratio ($\lambda = W_0/W_e$)
μ	constant, $\mu = g_0 R_0$
ρ	mass density, slugs/ft^3
σ	structural factor of step rockets
τ	period of revolution, sec
ψ	angle of thrust direction with horizontal

Subscripts

e	escape condition
max	maximum
s	satellite

Chapter 13

Rocket Testing

1   Type of Tests

Before liquid and solid propellant rockets are put into operational use, they are subjected to several different types of tests, some of which are outlined below in the sequence in which they are normally performed.

1. Manufacturing and assembly testing (pressure tests, leak checks, electromechanical checks).
2. Component tests (functional and operational tests on igniters, valves, injectors, structure, etc.).
3. Static rocket system tests (with complete rocket on test stand). (*a*) Simulated rocket operation (for proper function, calibration, ignition, operation—usually without establishing full combustion). (*b*) Complete engine tests (under rated conditions, off-design conditions, with intentional variations in environment or calibration).
4. Static vehicle tests (when rocket is installed in a restrained non-flying vehicle).
5. Flight tests. (*a*) On a specially instrumented flight test range with special flight test vehicle. (*b*) With production vehicle.

Each of these five types of tests can be performed on at least three basic types of programs:

1. The research on and the development or improvement of a new rocket.
2. The evaluation of the suitability of this new (or modified) rocket for a specified application.
3. The production of a rocket.

The first two types of programs concern themselves with a new or modified device and often involve the testing and measurement of new phenomena using experimental rockets. The testing of a new solid propellant grain, the development of a new control valve assembly, and the measurement of the thermal expansion of a nozzle exhaust cone during firing operation are examples of the problems to be encountered here.

Production tests concern themselves with the measurement of a few basic parameters on a relatively large number of production propulsion systems. During the Second World War thousands of solid rocket projectiles and assisted take-off units were production tested in this country and abroad, and some 3000 German V-2 power plants were statically fired. The test equipment and instrumentation used for these tests were usually designed so that they permitted the testing and measurement in a minimum of time.

In this case the five basic types of tests are performed to permit a quality control check on the production. Not all of the units fabricated need to be subjected to all the tests, for a statistical sample is often adequate. In some rocket designs, the article is suitable for single shot operation only, and selective sampling must be used for production testing.

Of course, it is implied that all rockets will undergo a certain amount of manufacturing testing in their normal inspection and fabrication process; this includes pressure tests of chambers, tanks, valves, and pipes, electromechanical checks, leakage tests, and material composition or heat treatment checks.

During the early development phases of a program, many special and unusual tests are performed on components and complete rockets to prove specific design features and performance characteristics. Special facilities and instrumentation or modification of existing test equipment are used in these tests. During the second type of program, some special tests will usually be conducted to determine the statistical performance and reliability of a rocket device by operating a number of units of the same design. During this phase tests are also made to demonstrate the ability of the rocket to withstand extreme limits of the operating conditions, such as high and low ambient temperature, variations in fuel compositions, changes in the vibration environment, or exposure to moisture and rain, and rough handling during storage.

2 Safety Precautions

Because of the physical hazards involved in handling propellants and controlling high pressure combustion processes,

FIGURE 13-1. Fragments of exploded experimental rocket thrust chamber.
(Courtesy North American Aviation, Inc.)

elaborate safety precautions govern the method of testing. Figure 13-1 shows the remains of an experimental rocket thrust chamber after a chamber explosion. This is the same uncooled liquid propellant thrust chamber type shown in Figure 5-3. The violence of the explosion can be seen from the complete fragmentation and deformation of the heavy steel pieces.

Almost all tests with actual propellants, therefore, are conducted by remote control from a protected barricade or blockhouse. In addition, precautions are usually taken to minimize the damage, in case of accident or explosion. Some of the more common safety features for rocket testing are:

1. Operators are protected by concrete walled blockhouses or barricades, which are located at some distance away from the test unit.

2. Control of valves, etc., is achieved by electric, hydraulic, or pneumatic means, so that the flow of hazardous propellants into the control station is not required.

3. An automatic or hand-actuated sprinkler system to extinguish possible propellant fires is almost always provided.

4. Operators view test operation through periscope type mirror arrangement or through a very thick layer of safety glass, which is often reinforced with iron grids. In some test installations television has been used for remote test observation.

5. Individual test stations, propellant or parts storage locations, and control stations are never located adjacent to each other; they are usually spaced sufficiently far apart so that an accident in any one establishment will not affect the remainder of the installation.

6. Warning signals are given to notify personnel to clear hazardous area prior to tests (siren, bell, flag, horn, or signal lights).

7. Separating of fuel and oxidizer storage reduces the fire and explosion hazard. The amount of propellant stored in any one installation is limited.

8. The test cell is usually barricaded on several sides so as to reduce shrapnel effect in case of explosion.

9. Instruments are of the remote indicating or remote recording type.

10. No smoking is permitted near a test station which uses ignitable propellants. Sparkproof shoes are worn by all personnel.

11. Personnel are permitted to work on test installation only if fuel and oxidizer are separated and not pressurized.

12. Personnel handling dangerous propellants have to wear safety equipment such as gloves, face shields, and with

some propellants even gas masks and rubber suits or aprons (see Figure 13–2).

Figure 13–2. Plastic safety suit, gloves, boots, and hood used by operating personnel in handling very hazardous or corrosive liquid propellants. Safety shower, which starts automatically when personnel steps onto platform, washes away spilled or splashed propellant. (Official U. S. Air Force Photograph.)

13. Establishment and rigid enforcement of safety rules will minimize carelessness.

Once a unit or a design has been proved or developed, it is possible to forego some of the safety precautions; for example, flight tests are usually performed only with proven and checked rockets.

3 Test Installation

Early rocket test stations consisted frequently of only a hole in the ground, in which the operator could hide, and a simple wooden rocket test stand some 20 feet from the hole. The valves were

FIGURE 13–3. Typical control and instrument panel inside blastproof control station used in sequencing, operating, and data recording of tests on rocket engine. Automatic chart recorders on left give permanent readings of measured quantities. Operating consoles with switches, indicating lights, and instruments are near heavy safety glass windows at right. (Courtesy North American Aviation, Inc.)

often operated by long strings from the dugout. A typical early test setup is shown in Figure 2–8.

A modern test station usually has a concrete control house in which all instruments and control equipment are housed. The test crew operates the unit from this control station. A typical operator's control panel is shown in Figure 13–3. The slots in the wall lead to windows which permit the viewing of the tests. An intercommunication system is used for contact between operator and test pit crew during servicing, repairs, and system checks. The lock in the panel controls a master switch. Keys are issued only to authorized operating personnel.

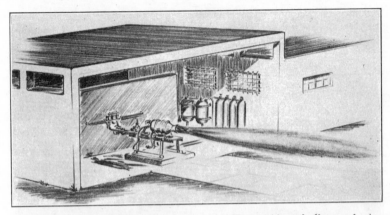

FIGURE 13–4. Static firing rocket test pit. Note grid on bulletproof windows. (Reproduced from G. P. Sutton, "Gaging Rocket Engine Forces and Flows," *Aviation*, April 1947.)

FIGURE 13–5. Static firing test in concrete test pit. (Courtesy North American Aviation, Inc.)

Close to the control house is the test bay or test pit in which the unit to be tested is located. The appearance of this test bay will vary, depending on the type and size of unit. Liquid propellant feed system components which use hazardous propellants require almost equally complex test stations as thrust chambers. The propellant storage tanks are usually outside the test pit itself in

FIGURE 13–6. Testing and servicing tower for experimental launching of surface-to-surface missiles at White Sands, New Mexico. Tower is on wheels and is moved away prior to launching. (Courtesy General Electric Company.)

order to reduce the explosion hazard. Equipment for servicing and repairing the test equipment and unit is located in an adjacent shop. Typical test stations can be seen in Figures 13–4 and 13–5. Note the blast walls on all sides except in the firing and

FIGURE 13–7. Static test stands like this one at the Experimental Rocket Engine Test Station, Edwards Air Force Base, are used to test large liquid rocket engines prior to installations in missiles or aircraft. (Official U. S. Air Force Photograph.)

viewing directions. A launching test and servicing station is shown in Figure 13–6. Since most rocket-propelled vehicles are bulky, heavy, and fragile, they require specially designed launching provisions. A test stand for testing large rocket engines for missile use in a vertically downward firing position is shown in Figure 13–7. A water basin for testing underwater rockets is shown in Figure 13–8.

Sections 9.1 and 9.3 of the Reference Bibliography give references for further study on test facilities and test operation.

FIGURE 13–8.   Towing channel designed for testing propulsion units for underwater vehicles.   (Courtesy Jet Propulsion Laboratory, California Institute of Technology.)

4   Instrumentation

General

Some of the physical quantities measured in rocket testing are discussed briefly in this section.   References to further study can be found in Section 9.2 of the Reference Bibliography.

1. Forces (rocket thrust, jet vane reaction).
2. Flows (hot and cold gases, fuel, oxidizer).
3. Pressures (chamber, fuel system, oxidizer system, igniter, pump discharge and suction, tank, inert gas system).
4. Temperatures (walls of chamber, nozzle, gas generator, propellants).

5. Operating sequences (timing and sequence of valve actuation, igniter operation, pressure switch functioning, etc.).

6. Stresses and vibrations (stress of various structural members of the rocket and acceleration in various locations).

7. Special instruments (as required for the specific tests).

Each of these measurements requires a *sensing element* (often called *pickup*) and an *indicating instrument* or more frequently a

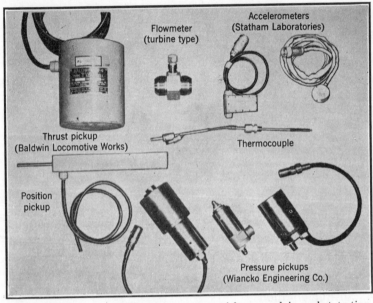

FIGURE 13–9. Typical sensing elements or pickups used in rocket testing. Their electrical outputs are modulated and recorded or sometimes displayed on an indicating instrument. (North American Aviation Photograph.)

recorder; some instruments require *amplifiers* or *modulators* to change the signal from the sensing element into a form suitable for recording or indicating. Typical sensing elements are shown in Figure 13–9 and typical chart recorders in Figure 13–3. A simple Bourdon type pressure gage, for example, has a curved tube sensing element which deflects under pressure, a linkage mechanism, which transforms the linear deflection of the tube into a rotary motion, and a needle with a calibrated dial to give visual indication of the measured pressure. Several significant definitions of terms used in instrumentation are listed below.

Range refers to the region extending from the minimum to the maximum rated value over which the instrument will give a true and linear response. Usually an additional margin is provided to permit temporary overloads of the instrument without damage to the instrument or need for recalibration.

Errors in measurements are usually of two types: *human errors* of improperly reading the instrument, chart, or record and of improperly interpreting or correcting this data; *instrument errors* usually fall into four classifications, which are static errors, dynamic response errors, drift errors, and hysteresis errors.

Static errors in the instrumentation are usually fixed errors due to fabrication and installation variations; these static errors can usually be detected by careful calibration. An appropriate correction can then be applied to the reading.

Drift error is the change in the instrument output over a period of time, usually caused by random wander and environmental conditions. To avoid drift error the instrument has to be calibrated at frequent intervals at standard environmental conditions against a known standard reference value over its whole range.

Dynamic response errors occur when the instrument fails to register the true value of the measured quantity while this quantity is changing, particularly when it is changing rapidly. A *maximum frequency response* of a given instrument refers to the maximum frequency (usually in cycles per second) at which the instrument will measure true values. The natural frequency of the instrument system is usually above the limiting response frequency. Generally a high frequency response requires more complex and expensive instrumentation. All of the instrument system (that is, sensing elements, modulators, and recorders) must be capable of a fast response. Most of the measurements in rocket testing are made with one of two types of instruments: those made under nearly steady static conditions, where only relatively gradual changes in the quantities occur, and secondly those made of fast transient conditions such as rocket starting and stopping. This latter type of instrument has frequency responses above 200 cycles per second, sometimes as high as 20,000 cycles per second.

These fast measurements are necessary to evaluate the physical phenomena of rapid transients as they occur in rockets.

Linearity of the instrument refers to the ratio of the input (usually pressure, temperature, force, etc.) to the output (usually voltage, deflection, etc.) over the range of the instrument. Very often the static calibration error indicates a deviation from a truly linear response. A non-linear response can cause appreciable errors in dynamic measurements.

Resolution refers to the minimum change in the measured quantity that can be detected with a given instrument.

Dead zone or *hysteresis* errors are often caused by energy absorption within the instrument system or play in the instrument mechanism; in part they limit the resolution of the instrument.

Sensitivity refers to the change in response or reading caused by special influences. For example, the *temperature sensitivity* and the *acceleration sensitivity* of an instrument refer to the change in measured value caused by temperature and acceleration. These are usually expressed in per cent change of measured value and this information can serve to correct readings to reference or standard conditions.

Automatic recording is usually preferred over visually indicating instruments. Data recording is described briefly in another section of this chapter.

Thrust

The stand which supports the rocket unit is designed so that it permits a slight motion in the direction of the thrust. The magnitude of the thrust is then measured by a thrust-sensing element or thrust jack, as shown in Figures 13–10 and 13–11. Care must be exercised in the design of the test stand installation to minimize thrust errors introduced by restraints, such as pressurized piping, bearing friction, or instrument connections.

Thrust jacks of this type may consist of a cradle pushing against a spring, the deflection of which indicates the applied force. This system, although simple, is difficult to be realized accurately.

A hydraulic thrust jack, as shown in Figure 13–11, has been used. Pneumatic thrust-sensing elements and strain gage type cells are also frequently used. By transmitting the fluid pressure from a hydraulic cylinder to a direct reading pressure gage through a throttling valve, which dampens out high frequency

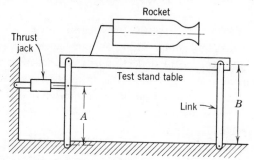

FIGURE 13–10. Thrust stand. (Rocket thrust = Force on thrust jack × A/B.) (Reproduced from G. P. Sutton, "Gaging Rocket Engine Forces and Flows," *Aviation*, April 1947.)

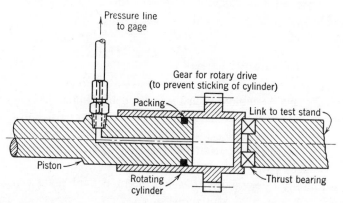

FIGURE 13–11. Hydraulic thrust-sensing element. (Reproduced from G. P. Sutton, "Gaging Rocket Engine Forces and Flows," *Aviation*, April 1947.)

pressure fluctuations, a direct low frequency response thrust measurement is obtained. The thrust jack in Figure 13–11 is rotated by a gear train to prevent sticking of the cylinder.

If it is desired to obtain a high frequency response thrust measurement, for example, during rocket starting and stopping, it can be accomplished by electronically measuring the fluid pressure in a hydraulic thrust jack or by a special strain gage element of the type shown in Figure 13–9. The instrument to be used for measuring such hydraulic cylinder pressures is similar to pressure pickups described in Section 4 below. To mount the whole test stand directly on scales has also been found to be very satisfactory.

Another method of determining instantaneous thrust is to mount the rocket unit on an elastic support, such as a steel beam, and to measure the beam deflections by means of strain gages. In such measurements, care has to be taken to prevent heat from the thrust chamber or radiation from the jet flame reaching the strain gage itself, since resistance changes in the strain gage wires may introduce considerable errors.

When it is desired to measure control forces induced by deflections of jet vanes immersed in the jet or the forces induced by auxiliary swiveled control rockets, it is necessary to measure not only the axial thrust but also side forces or moments produced by the test unit. This requires a complex thrust stand construction similar to a wind tunnel balance and several simultaneous force measurements.

Flow of Liquid Propellants

For many years only rough measurements of the total consumption of propellant have been made by determining the quantity of propellant in the storage tanks before and after each test. This permitted the evaluation of an average flow rate. Recently it has become practicable to use flow rate meters, such as certain type orifice meters and vane type rotary flowmeters.

An alternate method is to weigh the propellant tanks continuously by scales or by strain gage suspension.

However, all flow rate meters with which the author is acquainted have a considerable inertia, and a fast-responding research flowmeter that will give a high frequency response has yet to be devised.

Pressures

Steady state and gradually varying pressures have repeatedly been measured or recorded with ordinary commercial gages. In most rocket units all pressures are subject to some high frequency fluctuations; ordinary Bourdon gages and manometers usually give an average pressure only.

Pressure pickups capable of a high frequency response will give not only transient starting and stopping pressure changes but also a more correct picture of the actual course of the pressure. All these pickups are usually connected to recording oscillographs or to fluorescent oscilloscope screens for recording and photographic observation. A pressure pickup is a device in which mechanical pressure is converted into an electrical signal, which

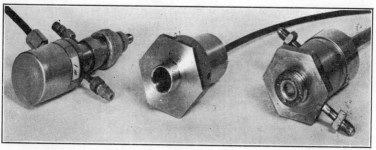

FIGURE 13–12. Three types of pressure pickups. Unit on either side has water cooling provisions. (Courtesy Aerojet-General Corporation.)

in turn is electronically modified and observed or recorded. Such pickups are capable of a response of several hundred cycles per second (in one instance several thousand cycles per second), have a linear characteristic between pressure and electrical output, are insensitive to temperature effects, and are readily calibrated.

One principle of pickup operation is to apply the pressure against a circular diaphragm, thereby causing a deflection of the diaphragm. This deflection changes a small air gap between the diaphragm and an adjacent plate, thereby causing a variation in the capacity of a condenser. By means of a frequency-modulated circuit it is possible to convert the variations in capacity into a useful electrical signal. Experimental pressure pickups are shown in Figures 13–9 and 13–12.

Other pickup types rely on strain gages, optical deflection of light beams, piezoelectric effects of certain crystals, inductance changes due to movable coils or small magnets or magnetostriction effects.

Temperature

Most of the ordinary temperature measurements in rocket testing are made with thermocouples; sometimes other instruments such as resistance thermometers and thermopiles are also used.

The successful measurement of combustion chamber wall and nozzle wall temperatures usually requires special design provisions for building the temperature-sensing elements directly into the wall of the unit. Unfortunately this insertion of thermo-

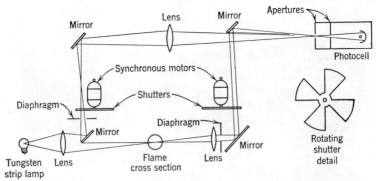

FIGURE 13–13. Absorption-emission-pyrometer with rotating shutters.

couples into the wall will often disturb the heat flux and temperature distribution in the vicinity of the thermocouple junction, thus causing it to indicate an erroneous value. Temperature measurements of metal parts, inert gases, and propellants (both solid and liquid) are quite common. Heat transfer rates are usually deduced from these measurements.

The measurement of hot gases above approximately 1500° F presents a problem, since the sensing element tends to cool itself by radiation to cooler surroundings and since the thermocouple materials present some limitations.

Measurement of gas temperatures above perhaps 2000° F is difficult and requires special instrumentation. This problem is aggravated not only by the extremely high temperature of the gases and their peculiar temperature gradient (sometimes over 2000° F differential), but also by the extremely high velocity of the gases especially at the nozzle section (1 mile per second or better). Means to measure these gas temperatures are usually only approximate. Some few measurements have been made using pyrometers and other optical means, but the methods are complicated and not always generally applicable to all usual types of rocket units. A few accurate optical or radiation type measuring instruments have been developed.

The sodium D line reversal method relies on matching the brightness of a black body radiation source with the sodium D line radiation (5893 Angstrom units) of sodium vapor introduced into the flame. A high accuracy tungsten lamp, which is used as the radiating source, has to be calibrated for non-black body radiation. This method lends itself to continuous or instantaneous recording. A schematic diagram of an instrument which compares the direct radiation of a reference source with the radiation across the jet is shown in Figure 13–13.

Operating Sequence

The time sequencing of events is of particular interest in rocket measurements. In simple solid rockets, the delays between the electrical signals, the actual functioning of the igniter, and the rise in chamber pressure are typical of the important quantities, which are usually specified by the customer. In liquid propellant rockets the functioning and time sequences of valve operations, arrival of first propellant at various stations, electrical signals to the control systems, pressure switch, and relay actuation may be of significance in specific rocket engines. Multiple channel sequence instruments are used for recording these events. In some of the more complex liquid rocket engines some 20 to 60 sequence signals are recorded.

The problem of referencing the time accurately to perhaps a few milliseconds on all recording instruments used during any one test usually requires some special devices. Measurements of relative motion and position of valves and control elements are also made to determine rocket operation and are sometimes recorded on sequence charts.

Stress, Vibration, and Accelerations

Measurements of stress in structural parts are not materially different from those used in conventional dynamic stress measurements. Strain gage methods with amplifiers and recording in-

struments are frequently used. Care must be exercised to reduce
temperature errors.

Vibration or acceleration measurements in several directions
have been made with high frequency response and rugged acceleration pickups. Under conditions of combustion vibration it
has been possible to record local, low amplitude accelerations in
excess of 500 g; this requires special instruments. These ac-
celerometer readings can usually be related with fluctuations in
the combustion pressure or the propellant or gas flow. The knowledge of the vibration spectrum of a rocket (frequency-amplitude
diagram) permits a more intelligent design of the vehicle.

Special Instruments

The categories of measurements given above comprise the bulk
of the instrumentation requirements for rocket testing. There
are a few other standard instruments, such as a tachometer for
pump speed indication, but there is usually only one or two of
these used in any one test. High speed photographic coverage is
also used frequently.

The other instruments are usually of a special nature and depend largely on the engine design and the special test program.
A few of these special instruments are discussed here to illustrate
the variety of problems encountered in rocket testing.

When a rocket engine is pivoted and hinged in its mounting
frame (to permit better attitude control of missiles) special instruments for recording angular position, angular velocity, and
angular acceleration are needed.

Direct jet velocity measurements are very difficult to perform.
It is common practice to calculate the effective exhaust velocity
from the thrust force and the propellant flow.

Measurements of the exhaust velocity of a high speed cold
air jet have been made by means of a high speed camera, determining the distance traversed by particles in the flame for the
small duration of the exposure time of the individual film frames.
A photographic determination of the Mach angle of shock waves
in supersonic jet flames will also permit an approximate determination of the jet velocity, provided the jet temperatures are
known.

The chemical composition of the flame determines the degree of completion of the combustion, and its determination is similar to a flue gas analysis. Samples of the exhaust gas are chemically analyzed. The probe which collects the sample from the hot gas stream has to be cooled in order to keep the probe from melting and in order to freeze the chemical equilibrium. Instruments have been designed which are capable of changing the position of the probe and drawing gas samples into different sampling bottles twenty times per minute.

It is also important to know the shape of the flame, in order to determine how close the adjacent air frame parts may be brought. Most flames are readily photographed because they are luminous. There are several types of propellants (for example, nitromethane) which show a relatively non-luminous flame, but the flame pattern can be made visible by coloring additives. Flame shapes are shown in Figures 13–4 and 13–5.

5 Flight Testing

Rocket airplane flight tests are usually carried out from experimental airfields. The pilots of experimental planes are usually protected by special safety features.

Missile and rocket projectile flight tests generally have to be conducted at unpopulated rocket test ranges. For heavy ground-to-ground missiles these test ranges have to be very large so that any uncontrolled missile will not damage inhabited installations. The observation of test missiles in flight (see Figure 13–14) and keeping the missile within the boundaries of the proving ground present special problems which require special equipment. Subsonic small missiles can be attached to airplanes as shown in Figure 13–15.

Strong blockhouses for controls and operating personnel of test ranges are frequently provided. The concrete control station at the White Sands Proving Grounds, New Mexico, shown in Figure 13–16, is strong enough to withstand the impact of a fully loaded V-2 missile. Optical and electrical tracking devices are provided on the range to plot the path of the missile and locate the point of impact.

Simulated flight tests are often conducted to save expense of aircraft and range usage. High speed tracks are sometimes used for this purpose (see Figures 2–15 and 13–17).

6   Recording of Data

The recording of data in permanent form has been found to be much more satisfactory than the mere indication and observation

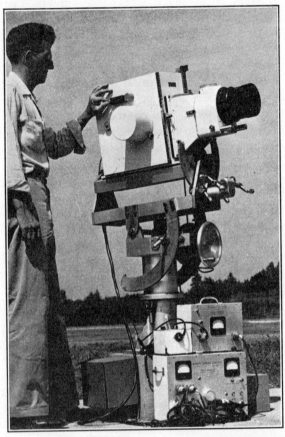

FIGURE 13–14. Camera used for determination of exterior ballistic characteristics of free flight projectiles. Film records the timing signal, elevation, and azimuth on the same film that photographs the rocket. (U. S. Army Photograph, Redstone Arsenal.)

of the measured quantities. A good part of the recorded data should be available immediately after a test to permit rapid evaluation of the results. Unfortunately, only the low frequency

FIGURE 13–15. Small guided rocket missile attached to airplane wing ready for flight test launching. (Official U. S. Navy Photograph.)

FIGURE 13–16. Launching station. At left is an observation tower and the control building, the latter roofed by nearly 30 feet of concrete. At right is the gantry crane, which surrounds the V-2 while it is being prepared for launching. (Courtesy General Electric Company.)

FIGURE 13–17. Track type rocket-propelled launcher carriage for projectile flight tests. Four 5-in. rockets are used to accelerate the carriage (gross weight of 390 lb) on the dual track to a velocity of 1300 ft/sec in a track distance of approximately 450 ft, at which time the rocket is released from the carriage. The rocket is fired to study the flight stability at high air speeds and at conditions of almost complete exhaustion of propellant. The 2.75-in. diameter test rocket has 4 folding fins, which are shown in the extended position. (Courtesy U. S. Naval Ordnance Test Station.)

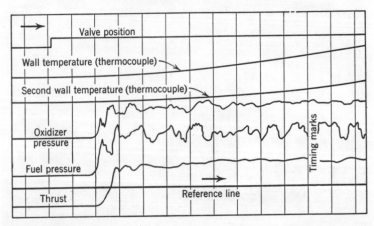

FIGURE 13–18. Oscillogram of typical experimental run. (Reproduced from G. P. Sutton, "Gaging Rocket Engine Forces and Flows," *Aviation*, April 1947.)

instrumentation lends itself readily to immediate inspection of its data; high frequency records do not readily lend themselves to rapid data reduction. The following types of data recording have been used.

1. Motion picture record of dial gages (low frequency).
2. Direct inking recording instruments using both the circular and strip chart record, with and without self-compensating amplifier (low frequency). See Figure 13–3.
3. Oscillograph with special photopaper (high frequency). See Figure 13–18.
4. High speed oscilloscope photographed by high speed camera (high frequency).
5. Magnetic tape recording with special analyzing instrument (high frequency).
6. Movie coverage of engine operation, sequence neon lights, and controls (high or low speed).

In flight testing the recording of measured data is more difficult, because the space and weight requirements of the flying vehicle do not permit the installation of many recording instruments. Directional movie cameras are often used to record the motion of airplanes with rocket take-off aides or of missiles near their launching station. Many military vehicles are expended and the salvage of instrument records becomes almost impossible in some of these cases. Two means of recording data for expendable missiles have been devised: one is to radio the data from the flying vehicle to some ground station at which the data will be recorded. This is commonly called *telemetering*. The other method is to house the recording instruments or records in a special impact resistant compartment in the missile, which can be salvaged after the missile has been expended.

Reference Bibliography

1.0 General Literature

1.1 Introductory References

1.101 M. J. Zucrow, *Principles of Jet Propulsion and Gas Turbines,* John Wiley & Sons, Inc., New York, 1949.

1.102 E. Sänger, *Raketenflugtechnik* (Rocket Flight Technique), R. Oldenburg, Munich, 1933.

1.103 E. Burgess, *Rocket Propulsion,* Chapman and Hall, Ltd., London, Revised 1954, 235 pp.

1.104 F. Zwicky, "Morphology and Nomenclature of Jet Engines," *Aviation,* June 1947.

1.105 A. Ananoff, *L'Astronautique* (Astronautics), Librairie Arthème Fayard, Paris, 1950, 498 pp.

1.106 J. Stemmer, *Die Entwicklung des Raketen Antriebes in allgemein verständlicher Darstellung* (Development of Rocket Propulsion, Simply Explained), Vols. 1, 2, and 3, E. A. Hofmann, Zürich, 1944.

1.107 H. K. Kaiser, *Kleine Raketenkunde* (Little Rocket Encyclopedia), Mundus Verlag, Stuttgart, Germany, 1949, 151 pp.

1.108 W. Ley, *Rockets, Missiles and Space Travel,* Viking Press, Inc., New York, 1951, 436 pp.

1.109 W. Dornberger, *V2—Der Schuss ins Weltall* (V2—The Shot into Space), Bechtle Verlag, Esslingen, Germany, 1952, 295 pp.

1.110 "Rockets for Peace and War," *Interavia,* No. 11, 1953, p. 627.

1.111 H. C. Urey, *The Planets, Their Origin and Development,* Yale University Press, New Haven, Connecticut, 1952, 245 pp.

1.112 R. H. Reichel, "Die heutigen Grenzen des Raketenantriebes und ihre Bedeutung für den Raumfahrtgedanken" (The Present Limits of Rocket Propulsion and Their Implications to Space Travel), *Zeitschrift des Vereines Deutscher Ingenieure,* Vol. 92, No. 32, Nov. 11, 1950.

1.2 Surveys and Bibliographies

1.201 H. H. Kölle and H. J. Kaeppeler, *Literature Index of Astronautics,* Pustet Verlag, Tittmoning, Germany, 1954, 100 pp.

1.202 E. F. Fiock and C. Halpern, *Bibliography of Books and Published Reports on Gas Turbines, Jet Propulsion and Rocket Power Plants*, National Bureau of Standards, Washington, D. C., July 1954, 110 pp.

1.203 G. P. Sutton, "Rocket Propulsion Progress: A Literature Survey," *Journal of the American Rocket Society*, Vol. 22, No. 1, Jan.–Feb. 1952.

1.204 G. P. Sutton, "Rockets Behind the Iron Curtain," *Journal of the American Rocket Society*, Vol. 23, No. 3, May–June 1953.

1.205 E. J. Gentle and J. W. Herrick, *Rocket Encyclopedia*, Aero Publishers, Los Angeles, California, 1956.

1.206 H. S. Seifert, "Twenty Five Years of Rocket Development," *Jet Propulsion*, Vol. 25, No. 11, Nov. 1955.

1.207 R. Youngquist and J. P. Layton, "Presentation of the Proposed American Standard Letter Symbols for Rocket Propulsion," *Jet Propulsion*, Vol. 25, No. 11, Nov. 1955.

2.0 History

2.1 Classical Publications

2.101 K. E. Ziolkowsky, *Space Investigations by Means of Propulsion Space Ships*, Kaluga, Leningrad, 1914.

2.102 H. Oberth, *Die Rakete zu den Planetenräumen* (By Rocket into Planetary Space), R. Oldenburg, Munich, 1923.

2.103 H. Oberth, *Wege zur Raumschiffahrt* (Means for Space Travel), R. Oldenburg, Munich, 1929.

2.104 *Die Rakete*, monthly magazine of the German Rocket Society, 1927–1930.

2.105 R. H. Goddard, "Liquid-propellant Rocket Development," *Smithsonian Institute, Washington, Miscellaneous Collection No. 3381*, 1936.

2.106 R. H. Goddard, A Method of Reaching Extreme Altitudes, *Smithsonian Institute, Washington, Miscellaneous Collections LXXI*, No. 2, 1919.

2.107 *Jet Propulsion, The Journal of the American Rocket Society*. (Formerly called *Astronautics* and originally called *Bulletin of the American Interplanetary Society*, started in 1931. Since Jan. 1, 1954, issued under title *Jet Propulsion*. Published by American Rocket Society, New York.)

2.108 H. Noordung, *Das Problem der Befahrung des Weltraums; Der Raketenmotor* (The Problem of World Space Travel; The Rocket Motor), Schmidt & Co., Berlin, 1929.

2.109 R. Esnault-Pelterie, *L'Astronautique* (Astronautics), Impremerie A. Lahure, Paris, 1930.

2.110 R. H. Goddard, *Rocket Development*, Prentice-Hall, Inc., New York, 1948.

2.111 P. E. Paulet, *Liquid Propellant Rocket*, El Commercio, Lima, Peru, 1920.

2.112 Sir W. Congreve, *The Details of the Rocket System*, Whiting, London, 1814.

2.113 M. Roy, *Recherches théoriques sur le rendement et les conditions de réalisation des systèmes motor propulseurs à Réaction*, E. Blondel, La Rougery, Paris, 1930.

2.114 *Journal of the British Interplanetary Society*, published by British Interplanetary Society, London.

2.115 *Weltraumfahrt* (World Space Travel), published by Gesellschaft für Raumfahrtforschung, Stuttgart, Germany.

2.2 Historical Accounts

2.201 W. Ley, *Shells and Shooting*, Viking Press, Inc., New York, 1942.

2.202 W. G. A. Perring, "A Critical Review of German Long-Range Rocket Development," *Journal of the Royal Aeronautical Society*, Vol. 50, No. 427, 1945.

2.203 R. Stanton, "Research and Development of the Jet Propulsion Laboratory, GALCIT," *Engineering and Science Monthly*, California Institute of Technology, Pasadena, California, July 1946.

2.204 A. Africano, "The Rocket Research of Dr. R. H. Goddard," *Journal of the American Rocket Society*, No. 71, Sept. 1947.

2.205 "H. Oberth, Shaper of Things to Come," *Interavia*, Sept. 1949.

2.206 J. W. Siry, "Early History of Rocket Research," *Scientific Monthly*, Vol. 71, Nov. 1950.

2.207 J. W. Siry, "Rocket Research in the Twentieth Century," *Scientific Monthly*, Vol. 71, Dec. 1950.

2.208 W. Ley, "Die ersten grossen Raketen" (The First Large Rockets), *Weltraumfahrt*, No. 1, 1951.

2.209 F. Ross, *Guided Missiles: Rockets and Torpedoes*, Lathrop, Lee and Shepard Co., Inc., New York, 1951, 186 pp.

2.210 T. L. Davis, "Early Chinese Rockets," *Technical Review*, Dec. 1948.

2.211 W. von Braun, "Survey of Development of Liquid Rockets in Germany and their Future Prospects," *Journal of the British Interplanetary Society*, Vol. 10, March 1951.

2.212   W. Dornberger, "European Rocketry after World War I," *Journal of British Interplanetary Society,* Vol. 13, Sept. 1954.

2.213   K. W. Gatland, *Development of the Guided Missile,* Philosophical Library, Inc., New York, 1954, 292 pp.

2.214   R. C. Truax, "The Pioneer Rocket Project of the U. S. Navy," *Journal of the American Rocket Society,* June 1948.

2.215   K. A. Ehricke, "The Peenemünde Rocket Center, Part 3," *Rocketscience,* Sept. 1950.

2.216   H. H. Kölle, "Fliegen durch den Weltenraum," (Flight through Interplanetary Space), *Die Weltluftfahrt* (The Airworld), Vol. 1, No. 1–2, Jan.–Feb. 1949.

2.217   F. W. F. Gleason, "Rockets in History," *Ordnance,* Vol. 32, 1947–1948.

2.218   H. K. Kaiser, "The Spirit of Astronautics in Germany in the Last 15 Years," *Journal of the British Interplanetary Society,* March 1949.

2.219   W. von Braun, *The Mars Project,* University of Illinois Press, Urbana, Illinois, 1954, 153 pp.

2.220   M. Subotowicz, "The Rocket Conceptions of K. Siemienowicz, 1650," *Journal of the British Interplanetary Society,* Vol. 14, No. 5, Sept.–Oct. 1955.

3.0   Thermodynamics, Gas Dynamics, and Combustion

3.1   General Thermodynamics

3.101   L. Prandtl and O. G. Tietjens, *Fundamentals of Hydro- and Aeromechanics,* McGraw-Hill Book Co., Inc., New York, 1934.

3.102   W. N. Barnard, F. O. Ellenwood, and C. F. Hirshfeld, *Heat-Power Engineering,* John Wiley & Sons, Inc., New York, 3rd Ed., Part I, 1926, and Part II, 1935.

3.103   J. H. Keenan, *Thermodynamics,* John Wiley & Sons, Inc., New York, 1941.

3.104   R. Sauer, *Theoretische Einführung in die Gasdynamik* (Introduction to the Theory of Gas Dynamics), J. Springer Verlag, Berlin, 1943.

3.105   H. W. Liepmann and A. E. Puckett, *Introduction to Aerodynamics of a Compressible Fluid,* John Wiley & Sons, Inc., New York, 1947.

3.106   F. P. Durham, "Supersonic Flow with Variable Specific Heat," *Journal of Applied Mechanics,* Vol. 19, March 1952.

3.107   N. P. Bailey, "The Thermodynamics of Air at High Velocities," *Journal of the Aeronautical Sciences,* July 1944.

3.108 F. J. Malina, "Characteristics of Rocket Motor Unit Based on the Theory of Perfect Gases," *Journal of the Franklin Institute,* Vol. 230, No. 4, 1940.

3.109 C. N. Satterfield, H. C. Hottel, and G. C. Williams, "Generalized Thermodynamics of High Temperature Combustion," *Transactions of the ASME,* Vol. 70, Aug. 1948.

3.110 J. Kaye, "Survey of Friction Coefficients, Recovery Factors and Heat-Transfer Coefficients for Supersonic Flow," *Journal of the Aeronautical Sciences,* Vol. 21, Feb. 1954.

3.111 M. Gilbert, L. Davis, and D. Altman, "Velocity Lag of Particles in Linearly Accelerated Combustion Gases," *Jet Propulsion,* Vol. 25, No. 1, 1955.

3.112 H. R. Anderson and F. R. Johns, "Characteristics of Free Supersonic Jets Exhausting into Quiescent Air," *Jet Propulsion,* Vol. 25, No. 1, 1955.

3.113 *High Temperature Thermodynamics,* Technical Report No. 2, National Bureau of Standards Report 3431, July 1954, 120 pp.

3.114 K. Scheller and J. A. Bierlein, "Isothermal Combustion Under Flow Conditions," *Journal of the American Rocket Society,* Vol. 22, No. 5, Sept.–Oct. 1952.

3.115 F. E. Osborne, "High Temperature Thermodynamic Processes; their Generalized Treatment, with Particular Application to Rocket Motors," *Aircraft Engineering,* Vol. 24, No. 284, Oct. 1952.

3.116 E. Sänger, "High Gas Discharge Velocities in Rocket Propulsion," *U. S. Department of Commerce, P.B. 96227,* Nov. 1946.

3.117 N. J. Bowman, "The Effect of Solid Particles in Rocket Exhausts," *Journal of Space Flight,* June 1951.

3.118 R. Engel and U. T. Boedewadt, "Influence of After-Burning on the Performance of Rockets" (in French), *La Recherche aeronautique,* No. 18, Nov–Dec. 1950.

3.119 W. E Moeckel, "Use of Aerodynamic Heating to Provide Thrust by Vaporization of Surface Coolants," *NACA Technical Note 3140,* Feb. 1954.

3.120 D. F. Rossini, Editor, *Thermodynamics and Physics of Matter,* Vol. I of *High Speed Aerodynamics and Jet Propulsion,* Princeton University Press, Princeton, New Jersey, 1955, 830 pp.

3.2 Flow through Nozzles

3.201 M. Summerfield, C. R. Foster, and W. C. Swan, "Flow Separation in Overexpanded Supersonic Exhaust Nozzles," Paper presented at Institute of Fluid Mechanics and Heat Transfer, Los Angeles, California, June 1948.

3.202 Y. W. Chen, "Supersonic Flow through Nozzles with Rotational Symmetry," *Communications on Pure and Applied Mathematics,* Vol. 5, 1952.

3.203 Y. W. Chen, "Flow through Nozzles and Related Problems of Cylindrical and Spherical Waves," *Communications on Pure and Applied Mathematics,* Vol. 6, May 1953.

3.204 R. Harrop, P. I. F. Bright, *et al.,* "The Design and Testing of Supersonic Nozzles," *Great Britain Aeronautical Research Council, Reports and Memoranda 2712,* 1953.

3.205 W. Bader, "Nozzle Flows with Friction" (in German), *Zeitschrift für Angewandte Mathematik und Mechanik,* Vol. 33, July 7, 1953.

3.206 S. S. Penner, "Thermodynamics and Chemical Kinetics of One-Dimensional Nonviscous Flow through a Laval Nozzle," *Journal of Chemical Physics,* Vol. 19, July 1951.

3.207 H. S. Seifert and D. Altman, "A Comparison of Adiabatic and Isothermal Expansion Processes in Rocket Nozzles," *Journal of the American Rocket Society,* Vol. 22, No. 3, May–June 1952.

3.208 H. S. Tsien, "The Transfer Functions of Rocket Nozzles," *Journal of the American Rocket Society,* Vol. 22, No. 3, May–June 1952.

3.209 W. Szablewski, "Contributions to the Theory of the Spreading of a Free Jet Issuing from a Nozzle," *NACA Technical Memorandum 1311,* Nov. 1951.

3.210 J. Kestin and J. A. Owczarek, "Critical Flow Through Convergent-Divergent Nozzles," *Aircraft Engineering,* Vol. 23, Oct. 1951.

3.211 E. L. Arnoff and H. S. Ribner, "Interaction between a Supersonic Stream and a Parallel Subsonic Stream Bounded by a Fluid at Rest," *NACA Technical Note 2860,* Dec. 1952.

3.212 D. Counsolo, "Calculation of the Shape of a Two-Dimensional Supersonic Nozzle in Closed Form," *NACA Technical Memorandum 1358* (translated from *Aerotecnica,* Vol. 31, Aug. 1951), Jan. 1953.

3.213 F. J. Krieger, "Chemical Kinetics and Rocket Nozzle Design," *Journal of the American Rocket Society,* Vol. 21, No. 6, Nov. 1951.

3.214 W. N. Hagginbottom and J. C. Thibodaux, "Aerodynamic Losses in Low-Pressure Tailpipe Exhaust Ducts for Rocket-Propelled Aircraft," *NACA Research Memorandum L8C25,* July 20, 1948 (declassified Sept. 1954).

3.215 K. Scheller and J. A. Bierlein, "Some Experiments on Flow Separation in Rocket Nozzles," *Journal of the American Rocket Society,* Vol. 23, No. 1, Jan.–Feb. 1953.

3.216 R. Kling and R. Leboeuf, "L'écoulement dans les orifices d'injection; Application aux moteurs-fusées" (Flow through Nozzle Orifices; Application to Rocket Motors), *La Recherche aeronautique,* Sept.–Oct. 1953. (Also, abridged in English, in *Engineering Digest,* Dec. 1953.)

3.217 I. E. Beckwith and J. A. Moore, "An Accurate and Rapid Method for the Design of Supersonic Nozzles," *NACA Technical Note 3322,* Feb. 1955.

3.218 F. P. Durham, "Thrust Characteristics of Underexpanded Nozzles," *Jet Propulsion,* Vol. 25, No. 12, Dec. 1955.

3.3 Thermochemistry

See also Section 4.0.

3.301 C. D. Hodgman and H. N. Holmes, *Handbook of Chemistry and Physics,* Chemical Rubber Publishing Co., Cleveland, 25th Ed., 1941.

3.302 F. R. Bichowsky and F. D. Rossini, *Thermochemistry of Chemical Substances,* Reinhold Publishing Corp., New York, 1936.

3.303 J. O. Hirschfelder, F. T. McClure, et al., "Thermodynamic Properties of Propellant Gases," National Defense Research Committee, *Report 1087,* Nov. 1942.

3.304 B. Lewis and G. Von Elbe, *Combustion, Flames and Explosions of Gases,* Cambridge University Press, London, 1938.

3.305 C. N. Satterfield, H. C. Hottel, and G. C. Williams, "Generalized Thermodynamics of High Temperature Combustion," Massachusetts Institute of Technology, Division of Industrial Cooperation, *Report DIC 6351,* May 1947. Also Preprint of the paper of the same title presented before the annual ASME convention, 1947.

3.306 I. C. Hutcheon and S. W. Green, "Calculated Data for the Combustion with Liquid Oxygen of Water-Diluted Alcohols and Paraffin in Rocket Motors," *Great Britain Aeronautical Research Council, Reports and Memoranda 2572,* 1951 (Oct. 1947).

3.307 A. B. P. Beeton, "I—Tabulated Thermal Data for Hydrocarbon Oxidation Products at High Temperatures; II—The Effect of Dissociation on Rocket Performance Calculations," *Great Britain Aeronautical Research Council, Reports and Memoranda 2542,* 1952 (Oct. 1946).

3.308 F. J. Martin and M. Yachter, "Calculation of Equilibrium Gas Compositions," *Industrial and Engineering Chemistry*, Vol. 43, Nov. 1951.

3.309 G. Klobe, "Der Adiabatenkoeffizient dissozierender Feuergase bei adiabatisch-isentropischer Entspannung" (The Adiabatic Coefficient of Dissociating Combustion Gases with Isentropic Expansion), *Zeitschrift für angewandte Mathematik und Physik*, Vol. II, Sept. 15, 1951.

3.310 E. Macioce, "Thermodynamic Charts of Combustion Products" (in Italian), *L'Aerotecnica*, Vol. 33, Aug. 1953.

3.311 L. Kowalczyk, "Thermal Conductivity and its Variability with Temperature and Pressure," *ASME Paper 54-A-90*, Oct. 1954.

3.312 L. C. Nelson and E. F. Obert, "Generalized pvT Properties of Gases," *Transactions of the ASME*, Vol. 76, Oct. 1954.

3.313 J. Hilsenrath and Y. S. Touloukian, "The Viscosity, Thermal Conductivity, and Prandtl Number for Air, O_2, N_2, NO, H_2, CO, CO_2, H_2O, He, and A," *Transactions of the ASME*, Vol. 76, Aug. 1954.

3.314 R. V. Meghreblian, "Approximate Calculations of Specific Heats for Polyatomic Gases," *Journal of the American Rocket Society*, Vol. 21, No. 5, Sept. 1951.

3.315 F. G. Keyes, "A Summary of Viscosity and Heat Conduction Data for He, A, H_2, O_2, CO, CO_2, H_2O, and Air," *Transactions of the ASME*, Vol. 73, July 1951.

3.316 N. A. Hall and W. E. Iberle, "The Tabulation of Imperfect Gas Properties for Air, Nitrogen and Oxygen," *Transactions of the ASME*, Vol. 76, Oct. 1954.

3.317 W. Jost, *Explosions- und Verbrennungs-vorgänge in Gasen* (Explosion and Combustion Processes in Gases), J. Springer Verlag, Berlin, 1939.

3.318 A. J. Donegan and M. Farber, "Solution of Thermochemical Calculations on a High-Speed Digital Computer," *Jet Propulsion*, Vol. 26, No. 3, March 1956.

3.4 Combustion—General

3.401 C. E. Frank and A. U. Blackham, "Reaction Processes Leading to the Spontaneous Ignition of Hydrocarbons," *Industrial and Engineering Chemistry*, Vol. 46, Jan. 1954.

3.402 D. M. Simon, "Flame Propagation: Active Particle Diffusion Theory," *Industrial and Engineering Chemistry*, Vol. 43, Dec. 1951.

3.403 "Symposium on Combustion Chemistry" (28 papers), *Industrial and Engineering Chemistry*, Vol. 43, Dec. 1951.

3.404 R. K. Neumann, D. Dembrow, *et al.*, "A Simplified Combustion Analysis System," *Journal of the American Rocket Society*, Vol. 23, July–Aug. 1953.

3.405 R. E. Wilfong, S. Penner, *et al.*, "An Hypothesis for Propellant Burning," *Journal of Physical and Colloid Chemistry*, Vol. 54, No. 6.

3.406 F. E. Marble and T. C. Adamson, Jr., "Ignition and Combustion in a Laminar Mixing Zone," *Jet Propulsion*, Vol. 24, No. 2, March–April 1954.

3.407 A. D. Baxter, "Combustion in the Rocket Motor," *Journal of the British Interplanetary Society*, Vol. 10, May 1951.

3.408 R. A. Gross and R. Esch, "Low-Speed Combustion Aerodynamics," *Jet Propulsion*, Vol. 24, No. 2, March–April 1954.

3.409 Y. B. Zeldovich, "Theory of Flame Propagation," *NACA Technical Memorandum 1282*, June 1951.

3.410 "Long Range Research Leading to the Development of Superior Propellants Mechanism of Burning," *Bureau of Mines Progress Report*, No. 53, March 1954, and No. 54, June 1954.

3.411 N. B. Setdikin, "Self Ignition Temperatures of Combustible Liquids," *Journal of Research, National Bureau of Standards*, Vol. 53, July 1954.

3.412 G. Porter, "The Mechanism of Carbon Formation," *Advisory Group for Aeronautical Research and Development* (NATO), AG 13/M9, May 1954.

3.413 B. Lewis, R. N. Pease, and H. S. Taylor, *Combustion Processes*, Vol. 2 of *High Speed Aerodynamics and Jet Propulsion*, Princeton University Press, Princeton, New Jersey, 1955, 670 pp.

3.5 Combustion—Liquid Propellant Rockets

3.501 D. Bellman, J. C. Humphrey, and T. Male, "Photographic Investigation of Combustion in a Two-Dimensional Transparent Rocket Engine," *NACA Report 1134*, 1953.

3.502 C. C. Graves and M. Gerstein, "Some Aspects of Combustion of Liquid Fuel," *Advisory Group for Aeronautical Research and Development* (NATO), AG16/M10, May 3–7, 1954.

3.503 E. T. B. Smith, "Some Simple Considerations of Combustion and Gas Dynamics in Liquid Propellant Rocket Motors," *Journal of the British Interplanetary Society*, March 1953.

3.504 K. Berman and S. H. Cheney, Jr., "Combustion Studies in Rocket Motors," *Journal of the American Rocket Society*, Vol. 23, March–April 1953.

3.505 K. Berman and S. E. Logan, "Combustion Studies with a Rocket Motor having a Full-Length Observation

Window," *Journal of the American Rocket Society*, Vol. 22, No. 2, March-April 1952.

3.506 J. H. Altseimer, "Photographic Techniques Applied to Combustion Studies—Two-Dimensional Transparent Thrust Chamber," *Journal of the American Rocket Society*, Vol. 22, No. 2, March-April 1952.

3.507 S. V. Gunn, "The Effects of Several Variables upon the Ignition Lag of Hypergolic Fuels oxidized by Nitric Acid," *Journal of the American Rocket Society*, Vol. 22, No. 1, Jan.–Feb. 1952.

3.508 H. L. Wood and D. A. Charvonia, "The Ignition of Fuel Droplets Descending Through an Oxidizing Atmosphere," *Journal of the American Rocket Society*, Vol. 24, No. 3, May–June 1954.

3.509 C.. W. Tait, A. G. Whittaker, and H. Williams, "Measurement of the Burning Rate of Liquid Propellants," *Journal of the American Rocket Society*, No. 85, June 1951.

3.6 Combustion—Solid Propellant Rockets

3.601 E. W. Price, "One-Dimensional, Steady Flow with Mass Addition and the Effect of Combustion Chamber Flow on Rocket Thrust. (With a Supplement on the Integration of the Burning Equation)," *Journal of the American Rocket Society*, Vol. 25, No. 2, Feb. 1955.

3.602 H. Muraour and G. Aunis, "Study of Laws of Combustion of Colloidal Powders" (in French), *Mémorial de l'artillerie française*, Vol. 25, No. 1, 1951.

3.603 O. K. Rice and R. Ginell, "The Theory of the Burning of Double-Base Rocket Powders," *Journal of Physical and Colloid Chemistry*, Vol. 54, No. 6, June 1950.

3.604 R. D. Geckler, "The Mechanism of Combustion of Solid Propellants," Advisory Group for Aeronautical Research and Development (NATO) Colloquium at Cambridge, England, Dec. 7–11, 1953, Preprint.

3.605 S. Patai and E. Hoffman, "Pre-Ignition Reactions of Some Combustible Substances with Solid Oxidants," *Journal of Applied Chemistry*, Vol. 2, Jan. 1952.

3.606 S. Patri and J. Jordan, "Combustion Profiles of a Double Base Nitrocellulose Propellant," *Journal of Applied Chemistry*, Vol. 1, April 1951.

3.607 E. Sänger, "Theorie der Pulverbrennung" (Theory of Powder Burning), *Zeitschrift für Physikalische Chemie*, Vol. 197, Aug. 1951.

3.608 H. Muraour and J. Faureau, "On the Burning Velocity of Double-Base Powders in Nitrogen under Pressures from 100 to 10,000 kg/cm², " *Chemie et Industrie,* Vol. 65, No. 1, Jan. 1951.

3.609 R. G. Parr and B. L. Crawford, Jr., "A Physical Theory of Burning of Double-Base Rocket Propellants," *Journal of Physical and Colloid Chemistry,* Vol. 54, No. 6.

3.610 J. H. Frazer and B. L. Hicks, "Thermal Theory of Ignition of Solid Propellants," *Journal of Physical and Colloid Chemistry,* Vol. 54, No. 6.

3.611 B. L. Crawford, Jr., C. Huggett, and J. J. McBrady, "The Mechanism of Burning of Double Base Propellants," *Journal of Physical and Colloid Chemistry,* Vol. 54, No. 6.

3.612 L. Green, Jr., "Erosive Burning of Some Composite Solid Propellants," *Jet Propulsion,* Jan.–Feb. 1954.

3.613 R. G. Rekers and D. S. Villars, "Flame Zone Spectroscopy of Solid Propellants," *Review of Scientific Instruments,* May 1954.

3.614 G. S. Sutherland, D. A. Mahaffy, and M. Summerfield, "Experimental Flame Temperatures of Ammonium Perchlorate Solid Propellant," *Jet Propulsion,* Vol. 25, Oct. 1955.

3.615 G. K. Adams and L. A. Wiseman, "The Combustion of Double-base Propellant," *Selected Combustion Problems,* Butterworth's Scientific Publications, London, 1954.

3.616 E. Sänger, "Steady Grain Burning in Rockets" (in German), *Astronautica Acta,* Vol. 1, No. 2, 1955.

3.617 G. S. Sutherland, D. A. Mahaffy, and M. Summerfield, "Experimental Flame Temperatures of Ammonium Perchlorate Solid Propellant," *Jet Propulsion,* Vol. 25, No. 10, Oct. 1955.

3.7 Combustion Stability

3.701 F. E. Marble, "Servo Stabilization of Low-Frequency Oscillations in Liquid Propellant Rocket Motors," *Zeitschrift für angewandte Mathematik und Physik,* Vol. 6, No. 8, Nov. 1954.

3.702 H. S. Tsien, "Servo-Stabilization of Combustion in Rocket Motors," *Journal of the American Rocket Society,* Vol. 22, No. 5, Sept.–Oct. 1952.

3.703 M. Summerfield, "A Theory of Unstable Combustion in Liquid Propellant Rocket Systems," *Journal of the American Rocket Society,* Vol. 21, No. 5, Sept. 1951.

3.704 I. Elias and R. Gordon, "Longitudinal Vibrations of Gas at Ambient Pressure in a Rocket Thrust Chamber," *Journal of the American Rocket Society,* Vol. 22, No. 5, Sept.–Oct. 1952.

3.705   Y. C. Lee, R. Gore, and C. C. Ross, "Stability and Control of Liquid Propellant Rocket Systems," *Journal of the American Rocket Society,* Vol. 23, No. 2, March–April 1953.

3.706   C. C. Ross and P. P. Datner, "Combustion Instability in Liquid-Propellant Rocket Motors—A Survey," Advisory Group for Aeronautical Research and Development (NATO) Colloquium at Cambridge, England, Dec. 7–11, 1953.

3.707   R. H. Sabersky, "Effect of Wave Propagation in Feed Lines on Low-Frequency Rocket Instability," *Jet Propulsion,* Vol. 24, No. 3, May–June 1954.

3.708   A. O. Tischler and D. R. Bellman, "Combustion Instability in an Acid-Heptane Rocket with a Pressurized-Gas Propellant Pumping System," *NACA Technical Note 2936,* May 1953.

3.709   D. F. Gunder and D. R. Friant, "Stability of Flow in a Rocket Motor," *Journal of Applied Mechanics,* Vol. 17, Sept. 1950.

3.710   S. I. Cheng, "Unconditional Stability of Low-Frequency Oscillation in Liquid Rockets," *Jet Propulsion,* Vol. 24, No. 5, Sept.–Oct. 1954.

3.711   S. I. Cheng, "High-Frequency Combustion Instability in Solid Propellant Rockets. Part 1 and 2," *Jet Propulsion,* Vol. 24, No. 1, Jan.–Feb. 1954.

3.712   S. I. Cheng, "Low Frequency Combustion Stability of Liquid Rocket Motors with Different Nozzles," *Jet Propulsion,* Vol. 25, April 1955.

3.713   L. Crocco, "Aspects of Combustion Stability in Liquid Propellant Rocket Motors. I—Fundamentals; Low-Frequency Instability with Monopropellants." *Journal of the American Rocket Society,* Vol. 21, No. 6, Nov. 1951.

3.714   L. Crocco and S. I. Cheng, "High-Frequency Combustion Instability in Rocket Motor with Concentrated Combustion," *Journal of the American Rocket Society,* Vol. 23, Sept.–Oct. 1953.

3.715   M. Barrère and A. Moutet, "Low-Frequency Combustion Instability in Bipropellant Rocket Motors—Experimental Study," *Jet Propulsion,* Vol. 26, No. 1, Jan. 1956.

3.716   Y. C. Lee, A. M. Pickles, and C. C. Miesse, "Experimental Aspects of Rocket System Stability," *Jet Propulsion,* Vol. 26, No. 1, Jan. 1956.

3.717   B. N. Smith, "Perturbation Analysis of Low-Frequency Rocket Engine System Dynamics on an Analog Computer," *Jet Propulsion,* Vol. 26, No. 1, Jan. 1956.

4.0 Propellants

4.1 General Propellant References

4.101 *International Critical Tables*, McGraw-Hill Book Co., Inc., New York, 1933.

4.102 *The Condensed Chemical Dictionary*, Reinhold Publishing Corp., New York, 1943.

4.103 P. F. Winternitz and P. Horvitz, "Rocket Propellant Performance and Energy of the Chemical Bond," *Journal of the American Rocket Society*, No. 85, June 1951.

4.104 J. Himpan, "Evaluating Rocket Propellant Performance," *Interavia*, Vol. 5, No. 10, Oct. 1950.

4.105 W. R. Maxwell, "Rocket Fuels Demonstration," *Journal of the British Interplanetary Society*, Vol. 11, No. 5, Sept. 1952.

4.106 S. S. Penner, "Quantitative Evaluation of Rocket Propellants," *American Journal of Physics*, Vol. 20, No. 1, Jan. 1952.

4.107 J. M. Carter, "How Much Rocket Thrust from Chemical Propellants?" *Aviation Age*, April 1955.

4.108 G. V. E. Thompson, "Cost and Availability of High-Energy Rocket Propellants," *Journal of the British Interplanetary Society*, Annual Report, 1952.

4.109 H. A. Campbell, "Interstate Commerce Commission Regulations for Transportation of Explosives and Other Dangerous Articles by Land and Water in Rail Freight Service and by Motor Vehicle (Highway) and Water Including Specifications for Shipping Containers," *Interstate Commerce Commission*, April 8, 1952.

4.2 Liquid Propellants—General

4.201 S. Krop, "The Toxicity and Health Hazards of Rocket Propellants," *Journal of the American Rocket Society*, Vol. 24, No. 4, July–Aug. 1954.

4.202 P. Bielkowicz, "Evolution of Energy in Jet and Rocket Propulsion," Parts I to V, *Aircraft Engineering*, March, April, May, June 1946.

4.203 A. S. Leonard, "Some Possibilities of Rocket Propellants," *Journal of the American Rocket Society*, No. 68, Dec. 1946, No. 70, June 1947, No. 72, Dec. 1947.

4.204 R. McLarren, "Rocket Engine Fuels," *Automotive and Aviation Industries*, Aug. 15, 1946.

4.205 G. A. Bleyle, R. B. Hinckley, and C. L. Jewett, "An Air-Transportable Liquid Oxygen Generator—Its Operation and Application," *Jet Propulsion*, Vol. 24, Sept.–Oct. 1954.

4.206   K. A. Ehricke, "A Comparison of Propellants and Working Fluids for Rocket Propulsion," *Journal of the American Rocket Society*, Vol. 23, Sept.–Oct. 1953.

4.207   M. Barrere, "Investigation of Propergol Rocket Propellants by Means of Micro Rocket Test Elements," *La Recherche aeronautique*, May–June 1951.

4.208   H. S. Tsien, "The Properties of Pure Liquids," *Journal of the American Rocket Society*, Vol. 23, No. 1, Jan.–Feb. 1953.

4.209   O. Nomoto, "Molecular Sound Velocity and Molecular Compressibility of Liquid Mixtures," *Journal of the Physical Society of Japan*, Vol. 8, July–Aug. 1953.

4.210   G. G. Kretschmar, "The Thermal Expansion of Some Liquids of Interest as Rocket Fuels," *Jet Propulsion*, Nov.–Dec. 1954.

4.211   G. G. Kretschmar, "The Isothermal Compressibilities of Some Rocket Propellant Liquids and the Ratios of the Specific Heats," *Jet Propulsion*, Vol. 24, No. 3, May–June 1954.

4.212   G. G. Kretschmar, "The Velocity of Sound in Some Rocket Propellant Liquids," *Journal of the American Rocket Society*, March–April 1953.

4.3   Specific Liquid Propellants—Monopropellants

4.301   A. V. Cleaver, "Using Hydrogen Peroxide," *Journal of the British Interplanetary Society*, May–June 1955.

4.302   H. Walter, "Experience with the Application of Hydrogen Peroxide for Production of Power," *Jet Propulsion*, Vol. 24, No. 3, May–June 1954.

4.303   C. N. Satterfield, G. M. Kavanagh, and H. Resnick, "Explosive Characteristics of H_2O_2 Vapor," *Industrial and Engineering Chemistry*, Vol. 43, Nov. 1951.

4.304   G. C. Williams, C. N. Satterfield, and H. S. Isbin, "Calculation of Adiabatic Decomposition Temperatures of Hydrogen Peroxide Solutions," *Journal of the American Rocket Society*, Vol. 22, No. 2, March–April 1952.

4.305   F. Bellinger, H. B. Friedman, W. H. Bauer, J. W. Eastes, and S. M. Edmonds, "Chemical Propellants—Analytical Studies and Characteristics of the System Hydrogen Peroxide-Permanganate," *Industrial and Engineering Chemistry*, Vol. 38, No. 6, June 1946.

4.306   J. Isemura and S. Nakamura, "Stabilizer for Hydrogen Peroxide," *Science (Japan)*, Vol. 19, 1949.

4.307   N. S. Davis, Jr., and J. H. Keefe, Jr., "Equipment for Use with High-Strength Hydrogen Peroxide," *Journal of the American Rocket Society*, Vol. 22, No. 2, March–April 1952.

4.308 "Handling Hydrogen Peroxide," *Flight,* Vol. 61, No. 2246, Feb. 8, 1952.

4.309 J. A. Williams, "Properties of Hydrogen Peroxide," *The Aeroplane,* Aug. 6, 1954.

4.310 C. N. Satterfield, P. J. Ceccotti, and A. H. F. Feldbrugge, "Ignition Limits of Hydrogen Peroxide Vapor," *Industrial and Engineering Chemistry,* Vol. 47, May 1955.

4.311 *Properties of Hydrogen Peroxide,* Buffalo Electro-Chemical Co., Buffalo, New York, Revised 1955.

4.312 L. J. Hillenbrand, Jr., and M. L. Kilpatrick, "The Thermal Decomposition of Nitromethane," *Journal of Chemical Physics,* Vol. 19, March 1951.

4.313 J. E. Troyan, "Properties, Production and Uses of Hydrazine," *Industrial and Engineering Chemistry,* Vol. 45, Dec. 1953.

4.314 L. P. Lessing, "Hydrazine," *Scientific American,* Vol. 189, July 1953.

4.315 L. F. Audrieth, "Autoxidation of Hydrazine," *Industrial and Engineering Chemistry,* Vol. 43, Aug. 1951.

4.316 T. C. H. Hill and J. F. Sumner, "The Freezing-Point Diagram of the Hydrazine-Water System," *Journal of the Chemical Society,* March 1951.

4.317 J. G. Burtle, "Vapor Pressure–Composition Measurements on Aqueous Hydrazine Solutions," *Industrial and Engineering Chemistry,* Vol. 44, 1952.

4.318 W. G. Cass, "Exothermic Decomposition of Nitromethane," *Aircraft Engineering,* Vol. 22, No. 258, Aug. 1950.

4.319 K. H. Mueller, "The Thermal Decomposition of Nitromethane at High Pressures," *Journal of American Chemical Society,* Vol. 77, July 5, 1955.

4.320 T. L. Cottrell, "The Thermal Decomposition of Nitromethane," *Transactions of the Faraday Society,* Vol. 47, June 1951.

4.321 J. P. McCullough, D. W. Scott, R. E. Pennington, I. A. Hossenlopp, and G. Waddington, "Nitromethane: The Vapor Heat Capacity, Heat of Vaporization, Vapor Pressure and Gas Imperfection; the Chemical Thermodynamic Properties from 0 to 1500° K," *American Chemical Society,* Vol. 76, Oct. 5, 1954.

4.322 H. Behrens, "Combustion of Liquid Mixtures with Tetranitromethane as the Oxygen Carrier" (in German), *Zeitschrift für Elektrochemie,* Vol. 55, 1951.

4.323 G. Edwards, "Vapor Pressure of Tetranitromethane," *Transactions of the Faraday Society,* Vol. 48, 1952.

4.324 M. R. Corelli, "L'Abbassamento del Punto di Congela-
mento del Tetranitrometano con Mezzi Chimici, e Nota
Preliminare sul Sistema: Tetranitrometano-Perossido
d'Azoto" (On the Lowering of the Freezing Point of
Tetranitromethane Using Chemical Means and a Preliminary Note on the System Tetranitromethane-Nitro-
gen Peroxide), *L'Aerotecnica*, Dec. 1953.

4.325 A. M. Eastham, "The Chemistry of Ethylene Oxide,"
Canadian Journal of Chemistry, Vol. 29, July 1951.

4.326 C. J. Walters and J. M. Smith, "Volumetric Behavior
and Thermodynamic Properties of Ethylene Oxide,"
Chemical Engineering Progress, Vol. 48, July 1952.

4.327 R. Landau, "Ethylene Oxide by Direct Oxidation,"
Petroleum Refiner, Vol. 32, Sept. 1953.

4.328 K. H. Mueller and W. D. Walters, "The Thermal Decomposition of Ethylene Oxide," *Journal of the American Chemical Society*, Vol. 73, 1951, and Vol. 76, Jan.
1954.

4.329 E. M. Wilson, "The Stability of Ethylene Oxide," *Journal of the American Rocket Society*, Vol. 23, No. 6,
Nov.–Dec. 1953.

4.330 H. W. Thompson and W. T. Cave, "Vibrational Spectrum of Ethylene Oxide," *Transactions of the Faraday
Society*, Vol. 47, 1951.

4.4 Specific Liquid Propellants—Bipropellants

4.401 A. B. McKeown and F. E. Belles, "Vapor Pressures and
Calculated Heats of Vaporization of Concentrated Nitric
Acid Solutions in the Composition Range 71 to 89 Percent Nitric Acid, 7 to 20 Percent Nitrogen Dioxide, 1
to 10 Percent Water and in the Temperature Range 10°
to 60° C," *NACA Research Memorandum E53L14*, Feb.
5, 1954.

4.402 H. H. Reamer, D. M. Mason, and B. H. Sage, "Volumetric Behavior of Red and White Fuming Nitric Acid,"
Industrial and Engineering Chemistry, May 1953.

4.403 F. T. Selleck, H. H. Reamer, and B. H. Sage, "Volumetric and Phase Behavior of Mixtures of Nitric Oxide
and Nitrogen Dioxide," *Industrial and Engineering
Chemistry*, April 1953.

4.404 H. H. Reamer, W. H. Corcoran, and B. H. Sage, "Volumetric Behavior of Nitric Acid," *Industrial and Engineering Chemistry*, Vol. 45, Dec. 1953.

4.405 G. D. Robertson, Jr., D. M. Mason, and B. H. Sage,
"Electrolytic Conductance of the Nitric Acid-Nitrogen
Dioxide-Water System at 32° F," *Industrial and Engi-
neering Chemistry*, Vol. 44, No. 12, Dec. 1952.

4.406 H. Zborowski, "Rocket Power Plants Based on Nitric Acid and Their Specific Propellant Weights," *NACA Technical Memorandum 1145*, 1948.

4.407 W. J. Dunning and C. W. Nutt, "Dissociation and Equilibria of Pure Liquid Nitric Acid," *Transactions of the Faraday Society*, Vol. 47, Jan. 1951.

4.408 C. Frejacques, "Kinetics of the Vapor-Phase Decomposition of Nitric Acid" (in French), *Comptes rendus*, Vol. 232, 1951.

4.409 T. R. Bump, P. F. Pagerey, J. P. Kern, D. W. Fyfe, C. R. St. Clair, and W. L. Sibbitt, "Thermal Properties of Commercial White Fuming Nitric Acid," *Jet Propulsion*, April 1955.

4.410 W. L. Sibbitt, C. R. St. Clair, T. R. Bump, P. F. Pagerey, J. P. Kern, and D. W. Fyfe, "Physical Properties of Concentrated Nitric Acid," *NACA Technical Note 2970* and *Technical Note 2969*, June 1953.

4.411 B. A. Reese and R. W. Graham, "Heat Transfer and Frictional Pressure Drop Characteristics of White Fuming Nitric Acid," *Jet Propulsion*, Vol. 24, No. 4, July–Aug. 1954.

4.412 R. Vandoni, "The Mixture Nitrogen Pentoxide-Nitric Acid. Total Pressures and Partial Pressures" (in French), *Mémorial des services chimiques de l'état*, Vol. 35, 1950.

4.413 C. H. Trent and M. J. Zucrow, "Behavior of Liquid Hydrocarbon with White Fuming Nitric Acid," *Industrial and Engineering Chemistry*, Vol. 44, No. 11, Nov. 1952.

4.414 S. V. Gunn, "The Effects of Several Variables upon the Ignition Lag of Hypergolic Fuels Oxidized by Nitric Acid," *Journal of the American Rocket Society*, Vol. 22, No. 1, Jan.–Feb. 1952.

4.415 C. H. Trent and M. J. Zucrow, "The Hypergolic Reaction of Dicyclopentadiene with White Fuming Nitric Acid," *Journal of the American Rocket Society*, Vol. 21, No. 5, Sept. 1951.

4.416 H. Wise and M. F. Frech, "Kinetics of Decomposition of Nitric Oxide at Elevated Temperatures. I. Rate Measurements in a Quartz Vessel," *Journal of Chemical Physics*, Vol. 20, Jan. 1952.

4.417 A. B. McKeown and F. E. Belles, "Vapor Pressures of Concentrated Nitric Acid Solutions in the Composition Range 83 to 97 Percent Nitric Acid, 0 to 6 Percent Nitrogen Dioxide, 0 to 15 Percent Water, and in the Temperature Range 20° to 80° C," *NACA Research Memorandum E53G08*, Sept. 17, 1953.

4.418 H. S. Johnston, "Interpretation of the Data on the Thermal Decomposition of Nitrous Oxide," *Journal of Chemical Physics,* Vol. 19, June 1951.

4.419 H. S. Johnston and D. M. Yost, "The Kinetics of the Rapid Gas Reaction Between Ozone and Nitrogen Dioxide," *Journal of Chemical Physics,* April 1949.

4.420 C. E. Frank and A. U. Blackham, "Reaction Processes Leading to Spontaneous Ignition of Hydrocarbons," *NACA Technical Note 2958,* June 1953.

4.421 A. B. P. Beeton, "An Approximate Method for Estimating the Performance of Oxygen-Oil Rockets," *Great Britain Aeronautical Research Council, Reports and Memoranda 2389,* 1950 (June 1946).

4.422 A. B. P. Beeton, "The Calculated Performance of Ethyl Alcohol-Water Mixtures as Rocket Fuels with Liquid Oxygen," *Great Britain Aeronautical Research Council, Reports and Memoranda 2816* (formerly ARC Technical Report 11534, Royal Aircraft Establishment, Technical Note 1943), 1953.

4.423 A. B. P. Beeton, "I—Tabulated Thermal Data for Hydrocarbon Oxidation Products at High Temperatures. II—The Effect of Dissociation on Rocket Performance Calculations," *Great Britain Aeronautical Research Council, Reports and Memoranda 2542,* 1952 (Oct. 1946).

4.424 J. L. Jackson, "Spontaneous Ignition Temperatures: Commercial Fluids and Pure Hydrocarbons," *Industrial and Engineering Chemistry,* Vol. 43, Dec. 1951.

4.425 J. E. Johnson, J. W. Crellin, and H. W. Carhart, "Spontaneous Ignition Properties of Fuels and Hydrocarbons," *Industrial and Engineering Chemistry,* Vol. 45, Aug. 1953.

4.426 D. J. Ladanyi, R. O. Miller, and G. Hennings, "Ignition-Delay Determinations of Furfuryl Alcohol and Mixed Butyl Mercaptans with Various White Fuming Nitric Acids Using Modified Open-Cup and Small-Scale Rocket Engine Apparatus," *NACA Research Memorandum E53E29,* Feb. 18, 1955.

4.427 W. Weltner, Jr., and K. Pitzer, "Methyl Alcohol: The Entropy, Heat Capacity and Polymerization Equilibria in the Vapor, and Potential Barrier to Internal Rotation," *Journal of the American Chemical Society,* Vol. 73, 1951.

4.428 I. C. Hutcheon and S. W. Green, "Calculated Data for the Combustion with Liquid Oxygen of Water-Diluted Alcohols and Paraffin in Rocket Motors," *Great Britain Aeronautical Research Council, Reports and Memoranda 2572,* 1951 (Oct. 1947).

4.429 R. C. Reid and J. M. Smith, "Thermodynamic Properties of Ethyl Alcohol," *Chemical Engineering Progress,* Vol. 47, Aug. 1951.

4.430 C. F. Cullis, "Structural Influences in the Oxidation of Aliphatic Amines," *Transactions of the Faraday Society,* Nov. 1952.

4.431 E. Wicke, "The Dissociation Energy of Fluorine," *Journal of Physical Chemistry,* Vol. 56, March 1952.

4.432 G. W. Elvern, Jr., and R. N. Doescher, "Physical Properties of Liquid Fluorine," *Journal of Chemical Physics,* Vol. 20, Dec. 1952.

4.433 W. H. Evans and others, "Bibliography on the Thermodynamic Properties of the Fluorine Compounds of Elements of Atomic Number 1 to 17," *National Bureau of Standards,* Jan. 21, 1952.

4.434 L. Haar and C. W. Beckett, "Thermal Properties of Fluorine Compounds: Heat Capacity, Entropy, Heat Content and Free Energy Functions of Diatomic Fluorine in the Ideal Gaseous State," *National Bureau of Standards,* Feb. 1, 1952.

4.435 M. D. Scheer, "Thermodynamic Properties of Chlorine Trifluoride," *Journal of Chemical Physics,* Vol. 20, May 1952.

4.436 A. Weber and S. M. Ferigle, "Thermodynamic Properties of Chlorine Trifluoride," *Journal of Chemical Physics,* Vol. 20, Sept. 1952.

4.437 M. J. Klein, F. T. Cleveland, and A. G. Meister, "Force Constants, Frequency Assignments and Thermodynamic Properties of Ozone," *Journal of Chemical Physics,* Vol. 19, Aug. 1951.

4.438 H. J. Hölzgen, "Die Verwendung von Ozon als Sauerstoffträger in Raketenmotoren" (The Application of Ozone as Oxidizer for Rocket Thrust Chambers), *Weltraumfahrt,* No. 4, 1951.

4.439 I. Bredt, "Hydrogen at High Temperatures" (in German), *Angewandte Naturforschung,* 6a, Feb. 1951.

4.440 H. L. Coplen, "Large-Scale Production and Handling of Liquid Hydrogen," *Journal of the American Rocket Society,* Vol. 22, No. 6, Nov.–Dec. 1952.

4.441 S. Prosad, "The Thermal Conductivity of Liquid Oxygen," *British Journal of Applied Physics,* Vol. 3, Feb. 1952.

4.442 S. Allen, "Liquid Oxygen as a Rocket Propellant," *Journal of the British Interplanetary Society,* May–June 1955.

4.443 G. W. Castellan, "Symmetry and Stability in Diborane

and Borine," *Journal of Chemical Physics,* Vol. 22, March 1954.

4.444   E. J. Bowen and A. W. Birley, "The Vapor Phase Reaction between Hydrazine and Oxygen," *Transactions of the Faraday Society,* Vol. 47, June 1951.

4.445   W. J. Barr and E. J. Wilson, Jr., "Calculated Thermochemical Properties for Hydrazine-Hydrogen Peroxide Reaction at High Pressures," *Journal of Chemical Physics,* Vol. 19, 1951.

4.446   H. A. Liebhafsky, "Use of Hydrazine Hydrate as a Fuel," *Chimie et industrie,* Vol. 56, 1946.

4.447   H. C. Brown, "The Borohydrides," *Chemical Engineering News,* Vol. 29, 1951.

4.448   J. H. Schroeder, "Effect of Vibrational Excitation on the Theoretical Performance of the Stoichiometric Carbon-Oxygen Propellant System," *Journal of the American Rocket Society,* Vol. 23, No. 1, Jan.–Feb. 1953.

4.5 Solid Propellants

4.501   R. Healy, "The Black Powder Rocket Charge," *Astronautics,* No. 53, Oct. 1942.

4.502   W. T. Osborn, "Construction and Performance of the Baka," *Journal of the American Rocket Society,* No. 65, March 1946.

4.503   J. Whetstone, "Solution to the Caking Problem of Ammonium Nitrate and Ammonium Nitrate Explosives," *Industrial and Engineering Chemistry,* Vol. 44, Nov. 1952.

4.504   G. Feick, *The Dissociation Pressure and Free Energy of Formation of Ammonium Nitrate,* Arthur D. Little, Inc., Cambridge, Massachusetts, 1954, 8 pp.

4.505   G. Feick, *On the Thermal Decomposition of Ammonium Nitrate Steady-State Reaction Temperature and Reaction Rate,* Arthur D. Little, Inc., Cambridge, Massachusetts, 1954, 10 pp.

4.506   R. M. Hainer, *The Application of Kinetics to the Hazardous Behavior of Ammonium Nitrate,* Arthur D. Little, Inc., Cambridge, Massachusetts, 1954, 17 pp.

4.507   R. M. Hainer and W. C. Lothrop, *Thermal Hazard in Ammonium Nitrate High-Percentage Ammonium Nitrate Materials,* Arthur D. Little, Inc., Cambridge, Massachusetts, 1954, 15 pp.

4.508   L. Friedman and J. Bigeleisen, "Oxygen and Nitrogen Isotope Effects in the Decomposition of Ammonium Nitrate," *Journal of Chemical Physics,* Vol. 18, 1951.

4.509   A. Glasner and L. Weidenfeld, "The Thermal Decomposition of Potassium Perchlorate and Perchlorate-Halo-

genide Mixtures: A Study in the Pyrolysis of Solids,"
Journal of the American Chemical Society, Vol. 74, May
20, 1952.

4.510 W. E. Garner and E. W. Haycock, "The Thermal Decomposition of Lithium Aluminum Hydride," *Proceedings of the Royal Society of London (A),* Vol. 211,
March 6, 1952.

4.511 J. D. Huffington, "The Burning and Structure of Cordite," *Transactions of the Faraday Society,* Vol. 47, 1951.

4.512 H. L. William, "Studies on RDX and Related Compounds," *Canadian Journal of Chemistry,* Vol. 29, Aug.
1951.

4.513 F. Pristera, "Analysis of Propellants by Infrared Spectroscopy," *Analytical Chemistry,* June 1953.

4.514 B. V. Erofeev and N. I. Mitskevich, "Kinetics of the
Transformations of the Polymorphous Modifications of
Ammonium Nitrate. II. Effect of the Previous Treat-
ment on the Rate of Transformation NH_4NO_3IV-
NH_4NO_3III" (in Russian), *Zhurnal Fizicheskoĭ Khimii,*
Vol. 26, 1952.

4.515 B. V. Erofeev and N. I. Mitskevich, "Kinetics of the
Polymorphic Changes in NH_4NO_3 General Character of
of the Kinetics of the IV-III Conversion," *Zhurnal
Fizicheskoĭ Khimii,* Vol. 24, 1950.

4.516 J. D. Huffington, "The Unsteady Burning of Cordite,"
Transactions of the Faraday Society, Vol. 50, Sept. 1954.

4.517 A. Zaehringer, "Treibstoffe für Feststoffraketen" (Propellants for Solid Propellant Rockets), *Weltraumfahrt,*
April 1955.

4.518 B. J. Wood and H. Wise, "Acid Catalysis in the Thermal
Decomposition of Ammonium Nitrate," *Journal of
Chemical Physics,* Vol. 23, April 1955.

4.519 A. J. Zaehringer, Processing Composite Rocket Propellants, *Chemical Engineering Progress,* Vol. 51, July 1955.

5.0 Heat Transfer

5.1 General References

5.101 McAdams, *Heat Transmission,* McGraw-Hill Book Co.,
Inc., New York, 3rd Ed., 1954, 532 pp.

5.102 M. Jakob, *Heat Transfer,* Vol. 1, John Wiley & Sons,
Inc., New York, 1949.

5.103 A. I. Brown and S. M. Marco, *Introduction to Heat
Transfer,* McGraw-Hill Book Co., Inc., New York, 1951.

5.104 R. F. Kayser, "Analogy among Heat, Mass, and Momentum Transfer," *Industrial and Engineering Chemistry,* Vol. 45, Dec. 1953.

5.105 P. L. Nichols, Jr., and A. G. Presson, "Heat Conduction in an Infinite Cylindrical Medium with Heat Generated by a Chemical Reaction," *Journal of Applied Physics,* Dec. 1954.

5.106 E. Mayer, "Heat Flow in Composite Slabs," *Journal of the American Rocket Society,* Vol. 22, No. 3, May–June 1952.

5.107 R. D. Geckler, "Transient Radial Heat Conduction in Hollow Circular Cylinders," *Jet Propulsion,* Vol. 25, No. 1, Jan. 1955.

5.108 O. A. Saunders, "Heat Transfer in a Nozzle at Supersonic Speeds," *Engineering,* Vol. 173, Aug. 29, 1952.

5.2 Heat Transfer in Liquid Propellant Rockets—General

5.201 S. Baxter, H. A. Vodden, and H. Davies, "A Rapid Method for the Determination of the Thermal Conductivity of Organic Liquids for Use in Heat Transfer Calculations," *Journal of Applied Chemistry,* Vol. 3, Part 10, Oct. 1953.

5.202 B. A. Reese and R. W. Graham, "Design of Apparatus for Determining Heat Transfer and Frictional Pressure Drop of Nitric Acid Flowing through A Heated Tube," *NACA Research Memorandum 52D03,* June 16, 1952.

5.203 C. M. Beighley and L. E. Dean, "Study of Heat Transfer to JP-4 Jet Fuel," *Jet Propulsion,* Vol. 24, No. 3, May–June 1954.

5.204 H. Ziebland, "A Review of the Current Techniques of Protecting and Cooling Rocket Motor Walls," *Journal of the British Interplanetary Society,* May 1954.

5.205 S. Greenfield, "Determination of Rocket-Motor Heat-Transfer Coefficients by the Transient Method," *Journal of the Aeronautical Sciences,* Vol. 18, No. 8, Aug. 1951.

5.206 H. Gartmann, "Cooling of the Rocket Combustion Chamber" (in German), *Weltraumfahrt,* Vol. 5, Oct. 1950.

5.207 M. E. Ellion, "New Techniques for Obtaining Heat Transfer Parameters of the Wall and Combustion Gas in a Rocket Motor," *Transactions of the ASME,* Vol. 73, No. 2, Feb. 1951.

5.208 M. Summerfield, "Recent Developments in Convective Heat Transfer with Special Reference to High-Temperature Combustion Chambers," *Heat Transfer, A Symposium,* University of Michigan, Ann Arbor, Michigan, 1952.

5.209 O. A. Saunders and P. H. Caulder, "Some Experiments on the Heat Transfer from a Gas Flowing Through a Convergent-Divergent Nozzle," *1951 Heat Transfer and*

Fluid Mechanics Institute, Preprints of papers presented at Stanford University, Palo Alto, California, June 20–22, 1951.

5.210 H. Ziebland, "Heat Transfer Problems in Rocket Motors," *Journal of the British Interplanetary Society,* Vol. 14, No. 5, Sept.–Oct. 1955.

5.211 R. H. Reichel, "On the Heat Release Problem of High Performance Rocket Propulsion," *Aeronautical Engineering Review,* Nov. 1955.

5.3 Heat Transfer in Liquid Propellant Rockets—Boiling Heat Transfer

5.301 R. H. Sabersky and C. W. Gates, Jr., "On the Start of Nucleation in Boiling Heat Transfer," *Journal of the American Rocket Society,* Vol. 25, No. 2, Feb. 1955.

5.302 E. A. Farber and R. L. Scorah, "Heat Transfer to Water Boiling Under Pressure," *Transactions of the ASME,* May 1948.

5.303 F. C. Gunther, "Photographic Study of Surface-Boiling Heat Transfer to Water with Forced Convection," *Transactions of the ASME,* Vol. 73, No. 2, Feb. 1951.

5.304 F. C. Gunther and F. Kreith, "Photographic Study of Bubble Formation in Heat Transfer to Subcooled Water," *Proceedings of Heat Transfer and Fluid Mechanics Institute, Berkeley, California,* printed by ASME, New York, 1949.

5.305 W. H. Jens, "Boiling Heat Transfer: What Is Known about It," *Mechanical Engineering,* Dec. 1954.

5.306 W. H. Lowdermilk and W. F. Weiland, "Some Measurements of Boiling Burnout," *NACA Research Memorandum E54K10,* Feb. 23, 1955.

5.307 M. S. Plesset and S. G. Zurick, "Growth of Vapor Bubbles in Superheated Liquids," *Journal of Applied Physics,* Vol. 25, April 1954.

5.308 M. Summerfield and F. Kreith, "Pressure Drop and Convective Heat Transfer with Surface Boiling at High Heat Flux," *Proceedings of Heat Transfer and Fluid Mechanics Institute, Berkeley, California,* 1949.

5.309 C. M. Beighley and L. E. Dean, "Study of Heat Transfer to JP-4 Jet Fuel," *Jet Propulsion,* May–June 1954.

5.4 Heat Transfer in Liquid Propellant Rockets—Film and Sweat Cooling

5.401 E. Knuth, "The Mechanics of Film Cooling—Part I and Part II," *Jet Propulsion,* Vol. 24, No. 6, 1954, and Vol. 25, No. 1, 1955.

5.402 R. H. Boden, "Heat Transfer in Rocket Motors and the Application of Film and Sweat Cooling," *Transactions of the ASME,* May 1951.

5.403 E. Mayer and J. G. Bartas, "Transpiration Cooling in Porous Metal Walls," *Jet Propulsion,* Nov.–Dec. 1954.

5.404 G. R. Kinney, F. Abramson, and J. L. Sloop, "Internal Liquid-Film-Cooling Experiments with Air-Stream Temperatures to 2000° F in 2- and 4-Inch-Diameter Horizontal Tubes," *NÁCA Research Memoranda E50F19, E51C13, E52B20,* 1950, 1951, 1952, *NACA Reports 1087,* 1952.

5.405 L. Crocco, "An Approximate Theory of Porous, Sweat, or Film Cooling with Reactive Fluids," *Journal of the American Rocket Society,* Vol. 22, No. 6, Nov.–Dec. 1952.

5.406 E. Duncombe, "An Experimental Investigation of Protection Achieved by Sweat Cooling on Porous Surfaces Adjacent to Non-porous Surfaces," *Canadian National Research Laboratories, Division of Mechanical Engineering, Report MT-20,* Jan. 22, 1951.

5.407 H. L. Wheeler, Jr., and P. Duwez, "Sweat Cooling," *Automotive Industries,* Vol. 103, No. 2, July 15, 1950.

5.408 L. H. Wilson, W. L. Sibbitt, and M. Jakob, "Flow of Gases in Porous Media," *Journal of Applied Physics,* Vol. 22, No. 8, Aug. 1951.

5.5 Heat Transfer in Liquid Propellant Rockets—Evaporation of Drops

5.501 H. L. Wood and D. A. Charvonia, "The Ignition of Fuel Droplets Descending through an Oxidizing Atmosphere," *Jet Propulsion,* May–June 1954.

5.502 K. Kobayasi, "The Evaporation Velocity of Single Droplets of Liquids," *Tokio University, Japan, Technical Report 2,* 1954; also *Engineering Digest,* Nov. 1954.

5.503 M. Goldsmith and S. S. Penner, "On the Burning of Single Drops of Fuel in an Oxidizing Atmosphere," *Journal of the American Rocket Society,* Vol. 24, No. 4, ·July–Aug. 1954.

5.504 E. F. Lype, "Kinetic Theory of Evaporation Rates of Liquids," *Transactions of the ASME,* Feb. 1955.

5.505 C. C. Miesse, "Ballistics of an Evaporating Droplet," *Jet Propulsion,* Vol. 24, No. 4, July–Aug. 1954.

5.506 S. S. Penner, "On Maximum Evaporation Rates of Liquid Droplets in Rocket Motors," *Journal of the American Rocket Society,* March–April 1953.

5.6 Heat Transfer by Radiation

See also Sections 5.1, 5.2.

5.601 S. S. Penner and S. Weinbaum, "Some Considerations of the Effect of Radiation on the Performance of Liquid Fuel Rockets," *Journal of the Optical Society of America*, Vol. 38, No. 7, July 1948.

5.602 S. S. Penner, M. H. Ostrander, and H. S. Tsien, "Emission of Radiation from Diatomic Gases. III. Numerical Emissivity Calculations for Carbon Monoxide for Low Optical Densities at 300° K and Atmospheric Pressure," *Journal of Applied Physics*, Vol. 23, Feb. 1952.

5.603 S. S. Penner and D. Weber, "Emission of Radiation from Diatomic Gases. II. Experimental Determination of Effective Average Absorption Coefficients of Carbon Monoxide," *Journal of Applied Physics*, Vol. 22, 1951.

5.604 W. H. Avery, "Radiation Effects in Propellant Burning," *Journal of Physical and Colloid Chemistry*, Vol. 54, No. 6.

5.605 R. H. Tourin, "Infrared Emission and Absorption of Thermally Excited Carbon Dioxide," *Journal of Chemical Physics*, Vol. 20, 1952.

5.606 C. Frejacques, "Vibration Spectrum of Nitric Acid in the Infrared," *Comptes rendus des séances de l'académie des sciences*, Vol. 234, 1952.

5.607 R. J. Holm, D. Weber, and S. S. Penner, "Emissivity for CO_2 at Elevated Pressures," *Journal of Applied Physics*, Vol. 23, Nov. 1952.

5.608 C. M. Auble and M. F. Heidmann, "The Application of Radiation Measurement Techniques to the Determination of Gas Temperatures in Liquid Propellant Flames," *Jet Propulsion*, Vol. 25, Sept. 1955.

5.7 Aerodynamic Heating

5.701 R. N. Thomas and F. L. Whipple, "Astroballistic Heat Transfer," *Journal of Aeronautical Science*, Vol. 18, Sept. 1951.

5.702 H. Hild, "Calculations of Skin Temperatures of the A-4 Guided Missile" (*Peenemünde, Heeresversuchsstelle, ZWB/PA/68/9*, Nov. 1940), *U. S. Air Force, Translation No. F-TS-3109-RE*, Feb. 1948.

5.703 M. A. Sulkin, "Aerodynamic Heating in High-Speed Flight," *Aviation Age*, Vol. 17, Sept. 1952.

5.704 R. J. Monaghan and J. R. Cooke, "The Measurement of Heat Transfer and Skin Friction at Supersonic Speeds," *Great Britain Aeronautical Research Council, Current Papers 138, 139,* and *140*, 1953.

6.0   Rocket Units

6.1   General—Liquid Propellant Rockets

6.101   W. P. Berggren, C. C. Ross, R. B. Young, and C. E. Hawk, "The Acid-Aniline Rocket Engine," *Journal of the American Rocket Society*, Vol. 73, March 1948.

6.102   H. Walter, "Report on Rocket Power Plants Based on 'T' Substance," *NACA Technical Memorandum 1170*, 1947.

6.103   H. S. Seifert, M. M. Mills, and M. Summerfield, "Physics of Rockets: Liquid Propellant Rockets," *Americal Journal of Physics*, Vol. 15, No. 2, 1947.

6.104   J. H. Wyld, "Problem of Rocket Fuel Feed," *Astronautics*, No. 34, June 1936.

6.105   J. Humphries, "The Design of Rocket Motors," *Journal of the British Interplanetary Society*, May 1949.

6.106   B. R. Diplock, D. L. Lofts, and R. A. Grimston, "I. Theory, II. Design, III. Development—Liquid Propellant Rocket Motors," *Journal of the Royal Aeronautical Society*, Vol. 57, No. 505, Jan. 1953.

6.107   V. Sivori, "Problemi Tipici Nel Progetto di Missili a Propellenti Liquidi" (Typical Problems in Design of Liquid Propellant Rockets), *L'Aerotecnica*, Feb. 15, 1953.

6.108   D. Altman and J. Lorell, "Effect of Local Variations in Mixture Ratio on Rocket Performance," *Journal of the American Rocket Society*, Vol. 22, No. 5, Sept.–Oct. 1952.

6.109   W. N. Neat, "Some Limiting Factors of Chemical Rocket Motors," *Journal of the British Interplanetary Society*, Vol. 12, Nov. 1953.

6.110   S. Allen, "Propulsion by Rocket," *Canadian Aviation*, Vol. 25, No. 3, March 1952.

6.111   "Britain Unveils Rocket Motor" (Fairey Aviation, Ltd.) *Aviation Week*, Oct. 9, 1950.

6.112   M. C. Sanz, "Five-Pound Thrust Liquid Monopropellant Rocket," *Journal of the American Rocket Society*, Sept.–Dec. 1948.

6.113   "De Havilland 'Sprite' Liquid Fuel Rocket," *Shell Aviation News*, Oct. 1949.

6.114   J. Humphries, "Liquid Propellant Rockets and Their Applications," *Machinery Lloyd, Overseas Edition*, Vol. 23, No. 24, Nov. 24, 1951.

6.2   Thrust Chambers and Injectors—Liquid Propellant Rockets

6.201   M. F. Heidmann and J. C. Humphrey, "Fluctuations in a Spray Formed by Two Impinging Jets," *Journal of the*

American Rocket Society, Vol. 22, No. 3, May–June 1952.

6.202 R. Kling and R. Leboeuf, "Flow in Injection Orifices, Application to Rocket Engines," *La Recherche aeronautique,* No. 35, Sept.–Oct. 1953.

6.203 K. R. Stehling, "Injector Spray and Hydraulic Factors in Rocket Motor Analysis," *Journal of the American Rocket Society,* Vol. 2, No. 3, May–June 1952.

6.204 R. H. Reichel, "Energy Loading of Combustion Chambers" (in German), *Weltraumfahrt,* Vol. 6, Dec. 1950.

6.205 J. Himpan, "The Calculation of the Volume of Rocket Combustion Chambers," *Aircraft Engineering,* Vol. 22, No. 257, July 1950.

6.206 J. E. Dalgleish and A. O. Tischler, "Experimental Investigation of a Lightweight Rocket Chamber," *NACA Research Memorandum E52L19A,* Dec. 1952.

6.207 H. H. Kölle, "Zur Bestimmung des optimalen Brennkammerdruckes von Raketen-Triebwerken" (On the Determination of the Optimum Combustion Chamber Pressure of Rocket Propulsion Systems), *Weltraumfahrt,* Jan. 1953.

6.208 E. Giffen and A. Muraszew, *The Atomisation of Liquid Fuels,* John Wiley & Sons, Inc., New York, 1953, 246 pp.

6.209 R. Novotny, "Determining the Minimum Combustion Chamber Volume by Nomogram," *Aero Digest,* Sept. 1955.

6.3 Rotating Machinery—Liquid Propellant Rockets

6.301 A. J. Stepanoff, *Centrifugal and Axial Flow Pumps,* John Wiley & Sons, Inc., New York, 1948.

6.302 A. H. Church, *Centrifugal Pumps and Blowers,* John Wiley & Sons, Inc., New York, 1944.

6.303 A. Stodola, *Steam and Gas Turbines,* McGraw-Hill Book Co., Inc., New York, 1927.

6.304 C. C. Ross, "Principles of Rocket-Turbopump Design," *Journal of the American Rocket Society,* No. 84, March 1951.

6.305 R. T. Knapp, "Cavitation Mechanics and Its Relation to the Design of Hydraulic Equipment," *Proceedings of the Institute of Mechanical Engineers,* Vol. 166, No. 2A, 1952.

6.306 R. F. Gompertz, "Turbopump Assembly for HWK 109–509 Rocket Motor," *U. S. Air Force, Interim Report F-IM-2127-ND,* Feb. 1948.

6.307 "Development of the Pump-Fed Rocket Motor," *Engineering,* Vol. 178, Sept. 17, 1954.

6.308   C. C. Ross, "Principles of Rocket Turbopump Design,"
        Aero Digest, Vol. 69, Sept. 1954.

6.309   A. J. Acosta, "An Experimental and Theoretical Investi-
        gation of Two-Dimensional Centrifugal-Pump Pro-
        pellers," *Transactions of the ASME*, Vol. 76, July 1954.

6.4   Tanks and Seals—Liquid Propellant Rockets

6.401   W. R. Sheridan, "Expellant Bags for Rocket Propellant
        Tanks," *Journal of the American Rocket Society*, No. 85,
        June 1951.

6.402   C. Giles, "Tank Pressure and Motor Efficiency," *Astro-
        nautics*, No. 48, 1941.

6.403   E. G. Chandler, "Tank Pressure from Combustion
        Chamber," *Journal of the American Rocket Society*,
        Sept.–Dec. 1948.

6.404   S. E. Logan, "Static Seals for Low Temperature Fluids,"
        Jet Propulsion, Vol. 25, No. 7, July 1955.

6.405   R. R. Ashmead, "Static Seals for Missile Applications,"
        Jet Propulsion, Vol. 25, No. 7, July 1955.

6.406   J. Kendall, "Generation of High Gas Pressure through
        Hydraulics," *Jet Propulsion*, Vol. 25, No. 9, Sept. 1955.

6.407   H. H. Bleich, "Longitudinal Forced Vibrations of Cylin-
        drical Fuel Tanks," *Jet Propulsion*, Vol. 26, No. 2, Feb.
        1956.

6.5   Controls—Liquid Propellant Rockets

6.501   M. Meyer, "Throttling Thrust-Chamber Control," *Jour-
        nal of the American Rocket Society*, June 1951.

6.502   G. P. Sutton, "Rocket Motor Hydraulics," *Machine De-
        sign*, May 1950.

6.503   D. B. Calloway, "Resonant Vibrations in a Water-Filled
        Piping System," *Journal of the Acoustical Society of
        America*, Vol. 23, Sept. 1951.

6.504   K. R. Stehling and P. M. Diamond, "Flow Controls,"
        Journal of the American Rocket Society, May–June
        1953.

6.505   Y. C. Lee, M. R. Gore, and C. C. Ross, "Stability and
        Control of Liquid Propellant Rocket Systems," *Journal
        of the American Rocket Society*, March–April 1953.

6.506   J. L. Dooley, "Pneumatic Relays," *Machine Design*,
        April 1949.

6.507   R. H. Reichel, "On Importance of Mixture Ratio Con-
        trol for Large Rocket Engines," *Jet Propulsion*, Vol. 25,
        No. 6, June 1955.

6.508   R. Kling and R. Leboeuf, "Velocity of Pressure-Wave
        Propagation in Fuel-Injection Lines in Motors" (in
        French), *La Recherche aeronautique*, No. 19, Jan. 1951.

6.509 E. W. Otto, H. Gold, and K. W. Hiller, "Design and Performance of Throttle-type Fuel Controls for Engine Dynamic Studies," *NACA Technical Note 3445,* April 1955.

6.6 Materials

6.601 E. Blaha, "Refractory Materials for Gas Combustion Equipment," *Industrial and Engineering Chemistry,* Vol. 46, Jan. 1946.

6.602 A. R. Bobrowsky, "Ceramic Developments at the National Advisory Committee for Aeronautics," *NACA Technical Data Digest,* March 1, 1949.

6.603 R. Steinitz, "Cermets—New High-Temperature Materials," *Jet Propulsion,* Vol. 25, No. 7, July 1955.

6.604 "Titanium—Most Modern Metal of Industry," *Aviation Age,* Vol. 17, No. 2, Feb. 1952.

6.605 R. L. Noland, "Strengths of Several Steels for Rocket Chambers Subjected to High Rates of Heating," *Journal of the American Rocket Society,* Vol. 21, No. 6, Nov. 1951.

6.606 W. H. Duckworth, "Rocket Linings," *Aviation Week,* Vol. 54, June 25, 1951.

6.607 G. M. Stokes, D. D. Davis, Jr., and T. B. Sellers, "An Experimental Study of Porosity Characteristics of Perforated Materials in Normal and Parallel Flow," *NACA Technical Note 3085,* April 1954.

6.608 "Nitric Acid Versus Construction Materials—Symposium," *Chemical Engineering,* Vol. 55, No. 2, 3, and 4, 1948.

6.609 H. H. Hilton, "Thermal Stresses in Bodies Exhibiting Temperature-Dependent Elastic Properties," *Journal of Applied Mechanics,* Vol. 19, Sept. 1952.

6.7 Solid Propellant Rockets

6.701 R. Healy, "Thrust of Powder Rocket Charges," *Astronautics,* No. 48, 1941.

6.702 E. W. Price, "Charge Geometry and Ballistic Parameters for Solid Propellant Rocket Motors," *Jet Propulsion,* Vol. 24, No. 1, Jan.–Feb. 1954.

6.703 L. Green, Jr., "Erosive Burning of Some Composite Solid Propellants," *Jet Propulsion,* Vol. 24, No. 1, Jan.–Feb. 1954.

6.704 E. W. Price, "Steady-State One-Dimensional Flow in Rocket Motors," *Journal of Applied Physics,* Vol. 23, No. 1, Jan. 1952.

6.705 R. D. Geckler and D. F. Sprenger, "The Correlation of

Interior Ballistic Data for Solid Propellants," *Jet Propulsion*, Vol. 24, No. 1, Jan.–Feb. 1954.

6.706 E. W. Price, "Theory of Steady Flow with Mass Addition Applied to Solid Propellant Rocket Motors," *Journal of the American Rocket Society*, July–Aug. 1953.

6.707 W. L. Rogers, "Determination of Thrust Alignment in Rocket Engines," *Journal of the American Rocket Society*, Vol. 23, No. 6, Nov.–Dec. 1953.

6.708 R. N. Wimpress, *Internal Ballistics of Solid Fuel Rockets*, McGraw-Hill Book Company, Inc., 1950, 214 pp.

6.709 L. W. Lassiter and R. H. Heitkotter, "Some Measurements of Noise from Three Solid-Fuel Rocket Engines," *NACA Technical Note 3316*, Dec. 1954.

6.710 R. D. Geckler, "Manifolds for Solid Propellant Rocket Motors," *Jet Propulsion*, Vol. 25, No. 10, Oct. 1955.

6.711 R. D. Geckler, "Thermal Stresses in Solid Propellant Grains," *Jet Propulsion*, Vol. 26, No. 2, Feb. 1956.

6.712 J. M. Vogel, "A Quasi-Morphological Approach to the Geometry of Charges for Solid Propellant Rockets: The Family Tree of Change Designs," *Jet Propulsion*, Vol. 26, No. 2, Feb. 1956.

6.713 R. S. Newman, "Solid Propellant Rocket Design," *Aero Digest*, Vol. 71, July 1955.

6.8 Nuclear Energy Rockets

6.801 M. D. Moller, "Nuclear Radiation Effects on Aircraft Materials," *Aviation Age*, Vol. 21, Jan. 1954.

6.802 C. Giles, "Atomic Powered Rockets," *Journal of the American Rocket Society*, No. 63, Sept. 1945.

6.803 H. J. Kaeppeler, "Zur Theorie Polarer Kräfte als Prinzip einer Anwendung von Atomenergie für Raketenantrieb" (On the Theory of Using Nuclear Forces from Atomic Energy as a Means of Rocket Propulsion), *Gesellschaft für Raumfahrt, Forschungsreihe*, Bericht 2, Dec. 1951.

6.804 H. J. Kaeppeler, "On the Problem of Cooling Nuclear Working Fluid Rockets Operating at Extreme Temperatures," *Journal of the British Interplanetary Society*, Vol. 14, March–April 1955.

6.805 L. N. Thompson, "Nuclear-Energy Propulsion," *Flight*, Vol. LX, Nov. 23, 1951.

6.806 D. J. H. Wort, "The Atomic Hydrogen Rocket," *Journal of the British Interplanetary Society*, Vol. 12, July 1953.

6.807 H. S. Seifert, "Is the Nuclear-Powered Rocket Feasible?" *Physics Today*, Vol. 2, May 1949.

6.808 E. Sänger, "Theory of the Photon Rocket," *Ingenieur-Archiv*, Vol. 21, 1953.

6.809 G. F. Forbes, "The Thrust Available from Electronic Accelerators," *Journal of Space Flight*, Vol. 4, No. 10, Dec. 1952.

6.810 L. R. Shepperd and A. V. Cleaver, "The Atomic Rocket," *Journal of the British Interplanetary Society*, Nov. 1948 and March 1949.

7.0 Applications

7.1 General

7.101 "New Power Packages for Missiles," *Aviation Week*, July 11, 1955.

7.102 "Rocket on Rails," *Journal of the American Rocket Society*, No. 74, June 1948.

7.103 "Rocket Engines on Helicopter Rotor Tips," *Automotive Industries*, Vol. 111, Oct. 1, 1954.

7.104 W. J. Coughlin, " 'Pinwheel' Power Package for Missiles; Auxiliary Unit's Design Saves Weight, Space," *Aviation Week*, Vol. 57, No. 14, Oct. 6, 1952.

7.105 K. W. Gatland, "Expendable Rockets," *Journal of the British Interplanetary Society*, Vol. 7, July 1948.

7.106 G. Merrill, "Testing Naval Pilotless Aircraft," *Journal of the American Rocket Society*, No. 69, March 1947.

7.107 M. M. Munk, "Reliability Analysis of Modern Weapons," *Aero Digest*, Vol. 63, Nov. 1952.

7.108 M. S. Jones, Jr., "A Method for Estimating Altitude Performance of Balloon Launched Rockets," *Jet Propulsion*, Vol. 25, Oct. 1955.

7.2 Military Applications

7.201 D. A. Anderton, "How a Weapon System Operates in Field," *Aviation Week*, April 18, 1955.

7.202 C. B. Millikan, "The Guided Missile—Precocious Problem Child of the Military Art," *Aeronautical Engineering Review*, Vol. 11, April 1952.

7.203 J. R. Randolph, "Rockets Today; the Military Potentialities of Jet Propulsion," *Ordnance*, Vol. 35, No. 184, Jan.–Feb. 1951.

7.204 J. T. McNarney, "What is Happening in the Field of Rockets, Jet Propulsion and Supersonic Flight," *Technical Data Digest*, Vol. 14, No. 2, Jan. 15, 1949.

7.205 A. G. Favret, "The First Guided Missile Group," *Antiaircraft Journal*, Vol. 95, No. 6, Nov.–Dec. 1952.

7.206 J. L. Homer, "Gunnery and Guided Missiles; Fort Bliss Lays the Foundation for Developing New Ordnance Techniques," *Ordnance*, Vol. 34, No. 176, Sept.–Oct. 1949.

7.3 Guided Missiles

7.301 D. L. Putt, "German Developments in the Field of Guided Missiles," *SAE Journal (Transactions)*, Vol. 54, No. 8, Aug. 1946.

7.302 J. F. Smith, "The State of the Art," *Interavia*, Vol. X, No. 5, May 1955.

7.303 A. R. Weyl, "Guided Missiles," *The Aeroplane*, Part I, Vol. LXXIV, No. 1929, May 28, 1948; Part II, Vol. LXXIV, No. 1931, June 11, 1948; Part III, Vol. LXXIV, No. 1933, June 24, 1948; Part IV, Vol. LXXIV, No. 1937, July 23, 1948; Part V, Vol. LXXIV, No. 1941, Aug. 1948; and Part VI, Vol. LXXIV, No. 1943, Sept. 3, 1948.

7.304 C. B. Millikan, "Design Trends—Guided Missiles," *Aeronautical Engineering Review*, Vol. 12, No. 12, Dec. 1953.

7.305 "First Air-to-Air Missile," *Aero Digest*, Dec. 1949.

7.306 K. W. Gatland, "Evolution of the Guided Missile," *Flight*, Vol. 60, Aug. 3, 1951.

7.307 A. L. Feldman, "The Evaluation of Competing Rocket Power Plant Components for Two-Stage Long-Range Vehicles," *Journal of the American Rocket Society*, Vol. 23, Sept.–Oct. 1953.

7.308 R. H. Reichel, "The Guided Anti-Aircraft Missile C-2 'Wasserfall,'" *Interavia*, Vol. VI, No. 10, Oct. 1951.

7.309 "Swiss Guided Missile; A Revealing Description of the Oerlikon Ground-to-Air Guided Missile, Type 54," *Flight*, Jan. 7, 1955.

7.310 J. B. Schrock, "Launching Control for Guided Missiles," *Electronics*, Feb. 1955.

7.311 E. Burgess, "German Guided and Rocket Missiles," *Engineer*, Vol. 184 and 407, 1947.

7.312 A. S. Locke et al., *Guidance*, D. Van Nostrand Co., Inc., 1955, 729 pp.

7.313 "The Fairey Guided Missile," *Engineer*, Vol. 183, 1947, and *Flight*, Vol. 51, 1947.

7.314 H. Gartmann, "X4 Germany's Smallest Liquid Rocket," *Interavia*, Sept. 1949.

7.315 M. R. Seldon and D. W. Pertschuk, "The Experimental Determination of Guided Missile Reliability," *Journal of the Operations Research Society*, Vol. 2, Feb. 1954.

7.316 P. W. Powers, "The Aerodynamics of Guided Missiles. I—What Makes Them Fly?" *Antiaircraft Journal*, Vol. 95, No. 4, July–Aug. 1952.

7.317 W. H. C. Higgins, "Project Nike," *Ordnance*, Sept.–Oct. 1954.

7.318 H. S. Fowler, "Shooting Down the 600-m.p.h. Bomber;

Are Ram-jet Missiles the Answer?" *Air Pictorial,* Vol. 14, No. 9, Sept. 1952.

7.319 "Special Engineering and Development Issue: Missiles," *American Aviation,* Oct. 25, 1954.

7.320 C. L. Bates, "Pilotless Aircraft; A Statement of the Problems," *Aeronautical Engineering Review,* April 1955.

7.321 N. J. Bowman, "U. S. Guided Missile Progress, 1954," *Journal of Space Flight,* March 1955.

7.322 J. B. Mauldin, "German Developments in the Field of Rocket-Powered Controlled Missiles," *Journal of the American Rocket Society,* No. 65, March 1946.

7.323 C. C. Martin, "Guided Missile Maintenance," *Ordnance,* Vol. 39, May–June 1955.

7.324 G. P. Sutton, "History, Problems and Status of Guided Missiles," *Jet Propulsion,* Vol. 25, No. 11, Nov. 1955.

7.4 Assisted Take-off

7.401 M. J. Zucrow, "Jet Propulsion and Rockets for Assisted Take-off," *Transactions of the ASME,* April 1946.

7.402 Z. Krzywoblocki, "Rocket Assisted Take-offs," *Aero Digest,* Dec. 1946.

7.403 R. Hawthorne, "The Sprite Rocket Motor (Aviation Design Progress)," *Aviation Age,* Vol. 17, No. 4, April 1952.

7.404 W. J. Merboth, "Jet Assisted Take-off," *Sailplane and Glider,* Vol. 20, No. 2, Feb. 1952.

7.405 C. M. Bolster, *The Assisted Take-off of Aircraft,* James Jackson Cabot Fund, Publication No. 9, Norwich University, Northfield, Vermont, 1950, 71 pp.

7.406 T. von Karman, "Jet Assisted Take-off," *Interavia,* Vol. VII, No. 7, 1952.

7.407 A. V. Cleaver, "Rockets and Assisted Take-off," *Journal of the Royal Aeronautical Society,* Feb. 1951.

7.408 M. Summerfield, "The Rocket's Future Influence on Transport Design," *Aviation,* Vol. 45, No. 1, Jan. 1946.

7.409 H. Gartmann, "De Hilfs- und Start-Raketen mit Fremdantrieb" (Auxiliary and Assisted Take-off Rockets with External Power Drive), *Weltraumfahrt,* No. 6, 1951.

7.5 Armament Rockets

7.501 L. Schoeni, "Aircraft Rocket Launchers; Continuing Developments in Mounting Aerial Armament," *Ordnance,* Sept.–Oct. 1953.

7.502 "Aircraft Rockets," *Interavia,* Vol. 6, No. 10, Oct. 1951.

7.503 H. E. Stein, "Bazooka Rocket Motor Testing Now Fully Automatic," *Iron Age,* Vol. 169, March 20, 1952.

7.504   E. J. McShane, J. L. Kelley, and T. V. Reno, *Exterior Ballistics,* University of Denver Press, Denver, Colorado, 1953, 834 pp.

7.6   Aircraft Rocket

7.601   B. Hamlin and F. Spencerley, "Comparison of Propeller and Reaction Propelled Airplane Performances," *Journal of the Aeronautical Sciences,* Vol. 13, No. 8, 1946.

7.602   A. Lippisch, "Flugmechanische Beziehungen der Flugzeuge mit Strahlantrieb" (Flight Mechanics Relations of Airplanes with Rocket Propulsion), *Forschungsbericht 1791,* 1937.

7.603   A. D. Baxter, "Prospects and Problems of Rocket Propulsion for Aircraft," *The Engineer,* Feb. 18, 1955.

7.604   R. W. Byrne, "A Method of Selecting Rocket Thrust for Experimental Supersonic Airplanes," *NACA Research Memorandum L6G22,* Aug. 1946.

7.605   R. W. Allen, "Range Comparison of Rocket-Powered Aircraft," *Aero Digest,* Dec. 1953.

7.606   E. Sänger, "Recent Results in Rocket Flight Technique," *NACA Technical Memorandum 1012,* 1942.

7.607   "Das erste Americanische Raketenflugzeug" (Northrup Rocket Wing—The First American Rocket Airplane), *Weltraumfahrt,* No. 6, 1951.

7.608   "French Point Rocket Plane to Mach 1.6," *Aviation Week,* April 9, 1956.

7.609   "SO 6025 Jet-Rocket Fighter Tested," *Aviation Week,* Vol. 57, Aug. 25, 1952.

7.610   E. Burgess, "Rocket Propelled Interceptor Fighters," *Journal of the American Rocket Society,* No. 65, March 1946, and *Aeroplane,* Vol. 70–36, 1946.

7.611   E. Burgess, "The HWK 109–507 Bi-fuel Rocket Unit," *Pacific Rockets,* Vol. 1, No. 4, March 1947.

7.612   J. Shesta, "RMI's Rocket Engine Which Powers Supersonic XS-1," *Aviation,* Vol. 46, No. 1, Jan. 1947.

7.613   Z. Plaskowski, "The Use of Auxiliary Rockets in High-Speed Aircraft," *Aircraft Engineering,* March 1951.

7.614   C. J. Libby, "The Story of Zero-Length Launching," *Aviation Age,* March 1955.

7.615   H. F. King, "Rocket Fighters," *Flight,* May 23, 1946.

7.616   D. Hurden, "The Development of the Armstrong Siddeley 'Snarler' Rocket Motor," *Journal of the British Interplanetary Society,* Vol. 14, July–Aug. 1955.

7.617   A. D. Baxter, "The Prospects and Problems of Rocket Propulsion for Aircraft," *Journal of the Royal Aeronautical Society,* Vol. 59, May 1955.

7.618 R. Gordon, "Superperformance Rockets for Fighter Aircraft," *Aeronautical Engineering Review,* Vol. 14, Aug. 1955.

7.7 Research Rockets

7.701 W. J. Coughlin, "Aerobee Rocket Probes Upper Air Riddles," *Aviation Week,* Feb. 1, 1954.

7.702 W. G. Purdy, "Designing the Viking Rocket," *Machine Design,* Vol. 24, March 1952.

7.703 "Aerodynamic Research with Rocket-Propelled Models," *The Engineer,* Vol. 194, No. 5039, Aug. 22, 1952.

7.704 R. P. Haviland, "A Report on the Bumper Programme," *Journal of the British Interplanetary Society,* Vol. 11, No. 1, Jan. 1952.

7.705 "Rocket Motors for Windtunnels," *Aviation Week,* Sept. 14, 1953.

7.706 G. L. Christian, "Rocket Model Does Work of Windtunnel," *Aviation Week,* Vol. 56, No. 23, June 9, 1952.

7.707 M. Summerfield, "Fundamental Problems in Rocket Research," *Journal of the American Rocket Society,* June 1950.

7.708 H. Tsien, "Instruction and Research at the Daniel and Florence Guggenheim Jet Propulsion Center," *Journal of the American Rocket Society,* June 1950.

7.709 J. A. Van Allen, "Rockets for Studying the Upper Atmosphere," *Aero Digest,* Vol. 61, Sept. 1950.

7.710 C. F. Green, "V-2 Rocket in Upper Atmosphere Research," *Aero Digest,* Nov. 1953.

7.711 H. E. Newell, Jr., *High Altitude Rocket Research,* Academic Press, Inc., New York, Dec. 1953, 298 pp.

7.712 S. F. Singer, "Research in the Upper Atmosphere with Sounding Rockets and Earth Satellite Vehicles," *Journal of the British Interplanetary Society,* Vol. 11, No. 2, March 1952.

7.713 H. S. Sicinski, H. W. Spencer, and W. G. Dow, "Rocket Measurements of Upper Atmosphere Ambient Temperature and Pressure in the 30–75 Kilometer Region," *Journal of Applied Physics,* Vol. 25, Feb. 1954.

7.714 D. L. Arenson, J. H. McClow, Jr., and H. W. Wiant, "Rocket Powered Test Vehicles," *Jet Propulsion,* Vol. 25, No. 9, Sept. 1955.

7.8 Space Flight

See also Sections 8.3 and 8.4.

7.801 F. J. Malina and M. Summerfield, "The Problem of Escape from the Earth," *Journal of the Aeronautical Sciences,* Vol. 14, No. 8, 1947.

7.802   G. A. Crocco, "I Fondamenti dell'Astronautica" (On the Fundamentals of Astronautics), *L'Aerotecnica,* April 1953.

7.803   "On the Utility of an Artificial Unmanned Earth Satellite" (A proposal prepared by the Space Flight Committee of the American Rocket Society), *Jet Propulsion,* Vol. 25, No. 2, Feb. 1955.

7.804   K. W. Gatland, A. M. Kunesch, and A. E. Dixon, "Minimum Satellite Vehicles," *Journal of the British Interplanetary Society,* Vol. 10, Nov. 1951.

7.805   K. A. Ehricke, "A Method of Using Small Orbital Carriers for Establishing Satellites," *Aviation Week,* Jan. 5, 1953.

7.806   J. C. Bellamy, "Instruments for Upper Atmosphere and Interplanetary Navigation," *Navigation,* Vol. 2, Dec. 1950.

7.807   K. A. Ehricke, "Take-off from Satellite Orbits," *Journal of the American Rocket Society,* Nov.–Dec. 1953.

7.808   A. Bastide, "An Introduction to Celestial Navigation," *Interavia,* Vol. 7, No. 1, 1952.

7.809   L. R. Shepherd, "The Problem of Interplanetary Propulsion," *Journal of the British Interplanetary Society,* No. 55, Nov. 1946.

7.810   L. Spitzer, Jr., "The Rocket—a Tool for Exploring the Universe (Abstract)," *Mechanical Engineering,* Vol. 69, 1947.

7.811   W. Schaub, "The Interplanetary Ocean," *Interavia,* Vol. 5, No. 10, Oct. 1950.

7.812   G. A. Crocco, "The Crucial Problem in Astronautics— Recovery of Multistage Vehicles," *Jet Propulsion,* Sept.– Oct. 1954.

7.813   H. B. Ketchum, "A Preliminary Survey of the Constructional Features of Space Stations," *Journal of Space Flight,* Vol. 4, No. 8, Oct. 1952.

7.814   M. W. Ovenden, "Meteor Hazards to Space-Stations," *Journal of the British Interplanetary Society,* Vol. 10, Nov. 1951.

7.815   H. Wexler, "Observing the Weather from a Satellite Vehicle," *Journal of the British Interplanetary Society,* Vol. 13, Sept. 1954.

7.816   F. Hecht, "Chemische Probleme des Weltraumfluges" (Chemical Problems of Space Flight), *Weltraumfahrt,* Jan. 1953.

7.817   W. Proell, "Some Effects of Interplanetary Hydrogen upon Spaceships," *Journal of Space Flight,* Vol. 4, No. 6, June 1952.

7.818 H. Haber, "Manned Flight at the Borders of Space; the Human Factor of Manned Rocket Flight," *Journal of the American Rocket Society*, Vol. 22, No. 5, Sept.–Oct. 1952.

7.819 H. Oberth, "Electric Spaceships," *Weltraumfahrt*, No. 5, 1951.

8.0 Flight

8.1 Rocket Flight Theory

8.101 F. J. Malina and M. Summerfield, "The Problem of Escape from the Earth," *Journal of the Aeronautical Sciences*, Vol. 14, No. 8, 1947.

8.102 J. B. Rosser, R. R. Newton, and G. L. Gross, *Mathematical Theory of Rocket Flight*, McGraw-Hill Book Co., Inc., New York, 1947.

8.103 J. M. J. Kooy and J. W. H. Uytenbogaart, *Ballistics of the Future*, Technical Publishing Co., H. Stam, Haarlem, Netherlands, 1947.

8.104 J. Ackeret, "Zur Theorie der Raketen" (On the Theory of Rockets), *Helvetica Physica Acta*, Vol. 19, 1946.

8.105 H. S. Seifert, M. M. Mills, and M. Summerfield, "Physics of Rockets: Dynamics of Long Range Rockets," *American Journal of Physics*, Vol. 15, No. 3, May–June 1947.

8.106 F. J. Malina and A. M. O. Smith, "Flight Analysis of the Sounding Rocket," *Journal of the Aeronautical Sciences*, Vol. 5, No. 5, 1938.

8.107 H. E. Newell, "Rockets and the Upper Atmosphere," *Journal of the British Interplanetary Society*, Vol. 13, Jan. 1954.

8.108 D. F. Lawden, "Stationary Rocket Trajectories," *Quarterly Journal of Mechanics and Applied Mathematics*, Dec. 1954.

8.109 H. S. Tsien, T. C. Adamson, and E. L. Knuth, "Automatic Navigation of a Long Range Rocket Vehicle," *Journal of the American Rocket Society*, Vol. 22, No. 4, July–Aug. 1952.

8.110 J. S. Rinehart, W. A. Allen, and W. C. White, "Phenomena Associated with the Flight of Ultra-Speed Pellets, Part I: Ballistics, Part II: Spectral Character of Luminosity, Part III: General Character of Luminosity," *Bulletin of the American Physical Society*, Vol. 26 (9), July 25–28, 1951.

8.111 I. Sinra, "On the Vertical Climb of Rocket," *Journal of the Japanese Society of Aeronautical Engineering*, March 1954.

8.112   A. V. Cleaver, "Mass Ratios," *Journal of the British Interplanetary Society,* Vol. 8, No. 5, Sept. 1949.

8.113   C. H. Harry, "Investigation of Some Parameters Affecting Over-all Rocket Performance," *Journal of the American Rocket Society,* June 1949.

8.114   W. E. Frye, "On the Accuracy of Long-Range Ballistic Rocket," *Journal of Applied Physics,* May 1951.

8.115   H. S. Tsien, "A Method for Comparing the Performance of Power Plants for Vertical Flight," *Journal of the American Rocket Society,* Vol. 22, No. 4, July–Aug. 1952.

8.116   A. R. Hibbs, "Optimum Burning Program for Horizontal Flight," *Journal of the American Rocket Society,* Vol. 22, No. 4, July–Aug. 1952.

8.117   H. S. Tsien and R. C. Evans, "Optimum Thrust Programming for a Sounding Rocket," *Journal of the American Rocket Society,* Vol. 21, No. 5, Sept. 1951.

8.118   H. S. Seifert, "The Effect of Variable Propellant Density on Rocket Performance," *Journal of the American Rocket Society,* Vol. 22, No. 4, July–Aug. 1952.

8.119   K. A. Ehricke, "A Comparison of Rocket Propulsion at Constant Thrust and at Constant Acceleration," *Rocketscience,* Vol. 5, Sept. 1951.

8.120   W. R. Sears, Editor, *General Theory of High Speed Aerodynamics,* Vol. 6 of *High Speed Aerodynamics and Jet Propulsion,* Princeton University Press, Princeton, New Jersey, 1955, 774 pp.

8.121   A Miele, "Optimum Climbing Technique for a Rocket-Powered Aircraft," *Jet Propulsion,* Vol. 25, No. 8, August 1955.

8.122   F. H. Friedrich and F. J. Dove, "The Dynamic Motion of a Missile Descending through the Atmosphere," *Journal of the Aeronautical Sciences,* Vol. 22, Sept. 1955.

8.2   Aerodynamics

See also Sections 7.3, 7.4, 7.6, and 7.7.

8.201   R. Drenick, "The Perturbation Calculus in Missile Ballistics," *Franklin Institute Journal,* Vol. 251, No. 4, April 1951.

8.202   W. Bollay, "Aerodynamic Stability and Automatic Control (Wright Brothers Lecture)," *Journal of the Aeronautical Sciences,* Vol. 18, Sept. 1951.

8.203   D. R. Chapman, "An Analysis of Base Pressure at Supersonic Velocities and Comparison with Experiment," *NACA Technical Note 2137,* July 1950.

8.204   R. E. Bolz, "Dynamic Stability of a Missile in Rolling Flight," *Journal of the Aeronautical Sciences,* Vol. 19, No. 6, June 1952.

205 A. B. J. Clark and F. T. Harris, "Free-Flight Air-Drag Measurement Techniques," Appendix, by R. E. Roberson, *Journal of the Aeronautical Sciences,* Vol. 19, No. 6, June 1952.

8.206 A. W. Peppers, "Aerodynamic Design of a High-Altitude Rocket," *Aeronautical Engineering Review,* April 1955.

8.207 R. F. Peck, "Flight Measurements of Base Pressure on Bodies of Revolution with and without Simulated Rocket Chambers," *NACA Technical Note 3372,* April 1955.

8.3 Space Flight—General

See also Sections 7.8 and 8.4.

8.301 A. E. Slater, "Astronautics at Stuttgart," *Aeroplane,* Vol. 83, Sept. 26, 1952.

8.302 *Problems of Cosmical Aerodynamics, Proceedings of the Symposium on the Motion of Gaseous Masses of Cosmical Dimensions,* held in Paris, Aug. 16–19, 1949, International Union of Theoretical and Applied Mechanics and International Astronomical Union, Central Air Documents Office (Army-Navy-Air Force), Dayton 2, Ohio, 1951, 237 pp.

8.303 L. Spitzer, Jr., "Interplanetary Travel between Satellite Orbits," *Journal of the American Rocket Society,* Vol. 22, No. 2, March–April 1952.

8.304 L. R. Shepherd, "Basic Principles of Astronautics, Part I," *Journal of the British Interplanetary Society,* Vol. 14, Jan.–Feb. 1955.

8.305 A. C. Clarke, *Interplanetary Flight,* Harper and Brothers, New York, 1951, 164 pp.

8.306 *The Artificial Satellite; Proceedings of the 2nd International Congress on Aeronautics, London, 1951,* Edited by L. J. Carter, London, British Interplanetary Society, 1952, 74 pp.

8.307 D. F. Lawden, "Fundamentals of Space Navigation," *Journal of the British Interplanetary Society,* Vol. 13, March 1954.

8.308 "Second International Congress on Astronautics," *Nature,* Vol. 168, Oct. 27, 1951.

8.309 A. C. Clarke, *The Exploration of Space,* Harper and Brothers, New York, 1952, 199 pp.

8.310 F. Haber, "Human Flight at the Limits of the Atmosphere; G-Forces and Weight in Space Travel," Lecture, Second Symposium on Space Travel, Hayden Planetarium, New York, Oct. 13, 1952, and *Journal of the British Interplanetary Society,* Jan. 1953.

8.311 *Space Medicine*, Edited by J. P. Marbarger, University of Illinois Press, Urbana, Illinois, 1951, 83 pp.

8.4 Space Flight Theory

8.401 S. Herrick, "Space Rocket Trajectories," *Journal of the British Interplanetary Society*, Vol. 9, No. 5, Sept. 1950.

8.402 S. Herrick, *Tables for Rocket and Comet Orbits*, National Bureau of Standards, Applied Mathematics Series No. 20, Washington, Superintendent of Documents, 1953, 100 pp.

8.403 L. N. Thompson, "Fundamental Dynamics of Reaction-Powered Space Vehicles," *Proceedings of the Institute of Mechanical Engineers*, Vol. 164, No. 3, 1951.

8.404 B. Thüring, "Kompensation von Bahnstöhrungen durch kontinuierlichen Raketenschub" (Compensating Trajectory Disturbances by Continuous Rocket Thrust), *Weltraumfahrt*, Oct. 1954.

8.405 J. P. Sellers, Jr., "Influence of Earth's Gravitation on the Requirements of the Vertical Trajectory Rocket with Special Reference to Escape," *Journal of the American Rocket Society*, Sept.–Dec. 1948.

8.406 L. Spitzer, "Perturbations of a Satellite Orbit," *Journal of the British Interplanetary Society*, Vol. 9, No. 3, May 1950.

8.407 B. Thüring, "Eine einfache Methode der Berechnung von Gravitations-komponenten; Anwendung auf ein Astronautisches Dreikörperproblem" (A Simple Method for Calculating Gravitational Components; Application to an Astronautical Three-body Problem), *Weltraumfahrt*, July 1954.

8.408 D. F. Lawden, "Perturbation Manoeuvres," *Journal of the British Interplanetary Society*, Nov. 1954.

8.409 D. F. Lawden, "Escape to Infinity from Circular Orbits," *Journal of the British Interplanetary Society*, March 1953.

8.410 D. F. Lawden, "Minimal Rocket Trajectories," *Journal of the American Rocket Society*, Vol. 23, No. 6, Nov.–Dec. 1953.

8.411 H. Krause, "Die Bewegung einer Aussenstation in einer elliptischen, zum Erdäquator geneigten Bahn um die Erde. I" (The Motion of a Space Station around the Earth in a Path Which is Elliptical and Inclined to the Earth's Equator, I), *Weltraumfahrt*, Jan. 1952, Part II, July 1952.

8.412 W. Schaub, "Möglichkeiten des Überganges aus einer Ellipsenbahn in eine Kreisbahn und umgekehrt. I" (Possible Transitions from an Elliptical Orbit into a Circular

Orbit and Vice Versa), *Weltraumfahrt,* July 1952, Part II, Oct. 1952.

8.413   H. H. Kölle, "Graphisches Verfahren zur Abschätzung der optimalen Konstruktionsgrundwerte von Raumfahrzeugen" (Graphical Method for Estimating the Optimum Design Parameters of Space Vehicles), *Weltraumfahrt,* April 1952.

8.414   H. Kuhme, "Zur Aerodynamik von Start und Landung der Satellitenrakete," *Weltraumfahrt,* April 1952.

8.415   K. A. Ehricke, "A New Supply System for Satellite Orbits—Part I," *Jet Propulsion,* Vol. 24, No. 5, Sept.– Oct. 1954, Part II, Vol. 24, No. 6.

8.416   J. G. Porter, "Interplanetary Orbits," *Journal of the British Interplanetary Society,* Vol. 11, Sept. 1952.

8.417   G. F. Forbes, "Powered Orbits in Space," *Journal of the British Interplanetary Society,* March–April 1955.

8.418   H. R. Wahlin, "The Incremental Space Rocket in Free Space," *Jet Propulsion,* Vol. 25, No. 7, July 1955.

8.419   H. G. L. Krause, "Allgemeine Theorie der Stufenraketen" (General Theory of Steprockets), *Weltraumfahrt,* No. 2, April 1953.

8.420   R. Engel, "Leistungsnomogramm für Stufenraketen" (Performance Nomograms for Step Rockets), *Gesellschaft für Raumfahrtforschung,* Report No. 6, 1950.

8.5 Atmosphere, Stratosphere, and Planets

8.501   L. E. Miller, "Chemistry in the Stratosphere and Upper Atmosphere," *Journal of Chemical Education,* Vol. 31, March 1954.

8.502   *The Atmospheres of the Earth and Planets,* Edited by G. P. Kuiper, University of Chicago Press, Chicago, Revised Ed., 1952, 450 pp.

8.503   D. W. R. McKinley and P. M. Millman, "Long Duration Echoes from Aurora, Meteors, and Ionospheric Backscatter," *Canadian Journal of Physics,* Vol. 31, Feb. 1953.

8.504   J. G. Vaeth, *200 Miles Up,* The Ronald Press Co., New York, 1951, 207 pp.

8.505   H. E. Roberts, "The Earth's Atmosphere," *Aeronautical Engineering Review,* Oct. 1949.

8.506   F. L. Whipple, "Results of Rocket and Meteor Research," *Bulletin of the American Meteorological Society,* Vol. 33, Jan. 1952.

8.507   V. A. Firsoff, "The Air of Other Worlds," *Journal of the British Interplanetary Society,* Vol. 10, Sept. 1951.

8.508   C. Hoffmeister, "Interplanetäre Materie" (Interplanetary Matter), *Die Naturwissenschaften,* Vol. 38, May 1951.

8.509 F. A. Paneth, "Chemical Exploration of the Stratosphere" (in French), *Bulletin de la société chimique de France*, Jan. 1953.

8.510 R. M. Goody, *The Physics of the Stratosphere*, Cambridge University Press, New York, 1954, 192 pp.

8.511 N. J. Bowman, "Mars, Planet of Mystery," *Journal of Space Flight*, Vol. 6, Jan. 1954.

8.512 P. A. Moore, "What We Know about the Moon," *Journal of the British Interplanetary Society*, Vol. 11, Jan. 1952.

8.513 V. A. Firsoff, *Our Neighbor Worlds*, Philosophical Library, Inc., New York, 1953.

8.514 J. Lentz and R. Bennett, "Automatic Measurement of Star Positions," *Electronics*, Vol. 27, June 1954.

8.515 W. S. Diehl, "Standard Atmosphere—Tables and Data," *NACA Technical Report 218*, 1940.

8.516 C. N. Warfield, "Tentative Tables for the Properties of the Upper Atmosphere," *NACA Technical Note 1200*, Jan. 1947.

9.0 Rocket Testing

9.1 Test Facilities

9.101 A. Kossiakoff and R. E. Gibson, "The Launching of Guided Missiles," *Coast Artillery Journal*, March–April 1947.

9.102 B. N. Abramson, D. S. Brandwein, and H. C. Menes, "The 350,000-Pound Thrust Rocket Test Stand at Lake Denmark, N. J.," *Jet Propulsion*, Sept.–Oct. 1954.

9.103 "RMI Rocket Test Stand Simulates Flight Attitudes," *Aviation Week*, Aug. 14, 1950.

9.104 "Pioneer Rocket Test Station," *Journal of the American Rocket Society*, No. 70, June 1947.

9.105 D. A. Anderton, "Air Force Tests Rocket Engines in Giant Stands," *Aviation Week*, Aug. 31, 1953.

9.106 R. D. Hulliken, "The Long Range Proving Ground," *Ordnance*, Vol. 36, July–Aug. 1951.

9.107 L. J. Carter, "Anglo-Australian Long Range Weapon Project," *Journal of the British Interplanetary Society*, Vol. 9, No. 1, Jan. 1950.

9.108 "Woomera: Post-War Progress with British Guided Missiles; The Australian Rocket Range," *Flight*, Vol. 59, April 13, 1951.

9.109 H. S. Seifert, "The Jet Propulsion Laboratory," *Engineering and Science*, Vol. XVI, Oct. 1952.

9.110 J. T. Lewis, "Guided Missile Center," *Ordnance*, Vol. 36, No. 191, March–April 1952.

Rocket Testing 475

9.111   G. A. Bleyle, R. B. Hinckley, and C. R. Jewett, "An Air-Transportable Liquid Oxygen Generator—Its Operation and Application, *Jet Propulsion*, Vol. 24, No. 5, Sept.–Oct. 1954.

9.112   "Aerojet Builds New Missile Rocket Plant," *Aviation Week*, March 19, 1956.

9.2   Instruments and Measurement

9.201   G. P. Sutton, "Gaging Rocket Engine Forces and Flows," *Aviation*, April 1947.

9.202   M. F. Behar, *The Handbook of Measurement and Control*, The Instruments Publishing Co., Inc., Pittsburgh, Pennsylvania, 1951, Part II, "Instruments and Automation," Dec. 1954, 216 pp.

9.203   R. W. Ladenburg, B. Lewis, R. N. Pease, and H. S. Taylor, Editors, *Physical Measurements in Gas Dynamics and Combustion*, Vol. 9 of *High Speed Aerodynamics and Jet Propulsion*, Princeton University Press, Princeton, New Jersey, 1955, 594 pp.

9.204   J. Venn, "The Instrumentation of Rocket Motor Test Beds," *Journal of the British Interplanetary Society*, Vol. 12, Sept. 1953.

9.205   R. J. Sweeney, *Measurement Techniques in Mechanical Engineering*, John Wiley & Sons, Inc., New York, 1953, 309 pp.

9.206   C. G. Hylkema, R. F. Stott, and H. S. Seifert, "A Central Data-Recording System for a Jet Propulsion Laboratory," *Electrical Engineering*, Vol. 70, Nov. 1951.

9.207   P. A. Hufton, F. G. R. Cool, and P. S. Saunders, "A Recording System for Flight Test Data," *Great Britain Aeronautical Research Council, Current Paper 44*, Dec. 20, 1951.

9.208   E. J. Bobyn, "Instrumentation in Armament Development," *Engineering Journal*, Dec. 1954.

9.209   E. Cartotto, "Instrumentation for Rocket Testing," *Instruments, Journal of the Southern California Meter Association Section*, April 1953.

9.210   J. D. Humphreys, "Thrust Measurement in Flight," *Aero Digest*, Vol. 69, Sept. 1954.

9.211   J. A. Bierlein and K. Scheller, "Methods of Measuring Thrust," *Journal of the American Rocket Society*, Vol. 23, No. 3, May–June 1953.

9.212   T. H. Skopinski, W. S. Aiken, Jr., and W. B. Huston, "Calibration of Strain Gage Installations in Aircraft Structures for the Measurement of Flight Loads," *NACA Technical Note 2993*, Aug. 1953.

9.213   J. B. Wynn, "Guided Missile Test Center Telemetering System," *Electronics*, Vol. 25, May 1952.

9.214   R. P. Haviland, "Telemetry Instrumentation for Rocket Flight Tests," *Aviation Week*, Jan. 5, 1953.

9.215   W. C. Moore, "Simultaneous AM and FM in Rocket Telemetering," *Electronics*, Vol. 25, March 1952.

9.216   S. Raynor, "Calibration of Pressure Gages for Work in Ballistics," *Journal of Applied Mechanics*, Vol. 19, No. 4, Dec. 1952.

9.217   D. C. Pressey, "Temperature-Stable, Capacitance Pressure Gauges," *Journal of Scientific Instruments*, Vol. 30, No. 1, Jan. 1953.

9.218   R. T. Eckenrode and H. A. Kirshner, "Measurement of Pressure Transients," *Review of Scientific Instruments*, Vol. 25, Jan. 1954.

9.219   Y. T. Li, "High Frequency Pressure Indicators for Aerodynamic Problems," *NACA Technical Note 3042*, Nov. 1953.

9.220   A. S. Iberall, "Attenuation of Oscillatory Pressures in Instrument Lines," *Transactions of the ASME*, Vol. 72, July 1950.

9.221   F. P. Adler, "Measurement of the Conductivity of a Jet Flame," *Journal of Applied Physics*, July 1954.

9.222   F. A. Friswold, "Television Monitors Rocket Engine Flame," *Electronics*, Oct. 1953.

9.223   K. Berman and E. H. Scharres, "Photographic Techniques in Jet Propulsion Studies," *Journal of the American Rocket Society*, Vol. 23, No. 3, May–June 1953.

9.224   P. J. Dyne and S. S. Penner, "Optical Methods for the Determination of Combustion Temperatures," *Journal of the American Rocket Society*, Vol. 23, No. 3, May–June 1953.

9.225   E. F. Fiock and A. I. Dahl, "The Measurement of Gas Temperature by Immersion-Type Instruments," *Journal of the American Rocket Society*, Vol. 23, No. 3, May–June 1953.

9.226   S. Silverman, "The Determination of Flame Temperatures by Infra-Red Radiation," *Journal of the Optical Society of America*, April 1949.

9.227   J. H. Hett and J. B. Gilstein, "Pyrometer for Measurement of Instantaneous Temperatures of Flames," *Journal of the Optical Society of America*, Nov. 1949.

9.228   A. G. Gaydon and H. G. Wolfhard, "The Spectrum Line Reversal Method of Measuring Flame Temperature," *Proceedings of the Physical Society of London*, Vol. 65, Part 1, Jan. 1, 1952.

9.229 M. F. Heidmann and R. J. Priem, "A Modified Sodium-Line Reversible Technique for the Measurement of Combustion Temperature in Rocket Engines," *Journal of the American Rocket Society,* July–Aug. 1953.

9.230 J. L. Beal and J. T. Grey, "Sampling and Analysis of Combustion Gases," *Journal of the American Rocket Society,* Vol. 23, No. 3, May–June 1953.

9.231 F. P. Bundy, H. M. Strong, and A. B. Gregg, "Measurement of Velocity and Pressure of Gases in Rocket Flames by Spectroscopic Methods," *Journal of Applied Physics,* Vol. 22, Aug. 1951.

9.232 J. Grey and F. F. Liu, "Methods of Flow Measurement," *Journal of the American Rocket Society,* Vol. 23, No. 3, May–June 1953.

9.233 R. C. Swengel, W. B. Hess, and S. K. Waldorf, "Demonstration of the Principles of the Ultrasonic Flowmeter," *Electrical Engineering,* Dec. 1954.

9.234 L. W. Fraser and R. S. Ostrander, "Photographic Determination of the Orientation of a Rocket," *Photographic Engineering,* Vol. 1, No. 4, Oct. 1950.

9.235 A. Wexle and W. S. Corak, "Measurement and Control of the Level of Low Boiling Liquids," *Review of Scientific Instruments,* Vol. 22, Dec. 1951.

9.236 A. S. Bassette, "Vibration Instrumentation," *SAE Journal,* Vol. 59, Nov. 1951.

9.237 P. Curti and F. Dubois, "Mechanical Recording and Calculating in Exterior Ballistics" (in German), *Archiv für technisches Messen,* No. 253, Dec. 1953.

9.238 E. Jones, "Cemented Piezoelectric Accelerometers," *Review of Scientific Instruments,* Vol. 24, Dec. 1953.

9.239 V. Paschkis, "Heat and Mass Flow Analyzer," *Scientific Monthly,* Vol. 73, Aug. 1951.

9.240 R. M. Davies, J. D. Owen, and D. H. Trevena, "The Measurement of the Velocities of Bullets with a Counter Chronometer," *British Journal of Applied Physics,* Vol. 2, Sept. 1951.

9.241 K. R. Honick, "An Electromagnetic Method of Measurement of Density or Specific Gravity of Liquids," *Journal of Scientific Instruments,* Jan. 1954.

9.242 A. Boodberg and I. Cornet, "Atmospheric Pressure Apparatus for Studying Ignition Delay," *Industrial and Engineering Chemistry,* Vol. 43, Dec. 1951.

9.243 R. Jackson, "Temperature Measurement in Gases and Flames. Radiation Methods," *Bulletin of the British Coal Utilization Research Association,* Vol. 15, 1951.

9.244 E. M. Winkler, "Design and Calibration of Stagnation Temperature Probes for Use at High Supersonic

Speeds and Elevated Temperatures," *Journal of Applied Physics*, Vol. 25, Feb. 1954.

9.245 I. Bredt, "Grundsätzliches über Spektroskopische Verfahren zur Messung von Temperaturen und Geschwindigkeiten sehr heisser und sehr schnell strömender Feuergase" (Fundamentals of Spectroscopic Means for Measuring Temperatures and Velocities of Very Hot and Very Rapidly Flowing Combustion Gases), *Zeitschrift der Elektrochemie, Berichte der Bunsen Gesellschaft für physikalische Chemie*, Vol. 56, Jan. 1952.

9.246 R. J. Havens, "Temperature and Pressure Measurements in Rockets," Paper 48–1–3, Instrument Society of America, Pittsburgh, Pennsylvania, Sept. 1948.

9.247 J. G. Ziegler and N. B. Nichols, "Dynamic Accuracy in Temperature Measurement," *Instruments*, Vol. 23, Jan. 1950.

9.248 H. B. Jones, Jr., "Recording Instruments in Rocket and Jet Engine Testing," *Journal of the American Rocket Society*, Vol. 23, No. 3, May–June 1953.

9.3 Test Operation

9.301 G. L. Elliott and R. Weller, "Some Navigation Problems at a Guided Missile Range," *Navigation*, Dec. 1954.

9.302 "New Methods Developed for Evaluating Rocket Motors," *Aviation Week*, Sept. 29, 1947.

9.303 C. M. Beighley and T. E. Cheatham, "Reduction of Rocket Motor Performance Data by Means of IBM Computing Machines," *Journal of the American Rocket Society*, Vol. 23, No. 3, May–June 1953.

9.304 D. Hurden, "Rocket Motor Testing," *Journal of the British Interplanetary Society*, Vol. 12, May 1953.

Index